Industrial Electronic Engineering

PRENTICE-HALL ELECTRICAL ENGINEERING SERIES

W. L. EVERITT, *Editor*

Industrial Electronic Engineering

by

WELLS L. DAVIS

CHIEF OF ENGINEERING DEVELOPMENT
THE BABCOCK & WILCOX COMPANY, TUBULAR PRODUCTS DIVISION

and

HERMAN R. WEED

ASSISTANT PROFESSOR OF ELECTRICAL ENGINEERING
THE OHIO STATE UNIVERSITY

New York PRENTICE-HALL, INC. 1953

PRINTED IN THE UNITED STATES OF AMERICA

PREFACE

It is assumed by the authors of this book that the reader already has a knowledge of a-c circuit theory, elementary theory of electronic circuits, and elementary differential equations. In the chapters on Servomechanisms, Regulation, and Radio Frequency Heating, where slightly more advanced mathematics is necessary, the mathematics is developed as needed for the application. Assuming the prerequisites above, it is unnecessary to devote a large part of the book to presentation of background material. However, since gas tubes are so widely used in industry, it was thought advisable to include a chapter providing enough of the theory of gas tubes for adequate understanding of their application in circuits.

Also as a consequence of the prerequisites assumed, the instructor or general reader may select the order of chapters to suit his own needs, since, except for the chapters on Servomechanisms and Regulation, the chapters are independent of each other.

Throughout the book, an attempt has been made to present basic methods of analyzing and solving problems. However, no attempt has been made to describe a large number of circuits, since the description of existing circuits is of limited help in the design of a new circuit for a new application. On the other hand, a familiarity with the fundamental methods of attacking a new problem can be of most general value. Therefore, circuits for specific applications have been described only to the extent necessary to provide a vehicle for illustrating principles.

We, the authors, are indebted to many sources and many people in the preparation of this book, and it is impossible to mention them all here. In particular, we are indebted to Professor E. E. Dreese of the Ohio State University for his encouragement in the preparation of the book, to Dean W. L. Everitt of the University of Illinois for his helpful suggestions, to many of our students, whose questions and comments have clarified numerous points, and to our wives, Ellen and Sylvia, whose ready help and cooperation were a continuing source of encouragement.

Beaver Falls, Pennsylvania
Columbus, Ohio

WELLS L. DAVIS
HERMAN R. WEED

CONTENTS

viii CONTENTS

ing a resistance weld. 6.10: Fundamental resistance welding circuit. 6.11: Simple automatic sequence timer. 6.12: Synchronous weld timer with heat control.

Industrial Electronic Engineering

CHAPTER 1

GAS TUBE CHARACTERISTICS

An understanding of the characteristics of gas tubes and their control depends upon a knowledge of the behavior of electric discharges in gases; this subject will be discussed first. The behavior of an electric discharge through a gas is intimately connected with a number of factors, the most important being the kind of gas and its pressure, the electrode materials and shapes, the physical dimensions, shape, and size of the container, and sometimes the gas temperature. The characteristics of the discharge vary widely as the above factors are changed, with the result that the discharges have been classified as belonging to one of several different groups, each of which has certain characteristic properties and applications. In some cases the line of demarcation between two classes of discharge is rather indefinite, so that it may be difficult to decide whether a certain discharge belongs to one class or the other. Or a certain kind of discharge may have some, but not all, of the characteristics of two easily distinguishable classes of discharge.

For the purposes of this discussion, electric discharges through gases will be classed as either nonself-maintaining, self-maintaining, or corona discharges. The first two will be discussed at some length, and there will be various subclasses under each. The corona discharge is mentioned merely to give it a proper orientation with respect to other discharges, but since it has little importance as far as gas tubes are concerned, it will not be discussed at length.

1.1 Nonself-maintaining Discharges

The character of a discharge can perhaps best be described by its volt-ampere characteristic. Suppose one imagines a pair of plane, parallel electrodes, both cold, sealed into an envelope or tube con-

1

taining a gas at a pressure in the range from 50 mm Hg to 0.1 mm Hg. The volt-ampere characteristic of such a tube may be found by connecting the tube in series with an adjustable source of potential and a variable resistor.   The tube current may then be measured as a function of the tube voltage.   Figure 1-1 shows the volt-ampere characteristic which might result from such measurement.   The voltage and current scales merely indicate orders of magnitude, and the curve is not intended to represent an actual volt-ampere characteristic.

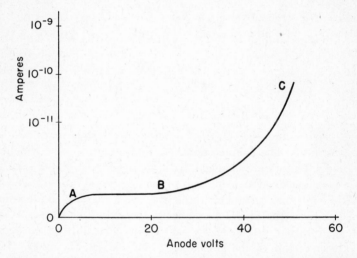

Fig. 1-1.   Volt-ampere characteristic for nonself-maintained discharge.

The shape of the curve is explained as follows.   There is always a small percentage of the gas atoms contained in the tube which are ionized.   The ionization may be caused by cosmic radiation, ultraviolet or visible radiation, x-rays, or other types of radiation. The cosmic radiation is always present, except under exceptional circumstances, and the presence or absence of the other types, which depend upon the surrounding conditions, may be controlled by the experimenter.   If a voltage is applied between the electrodes, the electrons and the ions are accelerated to the anode and cathode, respectively, producing a current.   As the voltage is increased the current increases until the point A, Fig. 1-1, is reached.   Further small voltage increases in the range from A to B do not produce any appreciable change of current. This saturation effect indicates that *all* the electrons produced by the external ionizing agent are being collected at the anode, and in this region the only way to change the current would be to change the intensity of the external ionizing radiation. Increases of voltage beyond point B cause the current to increase again, and in the region around C the rate of increase becomes very large. The rising characteristic in the region from B to C can be accounted for by the additional ionization of gas atoms by the original electrons freed by the external ionization. As the anode voltage is increased these original electrons can acquire energies great enough to cause ionization of neutral gas atoms by collision. These additional electrons are now accelerated toward the anode and contribute to the total current. Also, if the voltage is high enough, they may cause still further ionizations by collision. Thus, as the voltage increases, the effectiveness of this gas multiplication process increases. Even in this region, however, the existence of the current depends upon the presence of an external ionizing radiation, and if this radiation is removed, the current becomes zero. For this reason this type of discharge is called a *nonself-maintaining* discharge. It has also been called a Townsend[1] discharge after the man who carried out extensive and careful studies of the phenomenon.

Attempts to increase the anode voltage beyond the point C of Fig. 1-1 result in a very rapid increase of current into a region in which the discharge changes into a self-maintained discharge. This phenomenon will be discussed in later sections.

Nonself-maintained discharges occur in various practical devices, although there are relatively few tubes whose useful operating characteristics depend upon operation with this type of discharge. For example, many tubes, such as the various cold-cathode voltage regulator tubes, operate normally in the self-maintained discharge region, but before this kind of discharge begins the tube must pass through the nonself-maintained discharge condition. This transition is essential to the establishment of the self-maintained condition, as will become evident later.

The gas-filled phototube is an example of a tube whose normal operating characteristic is actually that of a nonself-maintained

---

[1] Townsend, J. S., *Electricity in Gases*, Oxford, Clarendon Press, New York, 1915.

discharge. A typical characteristic for such a tube is shown in Fig. 1-2. Here the necessary initial electrons are produced mostly by photoemission from a specially prepared cathode. The rising volt-ampere characteristic is due to the gas multiplication process already described. The curve shown in Fig. 1-2 is for a constant amount of radiation incident on the cathode. If the radiation were removed, the anode current would drop to virtually zero.

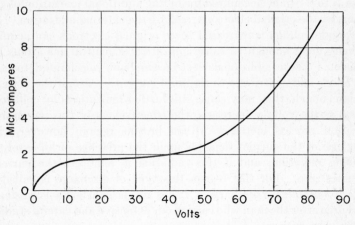

Fig. 1-2. Typical volt-ampere characteristic for a gas phototube with constant illumination.

1.2 Self-maintained Discharges

A large percentage of the gas-filled electron tubes in use today depend upon some form of self-maintained discharge, the two most important of which are the glow discharge and the arc discharge. Under arc discharges there are four important subclasses: the thermionic arc, the externally heated cathode arc, the high-field emission arc, and the metal arc. The first three are distinguished by the different mechanisms involved for producing the necessary electrons. In the thermionic arc they are produced by thermionic emission from an area of the cathode which is heated by ion bombardment. The electrons for the externally heated cathode arc come from a cathode heated by some means other than by an ion bombardment. The electrons for high-field emission are supplied by emission caused by very large gradients in the electric field at the surface of the cathode. The metal arc is the sort of arc occurring in circuit breakers, and here the mechanism for supplying electrons has not been definitely established. The metal arc does not occur in electron tubes and so will not be discussed here.

Except for the metal arc, the types of discharge mentioned above are commonly used in electron tubes and other devices. For example, the glow discharge occurs in regulator tubes, and the carbon arc lamp, used as a source of light, is an example of the thermionic arc. Sealed off hot-cathode gas diodes and triodes (thyratrons) operate as externally heated cathode arcs, and high-field emission arcs occur in ignitrons and other mercury pool type tubes.

1.3 Complete Volt-ampere Characteristic of a Gas Discharge

The nonself-maintained discharge has been discussed in Sec. 1.1, and Fig. 1-1 shows a volt-ampere characteristic for such a discharge. The complete volt-ampere characteristic for a gas discharge is shown in Fig. 1-3, in which the nonself-maintained region A-B-C is

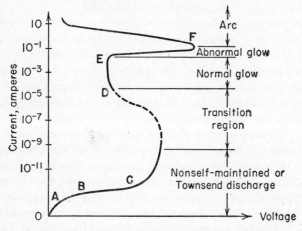

Fig. 1-3.   Volt-ampere characteristic of a gas discharge.

the same as Fig. 1-1. As the voltage is increased beyond the point C, there results a very rapid increase of current, accompanied by a drop in tube voltage, until the point D is reached. The discharge is now self-maintained, and it is accompanied by a visible glow in the tube. For this reason it is called a *glow discharge*. The external ionizing agency may now be removed, and the discharge continues without it. The volt-ampere curve is shown dotted in the region of transition between the nonself-maintaining and self-maintaining conditions, because operation in this region of negative slope is unstable unless the external circuit resistance is extremely large. In practical circuits where the resistance is not this large the transition is abrupt, and some references show the transition from C to D as a horizontal line to emphasize the abruptness of the change.

After the transition to the glow discharge, a further increase of supply voltage causes an increase of current but very little increase of tube voltage. This is the region between D and E of Fig. 1-3, and is called the *normal glow* region. In addition to the glow throughout the gas, normal glow operation is characterized by a brightly glowing area on the cathode known as the *cathode glow*. For small currents, near the point D of Fig. 1-3, only a small part of the total cathode surface is covered by this glow, and as the current is increased, the area of the glow increases linearly with the current. Thus the current density at the cathode remains constant in this region and is called the *normal current density*.

When the cathode becomes completely covered by the glow, a further increase of current is accompanied by an increase of voltage across the tube as shown by the curve from E to F of Fig. 1-3. This region of operation is called the *abnormal glow*. As the current is increased, the current density at the cathode begins to increase at one or more localized spots. Eventually one of these spots becomes hot enough, due to ion bombardment, so that thermionic emission begins. At this point the current may increase very rapidly, and the discharge undergoes another transition from the abnormal glow region to the *arc discharge* region of the characteristic. Here all the current flows to the one small spot on the cathode, the voltage drop across the arc drops to a value much less than that required for the normal glow, and the slope of the volt-ampere characteristic is negative. The current would rise to destructive values if a suitable current limiting resistor were not present in the external circuit.

The complete volt-ampere characteristic of a gas discharge has been described above, and in the sections to follow its various parts will be considered in more detail.

1.4 The Glow Discharge

The mechanism of the glow discharge and the difference between it and the nonself-maintained discharge can be explained by refer-

ence to Fig. 1-4.   Here the dotted lines indicate motions of ions, and
the solid lines indicate electron paths.   Part (a) of the figure indicates conditions existing in a nonself-maintained discharge.   In this
particular illustration the original primary electron produced by the

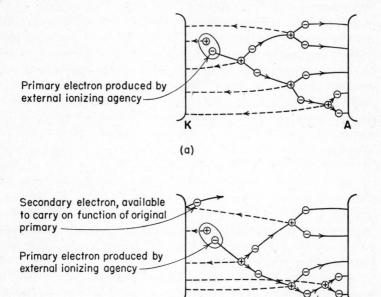

Fig. 1-4. Mechanism and comparison of nonself-maintained and self-
maintained or glow discharges.   In part (a) five ions arrive at K.   Five
electrons arrive at A.   Anode-cathode voltage is low, so that no secondary
electrons are produced at cathode.   Discharge is *nonself-maintained*.   In part
(b) five ions arrive at K.   Five electrons arrive at A.   One electron is liberated
at K by secondary emission.   The secondary electron may now replace original
primary electron, so that discharge is *self-maintained*.

external ionizing source results in four additional ionizations, on the
average, before it strikes the anode.   Also, on the average, five ions
reach the cathode for every five electrons striking the anode.   This
process is known as gas multiplication.   As the anode-cathode voltage is raised, the gas multiplication process described above becomes
more and more effective, since the electrons need not move as far
before attaining ionizing energy.   Also the ions strike the cathode

with greater and greater energies, until finally their energies become great enough to produce emission of the electrons at the cathode by the process known as secondary emission.   Not all the ions impinging on the cathode produce secondary electrons.   The ratio of the number of secondary electrons to the number of incident ions is dependent upon the kind of gas in the tube, the cathode material, and the anode-cathode voltage.   As the voltage is increased, each primary electron produced by external ionization results in liberation of more and more ions, which in turn strike the cathode with greater and greater energies.   Finally the production of secondary electrons at the cathode rises to the point where one secondary electron is produced for each group of ions caused by the single original primary electron.   When this condition is reached the secondary electron can take over the function of the primary electron produced by the external ionizing agency, and the external ionization becomes unnecessary for maintaining the discharge. This condition is shown in part (b) of Fig. 1-4.   When the discharge becomes self-maintained the current would increase without limit if there were no external resistance to limit it.   Assume that there is such a resistance and that it limits the current to the range from D to E of Fig. 1-3.

It should be pointed out to the reader at this point that the mechanism pictured in Fig. 1-4 is much simpler than what actually occurs.   For example, not every ion proceeds unimpeded from the point where it was formed to the cathode.   It may encounter and recombine with an electron before reaching the cathode, or it may go to the wall of the tube and recombine there.   These and other phenomena occur, but on the average it must always be true that the number of electrons per unit time striking the anode equals the number of ions striking the cathode per unit time plus the number of secondary electrons produced at the cathode per unit time.

So far nothing has been said about the ions striking the cathode. At the surface or even slightly inside the metal of the cathode they recombine with free conduction electrons.   The neutral atoms then evaporate from the surface back into the interelectrode space.

The glow discharge has been studied extensively by many investigators and from many points of view.   Some of the more important findings for our purposes will now be discussed.   The distributions of light intensity and of potential along the length of a long narrow discharge tube operating in the glow discharge region are shown in Fig. 1-5. The density of dots is intended to be proportional to intensity of light from the discharge. The potential distribution curve has been drawn so that its various parts correspond to the

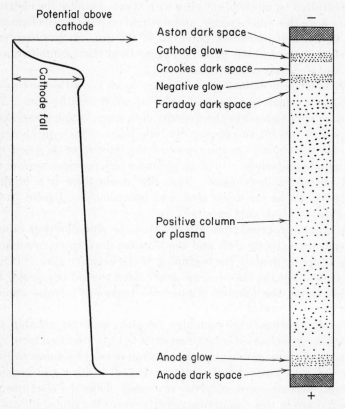

Fig. 1-5.   Distribution of light intensity and potential with respect to cathode along a glow discharge.

proper regions of the light intensity distribution diagram.   Immediately adjacent to the cathode is a dark space known as the *Aston dark space*. It is a region in which the secondary electrons have acquired only low velocities compared with the ions striking the cathode, so the region is characterized by a positive curvature of the potential distribution curve. The space is dark, because the electrons have not yet enough energy to cause ionization.   Next appears a soft, velvety glow known as the *cathode glow*. Often the Aston dark space is so short that it is not discernible, and the cathode glow appears to lie on the surface of the cathode. The cause of the cathode glow is not well understood. It almost surely is not caused by ionization by electron collision with atoms, because the electrons do not have this much energy, and the light emitted is not characteristic of the first ionization potential of the gas. It has been suggested that the cathode glow may come from the recombination of ions and electrons of the cathode.

Following the cathode glow is a dark space known as the *Crookes dark space*, which is followed by the so-called *negative glow*. The negative glow fades into the *Faraday dark space*, which merges into the *positive column*, or *plasma*. In long tubes of the type shown in Fig. 1-5 the plasma occupies most of the interelectrode space, and glows quite uniformly. It is the plasma which provides most of the light output of neon signs. Near the anode there is a brighter region known as the *anode glow*, and immediately adjacent to the anode is the *anode dark space*.

It will be observed from Fig. 1-5 that the potential rises rapidly through the cathode glow and the Crookes dark space, reaching a peak at approximately the beginning of the negative glow. It is in this region that the electrons are accelerated toward the anode, and in this region the number of electrons begins to increase rapidly with distance away from the anode. In this region (Crookes dark space) the electrons have such high velocities that the probability of excitation or ionization is low, and little light is produced here. At the edge of the negative glow the electron density becomes so great that the net charge density (summation of positive and negative charges) becomes zero and even reverses. Thus the electrons are slowed down in this region to a velocity where the probability of an electron causing an excitation or ionization of an atom becomes large. Thus there is an intense glow in the negative glow region. However, since the gradient in the negative glow region is negative (see Fig. 1-5), the electrons are retarded and gradually lose their ionizing and exciting ability, so that the intensity of glow drops off with distance, thus producing the Faraday dark space. The gradient now becomes positive again, so that the electrons may again acquire enough energy to cause excitation and ionization, thus forming the beginning of the plasma. From here on until close to the anode the gradient remains constant, indicating equal concentrations of positive ions and electrons. The plasma is a region of uniform light intensity. Since the net space charge is zero in the plasma, there is no space charge limitation on the amount of current it can carry, provided the electrons are made available. For this reason it is possible to carry relatively large currents through a plasma with little voltage drop across the plasma. As will be shown in Sec. 1.9, this is especially true of arc discharges, in which the supply of electrons available at the cathode is very large.

Since all current flow to the anode must be electron current, it follows that in normal operation the concentration of positive ions should decrease as the anode is approached. This results in a net negative space charge near the anode, so that the potential distribution curve rises. This change of voltage, called the anode fall, is rarely more than few volts in magnitude.

1.5   The Cathode Fall of Potential

The cathode fall of potential is the change of potential occurring in the glow discharge between the negative glow and the cathode. It is usually called simply the "cathode fall," and is so labeled on the potential distribution diagram of Fig. 1-5. The cathode fall not only constitutes most of the voltage drop across the tube, but it is *functionally the most important part of the discharge.* The reason for its importance is that the ions produced in the negative glow are accelerated to the cathode by the cathode fall of potential. As they fall through this potential the ions must acquire enough energy to produce the secondary electrons at the cathode necessary to maintain the discharge. *It is the principal function of the cathode fall to provide this energy,* for without it the discharge would not be self-maintaining. The cathode fall is substantially independent of pressure. However, as the pressure p is increased, the distance d from the cathode to the edge of the negative glow decreases. In fact, d adjusts itself so that the product pd is a constant which depends on the kind of gas. Thus in air at about atmospheric pressure the distance d is so short that the Aston dark space and Crookes dark space cannot be distinguished.

The magnitude of the cathode fall for a normal glow discharge varies with the electrode material and the gas through which the discharge occurs. For potassium electrodes in helium the cathode fall is 59 volts, and for cobalt electrodes in air it is 380 volts. Various other combinations[2] give values between these or even higher than 380 volts.   It is by suitable choice of electrodes and gas that voltage regulator tubes (see Sec. 1.7) can be made to maintain various voltages across their terminals.

It has been mentioned in Sec. 1.3 that a gas discharge operating in the normal glow region is characterized by a cathode glow whose area is proportional to the current.   It is possible at this point to explain why this should be true.   In the region of the cathode fall most of the tube current is carried by positive ions, and the net charge density in this region is therefore positive.   The electrons which do exist in this region have quite high velocities compared to the ion velocities (except *very* close to the cathode), so their presence may be neglected.   Hence, to a first approximation, the ion current in this region can be considered to be space-charge-limited.   Therefore the ion current density J is given by Child's law, the only differences between this case and the case of space-charge-limited electron flow being in the sign of the charges and the mass of the particles.   Thus

$$J = K \frac{E^{\frac{3}{2}}}{d^2} \text{ amp per sq. m,} \qquad (1.1)$$

where E is the cathode fall of potential and d is the distance from the negative glow to the cathodes.   It has already been mentioned that d depends on the pressure, which will be assumed constant here, so that d is also constant.   The cathode fall E is characterized entirely by the kind of gas and the electrode material.   Thus the ion current density, which is also the tube current density, must be constant, and it becomes evident at once that the area covered by the ion current, that is, the cathode glow area, must be proportional to the total current.

1.6   Comparison of Townsend and Glow Discharges

An interesting difference between the Townsend, or nonself-maintained, discharge and the glow discharge may now be pointed out. It will be recalled that the volt-ampere characteristic of a gas discharge shown in Fig. 1-3 displays a considerable decrease in voltage

---

[2] Cobine, J. D., *Gaseous Conductors*, McGraw-Hill Book Company, Inc., New York, 1941, page 217.

drop as the transition from Townsend to glow discharge occurs. What is the reason for this decrease?

To explain the decrease, a region of the Townsend discharge near the transition condition, say point C of Fig. 1-3, will be considered. At this condition of operation positive ions are being produced throughout the interelectrode space by external agents and by electron collisions with atoms. Conditions near the transition point are such that a large proportion of the ions are produced at a considerable distance from the cathode. Therefore most of the ions must move through a relatively long path to the cathode, and in so doing, encounter many collisions with atoms. Therefore the total cathode-anode voltage must be relatively large to accelerate the ions to the velocities necessary for appreciable secondary emission at the cathode, since the ions' free paths of flight between their last collisions with atoms and their collisions with the cathode are quite short. It is assumed here that the potential distribution between the electrodes in the Townsend discharge is essentially the same as if no charges were present, since the magnitude of the current in such a discharge is very small. Quite the opposite is true as soon as the glow discharge begins. Here most of the tube drop takes place at the cathode fall, which occurs in a relatively short distance from the cathode, as is shown in Fig. 1-5. The ions striking the cathode thus acquire most of their energy in this short distance, where impact with atoms en route to the cathode is unlikely. Since the total tube voltage is only slightly greater than the cathode fall, because of the potential distribution peculiar to the glow discharge, the total potential difference necessary to maintain the glow discharge is considerably less than the potential required to maintain the Townsend discharge near the transition point.

1.7 The Arc Discharge. Thermionic Arcs

If the current through a cold-cathode glow discharge tube be increased beyond the point where the cathode becomes completely covered by the cathode glow, the voltage across the tube rises sharply, as shown in Fig. 1-3, Sec. 1.3. The tube is then said to be operating in the abnormal glow region of its volt-ampere characteristic. The increased current must then cause an increase in the current density at the cathode. It turns out that the current density increases at a small, localized area or spot, and as the voltage and current increase, this spot is heated by the positive ion bombardment. If the voltage is increased far enough, the spot becomes hot enough to produce electrons by thermionic emission. The additional thermionic electrons allow the tube current to increase, which in turn increases the thermionic emission. This cumulative process continues until the tube current rises to a value limited only by the source voltage and the external circuit resistance. Under this condition, which is known as a thermionic arc, almost all the electrons necessary for the discharge are supplied by thermionic emission. The thermionic source of electrons in the arc is what distinguishes the thermionic arc discharge from the glow discharge, in which the electrons are supplied by secondary emission, and this difference is responsible for the fact that the voltage necessary to sustain an arc discharge is much less than for the glow discharge. The voltage across the glow discharge must be large enough to produce secondary electrons by positive ion bombardment of the cathode. However, the electrons are already available by thermionic emission in the arc, and the only voltage necessary is that required to accelerate the electrons to the energies necessary for ionization of gas atoms. The ionization is necessary in order to produce the plasma, the region of zero net space charge, so that the current is not space-charge-limited, and can attain large values. Therefore, the voltage across the arc discharge is of the order of 12 to 20 volts, which is the range of the first ionization potentials of the gases commonly used in commercial tubes. This is considerably lower than the voltages necessary to maintain a glow discharge, so that the volt-ampere characteristic of the discharge drops suddenly upon the transition from glow to arc. It will be noted from Fig. 1-3, Sec. 1.3, that the voltage across the arc decreases as the current increases.

1.8   Arc with Externally Heated Cathode

This type of arc discharge is one of the most important ones as far as engineering applications are concerned. Once the discharge has started, it is essentially no different than the thermionic arc already discussed. In differs from the thermionic arc in that the supply of electrons is produced by heating the cathode from an external source of power, as is done in the thyratron, for example.

The cathode is usually of the oxide-coated type, so that there is always a copious supply of electrons around the cathode whether the current is flowing or not. This is in marked contrast to the glow or thermionic arc discharges, which require a flow of current as the means of producing electrons at the cathode. For this reason the arc in a tube with an externally heated cathode can be established *without passing first through the glow discharge stage.* As the voltage across such a tube is increased from zero, current which flows at voltages below the value required for ionization is essentially the current which would flow in the same tube structure with no gas present; in other words, the current is space-charge-limited. It is, however, an extremely small current because of the tube geometry. As the potential required to produce ions is approached and a few ions are formed, the potential distribution curve is altered by the positive ions in such a way as to increase the field intensity near the cathode. Thus greater electron current leaves the cathode to produce more ions. This process is cumulative, so that in a very short time the tube "breaks down" or "fires" to form the arc discharge, in which the current is determined principally by the external circuit.

Some of the phenomena involved in the arc discharge of a hot-cathode tube may be visualized qualitatively with the aid of potential distribution diagrams. Figure 1-6 shows four such diagrams for the special case of a parallel plane diode, but the conclusions reached for this geometry should be valid for other configurations. For parallel planes, where the potential V is assumed to vary only with x, the differential equation to be satisfied is Poisson's equation:

$$\frac{d^2V}{dx^2} = -4\pi\rho. \tag{1.2}$$

Here ρ is the space-charge density, and must have associated with it a positive or negative sign depending upon whether the net charge density is positive or negative. Since the second space derivative of potential gives the curvature of the potential distribution curve, it follows that a negative space charge leads to a positive curvature. Thus at a voltage just below the value required to produce ions, the net space charge is negative, and the potential diagram has the shape of curve 1, Fig. 1-6. Under this condition the slope at the cathode is small, and the current is space-charge-limited. A slight increase of voltage causes the production of positive ions in great enough quantities to reverse the sign of the net space charge, except very close to the cathode. The resulting potential distribution is shown by curve 2, in which the voltage gradient at the cathode has been increased, so that a greater electron current can be drawn from

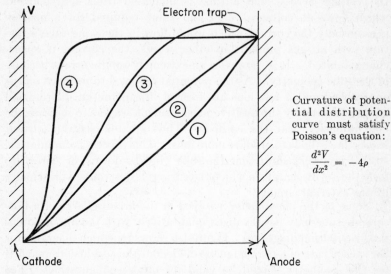

Curvature of potential distribution curve must satisfy Poisson's equation:

$$\frac{d^2V}{dx^2} = -4\rho$$

Fig. 1-6. Potential distribution curves for various space charge distributions in a hot-cathode parallel plane diode.

the cathode. The greater electron current produces more ions, which in turn produce greater negative curvature. This cumulative process may conceivably lead to the potential distribution diagram of curve 3. If such a distribution were to occur, electrons in the region of the potential maximum would experience a deceleration in their progress toward the anode because of the negative gradient. Electrons arriving at the potential maximum from the cathode have relatively small energies because of the many collisions suffered en route. Therefore most of them have insufficient energies to carry them to the anode through the decelerating field. They would therefore be trapped in the region of the potential maximum which we have supposed to be caused by an excess of positive ions. But

the trapped electrons neutralize the positive space charge, thus causing the potential distribution curve to flatten out into the form of
curve 4. Thus it is apparent that a distribution of the form of
curve 3 is not stable and would therefore not occur in the steady
state. The distribution of curve 4 is stable and has been observed
experimentally. Its stability is made apparent through the following argument. Suppose an excess of positive ions appears in the
flat part of curve 4. A hump would appear, which would immediately form an electron trap as described above, and the hump

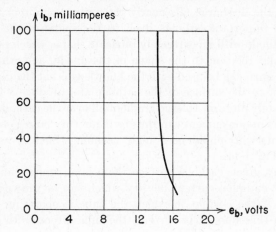

Fig. 1-7.   Volt-ampere characteristic of a hot cathode gas diode.

would immediately be flattened by the trapped electrons. If an
excess of electrons were to appear in the flat region of curve 4, the
curve would be depressed in the direction of curve 2. The consequent reduction of gradient at the cathode would reduce the electron
current, and the original excess of electrons would thus disappear.

The reader will realize from the above discussion that the principal function of the gas in a hot-cathode discharge tube is to neutralize the effect of negative space charge, so that relatively large
electron currents can be drawn from the cathode with relatively
small voltages across the tube. In fact, the voltage across the tube
need only be of the order of magnitude of that required to produce
ionization, and this voltage is almost independent of the amount of
current flowing through the tube. The volt-ampere characteristic
typical of a small gas filled tube is shown in Fig. 1-7.

1.9   Conditions at the Cathode of a Hot Cathode Tube

It has been explained in Sec. 1.8 that because of the relatively large voltage gradient at the cathode of a hot-cathode gas discharge tube it is possible to draw relatively large currents from the cathode. The actual *current density* at the cathode is not appreciably greater in a gas tube than it would be in a high-vacuum tube with the same voltage gradient at the cathode.   However, in a gas tube the useful cathode area per unit of anode area can be made enormously greater than is possible in a high-vacuum tube.   This is so because the plasma of the discharge fills nearly the entire volume of the tube, and, more important, adjusts itself to the shape of the cathode. Thus a cathode with an extremely intricate shape, which needs bear no particular relation to the shape of the anode, and which has a very large area, can be used with the knowledge that the plasma will shape itself to the surface of the cathode and produce a large and approximately uniform voltage gradient all over the cathode surface. The total emission current can thus be made very large compared to the currents obtainable in a high vacuum.   Such a cathode is shown in Fig. 1-11.

For any given cathode surface there is an upper limit to the thermionic emission current density which can be drawn from the cathode.   If the current in which the tube is operating demands more than this amount of current, the tube attempts to supply it by an increase in voltage drop across the tube.   Most of this drop appears close to the cathode, so that positive ions can bombard the cathode with sufficient energies to give secondary emission of electrons to supply the additional current requirements.   Unfortunately the voltages through which the ions must fall to produce appreciable secondary emission are also large enough to cause the ions to wear away the cathode surface by a process known as sputtering.   The process is not clearly understood, but the result is that the cathode surface is quite rapidly worn away.   In the case of oxide cathodes, which are used extensively in hot-cathode gas tubes, this sputtering soon destroys the emitting ability of the cathode.   It has been found experimentally that sputtering begins at a certain tube voltage which is characteristic of the particular gas and cathode material.   Thus for an oxide cathode in mercury vapor, the critical disintegrating voltage is about 22 volts, and for long tube life it is very important to keep the tube drop below this value.   Increase of the voltage across a hot-cathode gas tube with increasing current is an indication that the cathode can no longer supply the required current by thermionic emission alone.   This condition is to be avoided, because it leads to shortened tube life or immediate failure if the condition is severe.

1.10 Plasma of a Gas Discharge. Probes

The plasma conditions and the use of probes to be discussed in this section apply equally well to cold- or hot-cathode discharges, but the discussion is placed here because it has particular significance in connection with grid controlled hot-cathode tubes in which the grid can be considered as a probe.

It has already been pointed out that the plasma is a region which contains equal concentrations of positive ions and electrons.   There is also a great number of neutral gas atoms.   In fact, the number of positive ions is small compared to the number of neutral atoms, the ions representing perhaps 1 or 2 per cent of the total number of particles.   The ions and atoms, whose masses are nearly identical, are in a state of random motion.   The randomness arises from the chance collisions among the enormous numbers of particles.   If these collisions are assumed to be elastic, it is apparent that any individual particle may acquire any velocity from zero to quite large values, and this velocity may be in any direction.   Out of a very large number N of particles, it can be shown that the number dN_c having velocities in any direction between c and $c + dc$ is given by Eq. 1.3, which is known as the Maxwell-Boltzmann distribution function.

$$\frac{dN_c}{N} = \frac{4c^2}{\sqrt{\pi}\, c_0{}^3}\, \epsilon^{-c^2/\, c_0{}^2}\, dc \tag{1.3}$$

In this equation, c_0 is a constant equal to the most probable velocity, which may be thought of approximately as the velocity possessed by the largest number of particles at a particular instant.   It will be observed from Eq. 1.3 that the probability of a particle's having either a very small or a very large velocity is extremely small.   It is quite easy to show from Eq. 1.3 that the effective, or root-mean-square velocity C is

$$C = \sqrt{\frac{3}{2}}\, c_0 \tag{1.4}$$

Existing simultaneously with the ions and atoms are the electrons, which may be considered to behave as a gas also, and which have a velocity distribution function of the Maxwell-Boltzmann type. The law of equipartition of energy[3] states that two gases in equilibrium with each other have equal average kinetic energies. Therefore, if m and m_e represent the masses of an atom and an electron respectively,

$$\frac{mC^2}{2} = \frac{m_e C_e{}^2}{2},$$
(1.5)

where C and C_e are the rms velocities of atom (or ion) and electron, respectively. It is evident from Eq. 1.5 that the velocities attained by the two kinds of particles are inversely proportional to the square roots of the masses. Thus, for mercury vapor, the rms velocity of the electrons is about 608 times that of the atoms.

In addition to the random motion described, the electrons and ions also have slow drift velocities toward the anode and cathode, respectively. These velocities are usually relatively small, however, because the potential gradient in the plasma is quite small.

It is now possible to explain some of the conditions which exist at various kinds of surfaces which are either immersed in or bound the plasma. At surfaces made of insulating material, such as the glass walls of an enclosing tube, a negative surface charge accumulates. The reason for this accumulation is that in the steady state there can be no net current flow to the insulating surface. Since in the plasma the electrons have much higher velocities than the ions, the number of electrons per second striking an initially uncharged surface is much greater than the number of ions. Therefore a negative charge accumulates on the insulating surface. The field of this charge repels electrons and attracts positive ions, and in the steady state, the charge density adjusts itself so that the number of fast moving electrons which penetrates the repelling field is exactly equal to the number of relatively slow moving positive ions attracted to the surface by the field. In this way the requirement of zero current to the insulating surface is fulfilled. The region adjacent to a surface containing a charge such as that described is known as a *sheath*. Sheaths may form at conducting surfaces also, and the

[3] For a brief discussion of kinetic theory of gases, see Chapter I of Cobine, reference 2 above.

charge on the surface may be positive, negative, or zero, depending upon the amount and direction of current carried by the conducting surface.

Consider now a metallic probe immersed in the plasma of a discharge. If a probe is not connected to any external circuit, so that the probe current must be zero, the sheath which forms on the probe is exactly like that described for the insulating surface. However, if the potential of the probe with respect to one of the electrodes, say the cathode, is made adjustable, then as the probe is made more negative with respect to the cathode, and therefore with respect to the plasma, less and less electron current and more positive ion current flows to the probe. If the probe is made negative enough, the positive ion current reaches a saturation value determined by the random positive ion current density of the ions in the plasma. Under this condition the probe is covered by a positive ion space charge which is visible as a dark sheath covering the probe. If the thickness of this sheath is small compared with the mean free path of an ion, the ion current is space-charge-limited, and the current density J_+ can be represented approximately by Child's law:

$$J_+ = K \frac{E^{3/2}}{d^2} \tag{1.1}$$

This relation is only approximate because of the initial random velocities of the ions as they enter the sheath from the plasma, and a correction for this effect should be made at low voltages. It is not important for our purposes, however. Since further increases in probe voltage cannot result in more ion current, then according to Eq. 1.1 an increase in the thickness d of the sheath is the only result of making the probe voltage more negative. Under these conditions the potential distribution in the sheath is such that all electrons approaching the sheath are reflected back into the plasma. Also the entire potential difference between the probe and the plasma appears across the sheath, so that the negative potential of the probe has no effect upon the plasma except to draw a positive ion current from it. It is for this reason that the negative grid of a thyratron, to be discussed later, has no effect upon the plate current of the tube after conduction has started.

Suppose that the probe is now gradually made less negative to the cathode. At first the positive ion current stays unchanged, but the repulsion of electrons becomes less effective and electron current begins to reach the probe. The result is a decrease in the magnitude of the net probe current. As the probe voltage becomes zero with respect to the cathode, as at point B of Fig. 1-8, the current is still mostly ion current. As the voltage is made positive to the cathode the current soon becomes zero, as at point C. At this point exactly equal numbers of electrons and positive ions reach the probe per second. It should be pointed out that although the probe

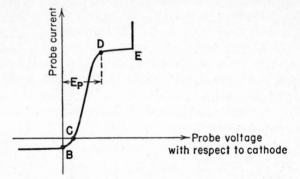

Fig. 1-8. Volt-ampere characteristic of a probe in a gas discharge. Positive ion current to the probe is plotted negative.

is positive to the cathode at this point, it is still negative to the plasma itself. The truth of this statement will be apparent when it is recalled that in the plasma the average velocity of the electrons is many times that of the ions, so that the probe must be made negative to the plasma if it is to collect equal numbers of electrons and ions. As the probe is made more positive to the cathode (and less negative to the plasma) the current increases again, but it is now predominately electron current. As the probe potential approaches that of the plasma, the probe receives the total random currents of both ions and electrons, and since the electron velocities are much greater, the net current is almost entirely electron current. This condition occurs at point D of Fig. 1-8, and the potential E_p is the potential of the plasma with respect to the cathode. Under this condition there is no net space charge at the probe surface, or in other words there is no sheath, and the plasma extends undisturbed to the surface of the probe. Further increase of the probe voltage does not increase the electron current, since at point D the probe already is receiving the maximum possible electron current as determined by the velocity distribution of the electrons. However, the relatively small ion current which also exists at point D is decreased rapidly to zero, so that there is a small increase in the total current. The volt-ampere characteristic then becomes flat and the current is all electron current. Further increase of the probe voltage may result in the transfer of the main discharge current from the anode to the probe, as at the point E of Fig. 1-8. In the region to the right of D an electron sheath forms around the probe.

1.11 High-field Emission Arcs

In Secs. 1.8, 1.9, and 1.10 the phenomena associated with externally heated cathode arcs were discussed. It may be mentioned here that although such arcs exhibit many of the characteristics of self-maintaining arcs, they really are not self-maintaining, since if the heater power be removed the anode-to-cathode voltage necessary to maintain the arc increases considerably. In this section we return to a consideration of certain truly self-maintaining arcs in which high-field emission is thought to play an important part in the mechanism of electron production at the cathode. It will be recalled that in any arc the phenomena at the cathode have the all-important task of producing the electrons necessary for the discharge.

In general, high-field emission is the phenomenon of electron emission from a surface due to the presence of an extremely high electric field intensity at the emitting surface. It may occur alone or simultaneously with thermionic emission. The relative importance of field emission as an electron producing mechanism in arc discharges is a somewhat controversial matter, since in most arc discharges it is difficult to determine whether the electron emission comes from thermionic emission as described in Sec. 1.7, or from high-field emission. The high-field theory has been proposed in order to explain the fact that the current densities obtained from certain cathodes are much greater than those obtainable by thermionic emission. This statement is based upon measurements of arc current, cathode spot area, and cathode spot temperature. The measurements of spot area and temperature are difficult and subject to considerable uncertainty, and therefore it is difficult to decide how much of the emission to attribute to thermionic emission and how much to other phenomena. In fact some investigators have proposed that the measured temperatures are much too low, and that actually the temperature may be high enough to account for the observed current by thermionic emission alone. However it is the concensus that in some kinds of arc, field emission is important.

The high field intensity necessary to produce field emission at the cathode exists in the cathode fall region in which there is a high concentration of positive ion space charge. The thickness of the cathode fall region is so small that it has not been measured directly, so that it is possible for large gradients to exist in this region in spite of the fact that the total cathode fall voltage is only a few volts.

Practical devices in which this form of emission is thought to occur are the various tubes and tank rectifiers employing mercury pool type cathodes. In such tubes the arc forms a localized spot on the cathode to which all the current flows, in the manner described in Sec. 1.7. In mercury pool type cathodes the spot is in continual random motion over the surface of the mercury, the speed of motion being of the order of 10 meters per second. This is one of the reasons why it is difficult to measure the size and temperature of the arc spot. In this form of discharge a considerable amount of cathode material is evaporated and sputtered away from the cathode spot. For this reason the mercury cathode has a great advantage over other solid types in that it is self-healing. The evaporated or sputtered material condenses on nearby surfaces and returns to the cathode pool as a liquid.

1.12 Characteristics of Hot Cathode Gas Diodes

The term *hot cathode* is used here in the same sense as the term *externally heated* cathode, which has been explained in previous sections of this chapter. The discharge in such a tube is nonself-maintaining, although, as is explained in Sec. 1.11, it has many of the characteristics of a self-maintaining discharge. These tubes are frequently referred to as phanotrons, and their use is extremely widespread.

The cathodes of phanotrons are almost always of the oxide-coated type, which give relatively large emission current at a rather low cathode temperature. They are most commonly filled with either an inert gas such as argon or neon at a pressure of the order of 0.01 mm Hg or with mercury vapor at a pressure of this order of magnitude. The inert gas is introduced into the tube after evacuation in gaseous form, whereas the mercury introduced is in liquid form.

The breakdown potential of the diode depends on the pressure of the gas. In general, the lower the pressure, the higher is the breakdown potential. This is because the number of ionizing collisions made by an electron in its flight from cathode to anode decreases with pressure, so that greater voltage must be applied to produce the ionization required to maintain the discharge. In tubes filled with mercury vapor the pressure depends upon the temperature of the condensed mercury. The temperature is above ambient temperature by some 15 or 20 degrees C because of the heater power and the loss due to tube drop. At an ambient temperature of 20°C, the vapor pressure of the mercury is 0.001 mm Hg, and at 40°C the pressure is about 0.006 mm Hg. Thus one would expect a decrease of breakdown potential as the tube warms up after heater power is applied, and this is found to be the case. The breakdown potential is of the order of one or two times the ionization potential of the gas contained in the tube. However, once conduction has started, the tube drop decreases rapidly with increasing current to a value of the order of, or less than, the ionization potential of the gas, and, as has been pointed out in Sec. 1.8, the tube drop then remains nearly constant over a relatively wide range of current (see Fig. 1-7). The drop is so nearly independent of current that in making circuit calculations where tube drop must be taken into account, the assumption is nearly always made that the tube drop is constant.

In the case of tubes filled with an inert gas, where the liquid phase does not exist in equilibrium with the gas as it does in the mercury vapor tubes, the gas pressure is directly proportional to the absolute temperature of the gas. Therefore a change of 20 degrees from ambient to operating temperature causes only very small changes in pressure and breakdown voltage. This is one advantage of the use of inert gases in gas tubes.

It has already been explained in Sec. 1.9 that the current which can be carried by the hot-cathode gas tube is limited to the thermionic emission current which can be drawn from the cathode. Any attempt to exceed this limit means that the additional current must be supplied by secondary emission through positive ion bombardment of the cathode, with the accompanying increase of the tube drop and shortening of cathode life.   Therefore it is important to design circuits utilizing gas tubes so that the anode current is within the tube rating, if long life and reliable operation are to be expected. This means that there must be a certain minimum resistance or impedance in the anode circuit, since the tube itself cannot limit the current.

The current through a phanotron can be reduced to zero, or the arc can be extinguished, by reducing the voltage across the tube to such low values that ionization cannot be maintained.   This result can be obtained by reducing the power supply voltage, by increasing the series resistance or impedance, or by other methods to be discussed later.

Gas-filled diodes are commercially available in a variety of forms and sizes whose average current capacities vary from $\frac{1}{8}$ ampere to about 100 amperes.

1.13   Voltage Regulator Tubes and Glow Rectifiers

The cold-cathode glow discharge operating over the normal glow range has an essentially constant voltage drop from anode to cathode, as has been mentioned in Sec. 1.3 and 1.5.   This is the range of operation from D to E of Fig. 1-3.   This property of the normal glow discharge has found wide application in voltage regulator tubes, where the constant drop across the tube is used as a source of relatively constant voltage.   One form of such a tube consists of a bare straight wire anode placed concentrically inside a hollow cylindrical cathode whose inner surface is usually coated with an oxide such as barium oxide.   It has already been pointed out that the voltage across such a tube is determined by the choice of gas and cathode material.   The cathode is made with a large area so that the tube operates in the normal glow condition over as large a current range as possible.   The shape and material of the anode are relatively unimportant as far as electrical characteristics are concerned.

The electrical characteristics of four commonly used regulator tubes are shown in Table 1.1.   The column headed Rated volts gives the nominal value of the voltage across the tube when operating within its rated current limits. The maximum rated current is the upper limit of current allowable for good tube life. It is the current which just completely covers the area of the cathode with the cathode glow. To increase the current beyond this value requires increased voltage, as in the abnormal glow region of Fig. 1-3, and such a voltage increase is in itself undesirable in a regulator. Also the increased energies of the bombarding ions would shorten the tube life by sputtering of cathode material. The exact mechanism of sputtering, which was mentioned in Sec. 1.9, is not thoroughly understood, but the net result is a removal of cathode mate-

Table 1.1   Characteristics of Voltage Regulator Tubes

Tube type	Rated volts	Rated ma		Approx. starting volts	D-c anode supply volts	Regulation, volts	
		Max.	Min.			5 to 30 ma	5 to 40 ma
VR 75	75	40	5	100	105	3	5
VR 105	105	40	5	115	133	1	2
VR 150	150	40	5	160	185	2	4
OA2	150	30	5	155	185	2	..

rial from the cathode surface. If this process is allowed to occur to any extent in tubes with coated cathodes, the life of the tube is seriously shortened.

The approximate starting volts is the voltage required to cause the tubes to fire when they are new. As the tubes age, the gas pressure slowly decreases, one of the chief reasons being that material sputtered from the cathode may trap gas atoms when the sputtered material condenses on nearby surfaces, such as the tube walls. The decrease of pressure is called gas cleanup, and it results in an increase in the required starting voltage. A well-designed circuit must then be able to supply more than the starting voltage for the new tube in order to insure firing of the tube as it ages. This higher voltage is given in the column headed D-c anode supply volts.

As the current in the normal glow region is varied, the voltage across the tube varies slightly. This variation is given in the column of Table 1.1 headed Regulation, volts. Thus the variation of voltage across a VR75 is 3 volts as the current varies from 5 to 30 ma, and it becomes 5 volts if the current varies from 5 to 40 ma.

The glow tube may also be used as a rectifier. This application requires that one electrode, a, be much smaller than the other electrode, b. Thus in the circuit of Fig. 1-9, when electrode b is the cathode, a relatively large current can flow through the load resistance R before the cathode becomes completely covered by the glow and the tube drop begins to increase. However, when the smaller electrode, a, becomes the cathode, its area becomes completely covered by the glow at a very low current.

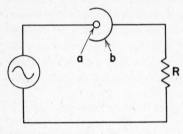

Fig. 1-9. The glow tube used as a rectifier.

Beyond this point the discharge goes into the abnormal glow region, where the voltage across the tube rises rapidly with current. Therefore the average current in this direction is much less than when electrode b is the cathode, and rectification is the result. Such a tube is limited to applications requiring relatively small current, of the order of 50 to 100 ma. Its advantage is that it is simple and requires no heater current.

1.14 Two-electrode Mercury Pool Rectifiers

In Fig. 1-10 is shown a sketch of a small sealed-off type mercury pool rectifier. In this particular tube there are two anodes for full-wave operation. The starting electrode is required in order to start conduction between either anode and the mercury pool cathode. Starting is accomplished by tipping the tube so that some of the mercury of the starting electrode runs into the larger cathode pool, thus closing an external circuit which is so connected that current flows from one pool to the other. The tube is then righted to its original posi-

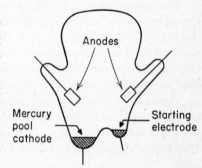

Fig. 1-10. Sealed-off mercury pool rectifier.

tion. When the circuit is broken, an arc occurs which causes enough ionization throughout the tube to permit conduction between either of the anodes and the cathode pool. One method of operating the tube is to use it as a full-wave rectifier in such a way that the arc shifts back and forth between two anodes so that there is ionization in the tube at all times. If for any reason the arc should go out, the ions would recombine in a short time, and the tube would have to be started again with the starting electrode. In some applications it may be necessary to allow the main arc to go out periodically. In such cases a tube with a "keep-alive" electrode may be used. Such an electrode is merely an auxiliary anode which carries a small continuous current sufficient to maintain the necessary starting ionization in the tube at all times. Such a tube is sometimes called an *excitron*.

Very large mercury pool rectifiers with many anodes have been built for polyphase rectification. They are built in steel tanks and are continuously pumped in order to maintain the necessary low pressure. Such units, which have been built to handle several thousand kilowatts, cannot be easily tipped, and so a movable starting electrode is provided inside the tank.

As was pointed out in Sec. 1.11, it is thought that the current in mercury pool cathode tubes is carried by high-field emission arcs. Such arcs can be made to carry much larger currents than can be carried in a hot-cathode tube because the cathode cannot be damaged by positive ion bombardment, or if it is damaged locally it is self-healing. This is the reason for using mercury pool cathode tubes for large-current applications.

1.15 The Thyratron

A thyratron is a hot-cathode gas-filled tube containing, in addition to the cathode and anode, a third electrode, the grid. Fig. 1-11 shows the electrode structure of a type FG-57 thyratron. It differs greatly from the structure of the conventional high-vacuum triode, the principal differences lying in the grid and cathode structures. In this tube the grid is a very large structure almost completely surrounding the anode and cathode and containing a baffle between the anode and the cathode. The cathode is indirectly heated by the centrally located heater spiral within the inner cylinder of the cathode. The oxide-coated surfaces are the radial vanes connecting the inner and outer cylinders, the outside of the inner cylinder, and the inside of the outer cylinder. This structure gives a very large emitting area in which the heater power is relatively low. The shaping of the plasma to fit the complicated shape of such a cathode has already been explained in Sec. 1.9.

The purpose of the grid is to determine the conditions under which the tube will break down. Because the grid almost completely shields the cathode from the anode, it is possible, by the application to the grid of a relatively small negative voltage with respect to the cathode, to nullify the effect on the voltage gradient at the cathode of a relatively large positive anode voltage. In this way the grid is able to control the anode voltage at which breakdown occurs. However, as soon as conduction starts and the plasma is established, *the grid no longer has any control whatever over the anode current,* which is determined then by the impedance of the external anode circuit and the applied voltage. This result is a consequence of the formation of a sheath around the grid, which then behaves like a probe immersed in the plasma. Several of the phenomena associated with probes have already been discussed at some length in Sec. 1.10. The most important facts to remember here in connection with the application of thyratrons are that the grid controls only the anode voltage at which the tube breaks down, and that the grid has no control of the anode current thereafter. The grid, however, draws a current to itself just as any other probe would, depending upon the voltage of the grid with respect to the plasma.

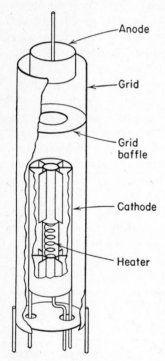

Fig. 1-11. Electrode structure of FG-57 thyratron.

The characteristics of a given thyratron are usually displayed by plotting anode breakdown voltage against grid voltage, both voltages being measured with respect to the cathode. Such a curve

is known as the control characteristic.   Control characteristics for
the type FG-57 thyratron are shown in Fig. 1-12.   This tube is filled
with mercury vapor, and therefore, as was explained in Sec. 1.12, the
breakdown potential depends upon the temperature of the condensed
mercury.   For this reason curves for several temperatures are
shown.   It will be observed that for a constant grid voltage the
breakdown voltage decreases with increasing temperature.   In the
case of tubes filled with one of the inert gases it is usually necessary

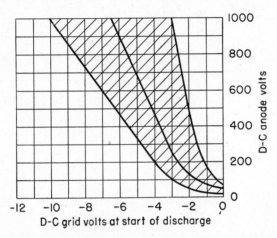

Fig. 1-12.   Control characteristics of a type GL-5559/FG-57 thyratron.
Intermediate curve is for condensed mercury temperature of 40°C.   (Courtesy
of General Electric Company.)

to give only one characteristic curve, since there is very little change
with temperature.

The type FG-57 tube is called a negative-grid thyratron, because
the grid is negative over the useful range of operation on the control
characteristics.   In some applications it is desirable to be able to
operate the thyratron with the grid positive.   Such a tube is the type
FG-33, which differs in construction from the FG-57 in that there are
three grid baffles instead of one between the anode and cathode,
and each of these baffles has several relatively small holes in it
instead of one large hole.   This grid structure so completely shields
the cathode from the anode that the grid must be made positive in
order to cause the tube to fire.   The control characteristics of this
tube are shown in Fig. 1-13.

In many applications it is important to know the ionization and deionization times of a tube. The ionization time is the time which elapses between sudden application of anode voltage and actual breakdown of the tube. The deionization time is the minimum

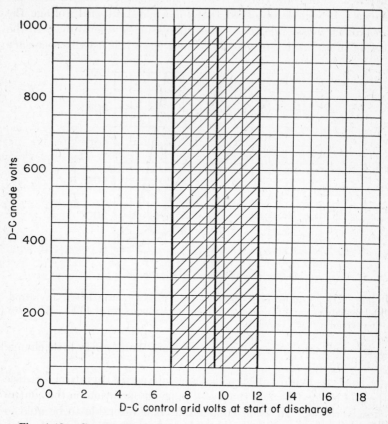

Fig. 1-13. Control characteristics of a type GL-5720/FG-33 thyratron for condensed mercury temperature range from 40°C. to 80°C. (Courtesy of General Electric Company.)

time required after anode current ceases to flow for the positive ions of the sheath around the grid to diffuse away and be neutralized to such an extent that the grid can control the tube when the anode is again made positive. The ionization time is small, usually of the order of 1 to 10 microseconds. In most applications it is not important because it is usually small compared to the deionization time. The latter is of the order of 100 to 1000 microseconds, depending upon a number of factors.   Increasing the gas pressure increases the deionization time, since the diffusion process is slower and because the probability of ion formation increases with pressure.   Large currents cause large deionization times because of the larger number of grid sheath ions which must recombine, the number of these ions depending on the plasma ion density.   On the other hand, large surface areas and close electrode spacings favor rapid deionization, and so do large negative voltages on the electrodes during the deionization period.

During World War II a special hydrogen-filled thyratron was developed for use in pulse generator circuits.   This development presented many special problems which are adequately discussed elsewhere.[4]   The tubes are mentioned here because of their very short ionization and deionization times.   The ionization time is of the order of 0.05 microsecond.   The deionization time is not known accurately, but it is of the order of 5 microseconds.   Ratings for three such tubes are contained in Table 1.2, p. 39.

1.16   Grid Current, Shield-grid Thyratrons

In the thyratron structures described in the preceding section, the grids may draw an appreciable grid current before the tube fires, especially in the case of a positive grid type such as the FG-33. This current is of the order of a microampere and may be completely negligible in many applications; but in any application requiring a high-impedance grid circuit as, for example, in phototube circuits, the grid current may be very disturbing.   To minimize this grid current, the shield-grid thyratron has been developed.

A cutaway view of the electrode structure of a type FG-95 shield-grid thyratron is shown in Fig. 1-14.   The control grid is located between the two baffles of the shield grid in such a way that the control grid is shielded from both the cathode and the anode.   In this way condensation of electron emitting material from the hot cathode onto the cool control grid is minimized, thus greatly reducing one of the principal causes of grid current.   Furthermore, the

[4] Hydrogen thyratrons and their properties are discussed in detail in *Pulse Generators*, Massachusetts Institute of Technology Radiation Laboratory Series, vol. 5, McGraw-Hill Book Company, Inc., New York, pages 335–354.

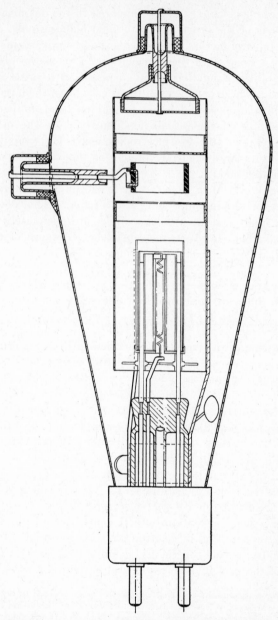

Fig. 1-14. Electrode structure of the type GL-5560/FG-95 shield-grid thyratron. (Courtesy of General Electric Company.)

electrostatic shielding between control grid and anode reduces the grid-to-anode capacitance to a small value.   In circuits where there are sudden changes in anode voltage during the nonconducting portions of the cycle of operation, the control grid voltage may change enough, due to grid-anode capacitance, to cause spurious firing of the tube.   For this reason a low ratio of grid-anode capacitance to grid-cathode capacitance is desirable.   In many applica-

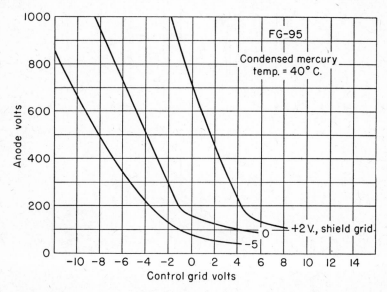

Fig. 1-15.   Control characteristics of a type GL-5560/FG-95 thyratron with various shield-grid voltages for condensed mercury temperature of 40°C.

tions the shield grid is connected to the cathode, and the tube is used as a three-electrode tube.   Another advantage of the shield grid is that it can also be used as an additional control on the firing of the tube, and there are a number of circuits which take advantage of this possibility.

The effect of the shield grid upon the control characteristics of an FG-95 is shown in Fig. 1-15, in which a number of characteristics are given for various shield-grid voltages.   Since this tube is a mercury vapor tube, all curves are for the same condensed mercury temperature, namely 40°C.

In Fig. 1-16 is shown a cutaway view of the electrode structure of a type 2050 shield-grid thyratron, which is a small inert-gas-filled tube. This structure is very different from the others shown and is included to show the great differences in geometry which can be

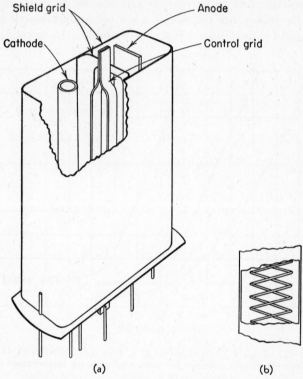

Shield grid ─

Anode

Cathode

Control grid

(a)

(b)

Fig. 1-16.   (a) Cutaway view of type 2050 shield-grid thyratron electrode structure.   (b) Cutaway view of cathode showing heater.

used in a gas tube.   The cathode is a long hollow cylinder, with the emitting material on the outside and a spiral heater coil on the inside.

1.17   Ratings of Thyratrons

In the application of thyratrons to practical circuits it is important that they be operated within the ratings specified by the manufacturer.   In this section the most important of these ratings will be discussed.

Cathode or heater voltage.   The tube may have either a directly heated filamentary type of cathode or an indirectly heated cathode.

In either case the manufacturer specifies a rated filament or heater voltage and current. In a gas-filled tube the best operating temperature range for the cathode is rather narrow. If the cathode is too cool, it may not provide adequate thermionic emission, and the tube will try to provide the additional electron requirement by positive ion bombardment of the cathode as explained in Sec. 1.9. Such bombardment very quickly destroys the cathode emitting surface. On the other hand, the cathode should not be operated at too high a temperature, for such operation causes an abnormally high rate of evaporation of emitting material, with consequent shortening of life. Therefore the manufacturer usually specifies that the filament or heater voltage be maintained within a certain percentage of its nominal rated value, usually of the order of plus or minus 5 per cent.

Heating time. In mercury-filled tubes it is important to maintain the temperature of the condensed mercury at a certain minimum value, as has been explained in Sec. 1.12. It is a secondary function of the heater or filament of such a tube to bring the temperature of the condensed mercury up to the proper operating temperature *before anode voltage is applied.* In the case of mercury-vapor-filled tubes, the *heating time* is the time necessary to bring about this temperature increase. It is usually of the order of 1 to 5 minutes, although it may be shorter or longer than this. In the case of inert-gas-filled tubes the specified heating time is merely the time required to bring the cathode to operating temperature, and this time is usually of the order of a few seconds to half a minute.

Maximum peak inverse voltage. This is the maximum safe voltage by which the anode may be made negative to the cathode. It is determined principally by arc-back, that is, the formation of an arc between anode and cathode when the anode is negative to the cathode. Arc-backs may disrupt the operation of some circuits or they may cause damage to the tubes in which they occur. The maximum peak inverse voltage is the largest instantaneous voltage which should ever be allowed to appear across the tube in the inverse direction if the probability of arc-back is to be kept negligibly small.

Maximum peak forward voltage. This is the maximum instantaneous anode voltage in the forward direction which a suitably controlled grid can prevent from firing the tube.

Maximum instantaneous anode current. This current is the greatest instantaneous periodic anode current which the tube can carry without overheating the anode or damaging the cathode by positive ion bombardment. The permissible duration and frequency of this peak current are functions of the thermal properties of the tube. These are, in effect, specified by the maximum average anode current rating.

Maximum average anode current. This rating is the greatest permissible average anode current based upon the greatest allowable temperature for any part of the tube. In conjunction with this current rating there must also be specified a *maximum averaging time* over which the above average current may be determined. The reason for specifying the maximum averaging time is made apparent from the following example. Suppose the maximum average anode current of a tube is 10 amperes, and the maximum averaging time is 10 seconds. The average current of 10 amperes may be obtained from an infinite number of periodic wave shapes, but not all of these are permissible. Thus a periodic square wave in which the current is 20 amperes for 0.5 second and zero for 0.5 second gives an average current of 10 amperes. The minimum time required to determine the average value of this current is one complete cycle, or 1 second in this case. This is well within the maximum averaging time and is therefore permissible. However, the same average current could be obtained from a square wave in which the current is 20 amperes for 9 seconds and zero for 9 seconds. Here the current must be averaged over a minimum time of 18 seconds to obtain the true average value. This is greater than the specified maximum averaging time, and therefore this wave form could not be handled by the tube, although the average value of the current is within the tube's rating. In this case the period of the repetitive current is so great compared with the thermal time constant of the tube that one or more of the electrodes would experience periodic temperature increases greater than should be permitted for long tube life. It is in order to prevent abuse of the tube in this way that the maximum averaging time is specified in addition to the maximum average anode current.

Maximum surge current. This is the maximum instantaneous anode current which the tube can safely carry occasionally, such as the current which might occur in case of an occasional short circuit. The circuit should not be designed to allow such an anode current in

Table 1.2 Ratings and Operating Data of Some Thyratrons

Type	No. of electrodes	CATHODE			ANODE						Tube Drop, volts		Kind of gas
					Peak volts			Amperes					
		Volts	Amperes	Heating time	Forward	Inverse	Max. inst.	Max. avg.	Surge	Avg'g. time, sec.	Max.	Min.	
GL-2D21	4	6.3	0.6	10 sec	650	1300	0.5	0.1	10	30	8		Inert
GL-3C23	3	2.5	7.0	15 sec	1250	1250	6.0	1.5	120	5	16		Hg & inert
FG-17	3	2.5	5.0	5 sec	2500	5000	2.0	0.5	20	15	16		Hg
FG-57	3	5.0	4.5	5 min	1000	1000	15.0	2.5	90	15	16		Hg
FG-95	4	5.0	4.5	5 min	1000	1000	15.0	2.5	200	15	16		Hg
FG-105	4	5.0	10	5 min	2500	2500	40.0	6.4	200	15	20		Hg
FG-172	4	5.0	10	5 min	2000	2000	40.0	6.4	400	15	16		Hg
GL-414	4	5.0	20			2000	100	12.5				10	Hg
GL-678	3	5.0	7.5			15000	6	1.6					Hg
2050	4	6.3	0.6	10 sec	650	1300	1.0	0.1	10	30	8		Inert
ELC1B/A	3	2.5	6.3	25 sec	750	1250	8.0	1.0	77		14	8	Xe
ELC3J/A	3	2.5	9	30 sec	1000	1250	30	2.5	300	4.5	14	10	Xe
ELC6J	3	2.5	21	60 sec	750	1250	77	6.4	770	6	12	9	Xe
ELC16J	3	2.5	31	60 sec	1000	1250	160	16	1000	4.5	14	11	Xe
3C45	3	6.3	2.4	5 min	3000	3000	35*	0.045			~90		H_2
4C35	3	6.3	6.3	5 min	8000	8000	90*	0.100			~90		H_2
5C22	3	6.3	10.3	5 min	16000	16000	325*	0.200			~90		H_2

* For maximum pulse duration of 6 microseconds.

normal operation even if the surges were separated by considerable time intervals, because the tube normally can stand only a limited number of such surges.

Maximum average grid current and maximum instantaneous grid current. These grid current ratings are defined in the same way as the corresponding anode current ratings.

Table 1.2 gives some of the ratings and operating data on a number of typical thyratrons.

1.18 Ignitrons

An ignitron is a sealed-off tube containing an anode, a mercury pool type cathode, and a third electrode called the ignitor. These

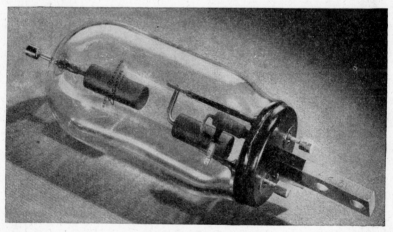

Fig. 1-17.   Construction of the type GL-5579 ignitron.   (Courtesy of General Electric Company.)

electrodes are shown in Fig. 1-17, which is a cross section of a type GL-5579 ignitron.   The function of the ignitor is to initiate conduction in the tube.   Ignition is accomplished by passing a current pulse of short duration and large magnitude from the ignitor to the mercury pool, the ignitor being made positive to the mercury pool. The ignitor rod is made of a refractory material such as silicon carbide, boron carbide, or carborundum.   The anode is usually made of carbon.

The ignitron shown in Fig. 1-17 is one of the smallest types made. For larger current ratings the tube is usually enclosed in a water-jacketed metal envelope, the water being necessary to carry away the heat developed in the tube by the tube drop and ignitor circuit losses.   Figure 1-18 shows the construction of three such tubes.

The exact mechanism by which the ignitor causes the tube to fire is not known.   One theory is that the voltage drop along the

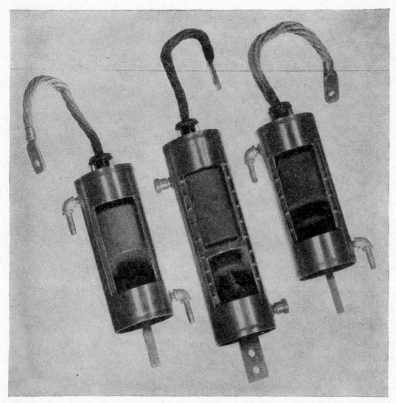

Fig. 1-18.   Construction of the types GL-5552/FG-235-A, GL-5554/FG-259-B, and GL-5822 ignitrons, left to right.   (Courtesy of General Electric Company.)

ignitor rod due to the flow of ignitor current (of the order of 30 amperes) is sufficient to cause local ionization, which in turn permits the anode to carry current.   Another theory is that the ignitor current, flowing from the ignitor rod to the mercury, causes a tiny arc at the mercury surface which produces sufficient ionization and electron emission to initiate the main discharge to the anode if the latter is positive enough to the cathode. At any rate, a short pulse of ignitor current of suitable magnitude and duration causes the tube to fire, and if the ignitor current is accurately controlled, the anode current is also accurately controlled. The advantage of the ignitron is that, like any mercury pool cathode tube, relatively large currents can be carried. Furthermore no cathode heater power

Fig. 1-19. Construction of the type GL-5555/FG-238-B ignitron showing baffle for rectifier service. (Courtesy of General Electric Company.)

is required, and of course no cathode warm-up period is required before operation.

In one sense the ignitor performs the same function for an ignitron as the grid does in a thyratron, that is, both control the time at which the anode current starts. There is, however, a basic difference in the way in which this control is effected. In the thyratron the action is *preventive*, that is, the field set up by the grid voltage prevents the anode voltage from firing the tube until either the grid voltage is reduced or the anode voltage is increased. In the ignitron, on the other hand, the action of the ignitor is *causative*, since ignitor current must flow to cause the initial production of electrons or ions required to start the discharge.

1.19 Ratings of Ignitrons

The manufacturers of ignitrons usually specify two sets of ratings for their tubes, one for intermittent rectifier service, the other for welder service. The ratings which follow apply to *intermittent rectifier service*.

Maximum peak anode voltage. The maximum inverse and forward peak anode voltages are the greatest instantaneous negative and positive anode voltages, respectively, which can be applied to the anode without firing the tube when no ignitor current is flowing.

Maximum instantaneous anode current. This is the greatest instantaneous periodic anode current which the tube can safely carry without damage by overheating.

Maximum average anode current. This rating is the greatest allowable average anode current for the tube. Just as in the case of thyratrons, a *maximum averaging time* must be specified for use in determining this rating, and the discussion of this matter for thyratrons in Sec. 1.17 applies equally here.

Maximum anode surge current. This current is defined in the same way as for thyratrons.

The following ratings are for *a-c welder control service*. In circuits of this kind two ignitrons are usually used connected in inverse parallel, or back to back, so that in effect they act as an a-c switch. For this reason the ratings for such service are given in rms values wherever possible, and it is assumed that each tube conducts for a full half cycle.

The *demand current* is the instantaneous rms current carried by a pair of ignitrons connected back to back.

The *maximum kilovolt-ampere* demand is the product of the supply voltage in rms kilovolts and the maximum current. This rating is valid only as long as the supply voltage lies within the voltage range specified by the manufacturer, and for voltages less than the minimum of this range the kva demand is to be computed as though the specified minimum voltage were being used.

There are two average anode currents. One is the *average anode current* corresponding to the kva demand, and it is defined as 54 per cent of the maximum average anode current. It is a true average value based on one tube only, and it is the largest average anode current which one tube can carry when both tubes are supplying the maximum kva demand.

The maximum average anode current is the largest true average current which one tube may carry as determined over an averaging time not to exceed the specified maximum averaging time. This rating is valid for a kva demand not to exceed one-third the maximum.

The *maximum surge current* is the maximum instantaneous value of current which the tube can handle in this type of service,

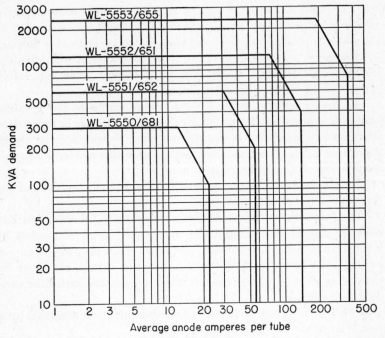

Fig. 1-20. Average ignitron anode current per tube as a function of demand kva for two tubes back-to-back, for four types. (Courtesy of Westinghouse Electric Corporation.)

and its magnitude in amperes is usually given as a per cent of the maximum rms demand current.

Three sets of curves are commonly given on the data sheets for ignitrons. Examples are shown in Figs. 1-20 and 1-21. In Fig. 1-20 are shown a set of curves of average anode current plotted against demand kva for several tubes. The upper break point in each curve occurs at the average anode current corresponding to the maximum kva demand, and the lower break point comes at the maximum average anode current. Figure 1-21 gives per cent duty

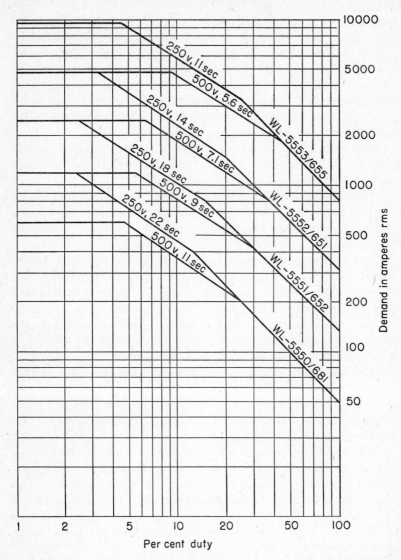

Fig. 1 21. Demand current for two ignitrons back-to-back as a function of per cent duty for 250 and 500 volts supply voltage, for four types. Averaging time is marked in seconds on each curve. (Courtesy of Westinghouse Electric Corporation.)

as a function of demand current for supply voltages of 250 and 500 volts rms. Per cent duty as read from the curves multiplied by maximum time of averaging anode current will give the greatest allowable time during which the given demand current can be carried continuously. A block of current having this magnitude and duration can be repeated periodically with a period equal to the maximum time for averaging anode current.   Ignitor ratings are the same for both classes of service.

The *maximum instantaneous allowed ignitor potential*, ignitor positive, is the greatest positive potential which the ignitor is designed to withstand.

The maximum instantaneous required ignitor potential, ignitor positive, is the potential which, when applied between ignitor and cathode for the maximum ignitor ignition time, will surely cause the ignitron to fire.

The maximum instantaneous allowed ignitor potential, ignitor negative, is the greatest negative potential which the ignitor is able to withstand, because too great a negative ignitor current will destroy the ignitor.

The maximum instantaneous allowed ignitor current is the greatest instantaneous current which should ever be allowed to flow in the positive direction through the ignitor.

The maximum instantaneous required ignitor current is that current, which, when allowed to flow for the maximum ignitor ignition time, will surely cause ignition.   Ignition will also occur if maximum instantaneous required ignitor potential is applied for the maximum ignitor ignition time.

The maximum average allowed ignitor current is the greatest average value the ignitor current can attain during periodic operation of the tube without overheating the ignitor circuit. This maximum average is to be determined in a time not to exceed the maximum ignitor current averaging time, which is defined in the same way as for the corresponding time for a thyratron, defined in Sec. 1.17.

The impedance of the ignitor circuit may be approximated by considering it to be a pure resistance equal to the ratio of the maximum instantaneous allowed ignitor potential to the maximum instantaneous allowed ignitor current. This ratio gives resistances of the order of 3 to 10 ohms.

CHAPTER 2

BASIC GASEOUS TUBE CIRCUITS

The theory and characteristics of the most important types of gaseous tubes have been discussed at some length in Chapter 1. The purpose of the present chapter is to discuss some of the more important basic circuits which are used in conjunction with these tubes. A few of the circuits considered will be essentially complete in themselves, as for example, the glow tube regulator circuit, but most of them will be only parts of circuits, such as the various circuits for controlling the grid of a thyratron. These circuits may appear frequently in a wide variety of complex circuits, all of which could not possibly be included in a book such as this, but if the basic circuits from which the complex whole is built are well understood, there should be little difficulty in understanding the operation of the more complicated circuits. Furthermore, if a new circuit is to be invented and designed to perform a new task, it is usually conceived in the mind of the engineer in the form of a combination of component circuits whose individual behavior is already familiar to him.

2.1 The Glow Tube as a Voltage Regulator

The glow tube has already been mentioned in Sec. 1.13 as a means of regulating voltage. Figure 2-1 shows a circuit for voltage regulation by means of a glow tube. The purpose of this circuit is to supply a constant voltage E_L to the load resistance R_L, regardless of changes in load resistance or supply voltage E. The circuit will do this within certain limits of operation which will become apparent with the following discussion.

The load voltage is determined by the amount of current flowing through the glow tube, or regulator tube, and therefore, if constant voltage is to be maintained, the current I_R must be kept within the straight-line part of the volt-ampere characteristic of the tube. If the tube has the characteristic shown in Fig. 2-1(b), then I_R must stay between 5 and 30 ma. The load voltage then remains constant at 150 volts. Suppose, for example, that the load current is 50 ma and the tube current is 20 ma. Then the current I through R is 70 ma. If the load current decreases to 40 ma because of an increase

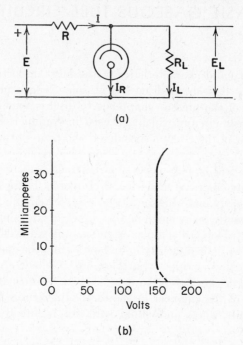

(a)

(b)

Fig. 2-1.   (a) Circuit for voltage regulation by means of a glow tube.   (b)
Volt-ampere characteristic of a typical glow tube.

in R_L, the tube current increases to 30 ma, leaving the total current I unchanged. Thus the drop IR stays unchanged, and if E is constant, E_L remains unchanged. Thus the regulator tube has changed its current in such a way that the load voltage remains constant. Suppose now that with this new condition the supply voltage E increases, causing a small increase in I. All this current increase flows through the regulator tube as long as the total tube current stays within the linear part of the tube characteristic. Therefore the voltage across the load remains constant, and the increase of supply voltage has been compensated for by an increased voltage drop, IR.

Thus it is apparent that, within the current range of the regulator tube, the circuit of Fig. 2-1 regulates against changes of load current or supply voltage. The relations discussed above can be expressed quantitatively by writing the voltage equation around either loop of the circuit and the current equation at one junction.

$$E = RI + E_L \tag{2.1}$$

$$I = I_R + \frac{E_L}{R_L} \tag{2.2}$$

$$\therefore \quad R = \frac{E - E_L}{I_R + \dfrac{E_L}{R_L}} \tag{2.3}$$

In these equations I_R, the regulator tube current, must be held within the operating range specified by the manufacturer. If this is done, the load voltage E_L, which is also the tube voltage, is equal to the rated tube voltage as specified by the manufacturer. Ratings are given for several typical tubes in Table 1.1, Sec. 1.13.

In the design of a regulator circuit, consideration must be given to the fact that the voltage required to start the tube is considerably larger than the operating voltage. For example, Table 1.1 shows that the starting voltage for a VR150 tube is about 160 volts. The voltage across the tube before it fires is

$$E_L = \frac{ER_L}{R + R_L} \tag{2.4}$$

because I_R is zero. Thus, in a circuit utilizing a type VR150 tube, the voltage given by Eq. 2.4 must be at least 160 volts.

Voltage regulator tubes of equal current ratings may be operated in series to provide various magnitudes of regulated voltages or to permit tapping of a voltage supply. Regulator tubes may not be operated in parallel because of slight variations in characteristics from tube to tube. For example if the firing voltages of two tubes in parallel differ by any amount whatever, one tube will fire first, thus reducing the voltage across the pair so that the other tube will never fire. However, a regulator tube in series with a resistor of the order of 100 or 200 ohms may be operated in parallel with another such series combination. The disadvantage of such a series combination is that poor regulation results because of the resistors.

2.2   The Glow Tube as an Oscillator

The circuit of Fig. 2-2 shows how a glow tube may be used in a circuit to produce oscillations. The operation of the circuit is

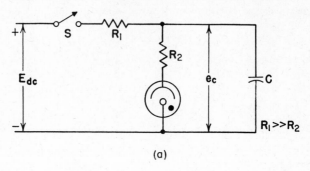

(a)

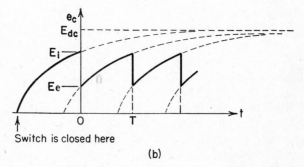

(b)

Fig. 2-2.   Relaxation oscillator circuit using a glow tube.

explained with the help of Fig. 2-2(b). It is assumed that before the switch s is closed there are no currents flowing and no charge on capacitor C. When the switch is closed, the voltage across the capacitor begins to rise along an exponential curve which would approach E_{dc} as a limit if no interruptions were to occur. During this initial period no current flows in the glow tube, and the voltage across the tube is the same as that across the capacitor. When the tube voltage reaches the ignition or ionization potential E_i, the tube fires and partially discharges the capacitor through R_2. The discharge occurs in a time which is very short compared to the charging time, because R_2 is very much smaller than R_1. In fact, R_2 is in the circuit only to limit the capacitor discharge current to a value which does not damage the tube. The discharge continues until the voltage across the tube falls to a value too low to maintain the discharge, whereupon the tube circuit opens. The extinction voltage of the tube is designated E_e. After extinction of the tube current, the capacitor begins recharging along the exponential curve characterized by R_1 and C until ignition potential is again attained. The cycle of firing, extinction, and recharging then repeats periodically with a period T. The period may be calculated by solving the differential equation of the series R_1-C circuit.

$$E_{dc} = e_c + R_1C \frac{de_c}{dt},$$

$$e_c = E_{dc} + A\epsilon^{-t/R_1C}. \tag{2.5}$$

At $t = 0$, Fig. 2-2(b), $e_c = E_e$. Therefore

$$A = -(E_{dc} - E_e),$$

and $$e_c = E_{dc} - (E_{dc} - E_e)\epsilon^{-t/R_1C}. \tag{2.6}$$

At $t = T$, $e_c = E_i$, and solution of Eq. (2.6) for T gives

$$T = R_1C \ln \frac{E - E_e}{E - E_i}. \tag{2.7}$$

It has been assumed in this calculation that the discharge time is so small in comparison with T as to be completely negligible.

This oscillator is frequently called a relaxation oscillator. In general the sloping portion of the sawtoothed wave is curved. For many applications it is desirable to have the sloping part a straight line. This condition can be approximated very well by making the ratio of $E_i - E_e$ to E_{dc} small.

The relaxation oscillator has a practical upper limit on frequency which is determined by the deionization time of the tube. The capacitor voltage must not be allowed to build up so rapidly that the tube refires because of residual ionization before the tube voltage has built up to its normal ignition voltage. If this happens the tube conducts continuously, and if the current is in the normal glow range, the circuit behaves like the regulator circuit discussed in

Sec. 2.1. The use of relaxation oscillators of this type is generally limited to frequencies less than 10,000 cycles per second.

It is quite feasible to use hot-cathode diodes or thyratrons in relaxation oscillators. The basic principles are the same as for the glow tube, and so this matter will not be discussed further. Problem 2 illustrates the use of the thyratron in such a circuit.

2.3 Hot Cathode Diodes

Hot-cathode diodes, both high-vacuum and gaseous types, are used in industrial applications almost entirely for rectification. In such applications the high-vacuum types are used in rectifiers for supplying power at relatively high voltages and low currents, and where good filtering is required. The gas-filled types are used in applications requiring relatively large amounts of power. Such applications are so important that Chapter 3 has been devoted to the discussion of rectifiers and inverters, and they will therefore not be discussed here. The remaining applications of hot cathode diodes are so varied that it is difficult to treat them as a group, and so these cases will be discussed as they occur in various circuits.

2.4 Thyratron Circuits

Thyratron circuits may be classed broadly as d-c circuits or a-c circuits, depending upon whether the source of power for the anode circuit is a d-c source, such as a rectifier and filter circuit, or an a-c source, such as the secondary winding of a transformer. In any thyratron circuit the principal problem is control of the anode current. It has been explained in Chapter 1 that once the anode current starts to flow, it is limited only by the external circuit. Therefore the only way in which the thyratron circuit can effect any control is to determine when the current begins to flow and when it stops flowing. In a-c circuits the grid can determine when the tube fires, and the fact that the anode supply voltage goes negative every half cycle takes care of extinction of the anode current. In d-c circuits the grid determines when the tube fires, but since the grid cannot control the current once it starts to flow, some auxiliary means of extinguishing the current must be provided. Thus in d-c circuits the principal problem is the method of extinction, whereas in a-c circuits the method of controlling the grid is of paramount importance.

2.5   Direct-current Thyratron Circuits

An extremely simple way to ensure the extinction of thyratron anode current in some applications is the use of a large series resistor between the power supply and the anode.   Such a circuit, which is a close relative of the relaxation oscillator, is shown in Fig. 2-3.   The purpose of this circuit is to produce a large negative voltage pulse across R_2 when a small positive triggering pulse is applied to the grid.   In operation, the grid is biased so as to prevent the thyratron from firing.   The capacitor C then charges to the supply voltage E through R_1 and R_2, thus applying voltage E to the anode. When the triggering pulse occurs, the thyratron fires, producing

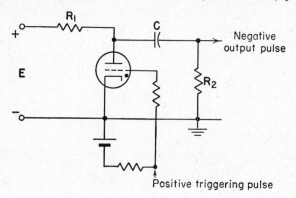

Fig. 2-3.   D-c circuit illustrating the use of a large series resistor to aid in extinction of the thyratron.

the desired negative pulse across R_2 and discharging C to such a low voltage that the thyratron current cannot be maintained.   The thyratron remains nonconducting if R_1 is so large that the voltage across the capacitor does not rise appreciably before deionization occurs and the grid can regain control.   Also, R_2 must be small compared to R_1, for otherwise these resistors would form a voltage divider which would cause an appreciable part of E to appear across the thyratron at the beginning of the recharging period. This particular circuit is of limited importance because of its rather special behavior, but it has been included to show that a limited sort of control over a thyratron may be achieved in a d-c circuit by means of a large plate circuit resistor.   Other variations of this circuit will doubtless occur to the reader.

2.6 Basic Parallel Control Circuit

A very effective way to cause anode current extinction in a d-c circuit is to drive the thyratron anode negative to the cathode by some electrical means for a time long enough for deionization to

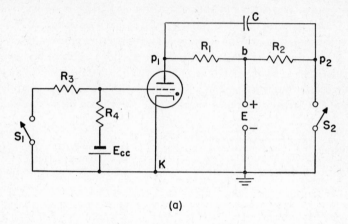

(a)

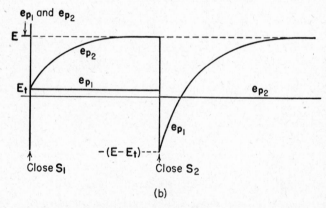

(b)

Fig. 2-4.   (a) Basic parallel control circuit.   (b) Voltages of points p_1 and p_2 referred to cathode.

occur.   The basic circuit for this purpose is shown in Fig. 2-4.   The circuit operates as follows.   Resistors R_3 and R_4 may be so designed that closing switch s_1 causes the tube to fire.   The voltages of points p_1 and p_2 drop at once to the tube drop voltage E_t, as shown in Fig. 2-4(b), where all voltages are referred to the cathode.   The voltage

e_{p_1} stays at the value E_t as long as the tube conducts, but e_{p_2} rises exponentially toward E as C charges through R_2 and the tube to a voltage which approaches $E - E_t$ in the steady state. If switch s_2 is closed after the voltage across C has reached essentially the steady state, the potential of point p_2 is suddenly reduced from E to 0. The potential of point p_1 is thus forced to a voltage $E - E_t$ below cathode potential, since the voltage across the capacitor cannot be changed instantaneously. The anode current is therefore very suddenly cut off, and if in the meantime the grid circuit switch s_1 has been opened, the grid can regain control of the tube. As long as switch s_2 remains closed, the potential of point p_1 rises exponentially toward E as C charges through R_1.

2.7 Basic Parallel Inverter

The essential features of operation of the parallel control circuit of Fig. 2-4 are unchanged if the switch s_2 is replaced by another

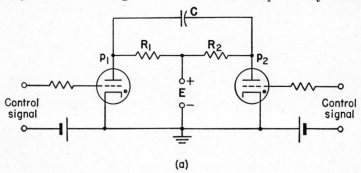

(a)

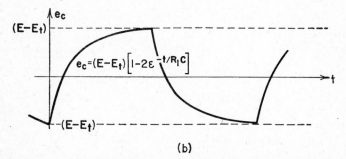

(b)

Fig. 2-5. (a) Parallel control circuit which is basis of parallel inverter. (b) Wave form of voltage across C.

thyratron, and if both grids are controlled by voltages or control signals supplied from an appropriate external circuit. Such an arrangement is shown in Fig. 2-5(a), and this circuit forms the basis for the parallel inverter, which is discussed in detail in Chapter 3. This circuit is also basic to certain counter circuits in which the quantity or phenomenon to be counted causes voltage pulses to appear at the grids of the tubes. The rate of counting for such a circuit is limited by the deionization time of the tubes. For inverter type operation the grids must be supplied with periodic positive pulses. If these pulses are so spaced that the voltage across the nonconducting tube attains essentially the steady-state condition before that tube is fired, the wave form of the voltage across the capacitor C is as shown in Fig. 2-5(b). It is left for the reader to convince himself that this is so by sketching separately the voltages of points p_1 and p_2 and subtracting one curve from the other. It is the function of an inverter to provide a voltage of periodically alternating polarity from a constant voltage source of energy. It is apparent from Fig. 2-5(b) that this circuit performs this function. As will be discussed in Chapter 3, it is possible to make the output voltage very nearly sinusoidal.

2.8 Series Control Circuit

A series control circuit is displayed in Fig. 2-6(a) in which the load resistor and a capacitor C are connected in series with the d-c power supply and tube 1. Let us suppose that initially neither tube is conducting. The capacitance C is very much greater than either of the plate-to-cathode capacitances C_{pk}, so that most of the d-c supply voltage E appears across tube 1. A positive control voltage on this grid therefore causes tube 1 to fire, and the voltage of the point a with respect to ground suddenly drops to $-(E - E_t)$, assuming zero initial voltage across C. The capacitor then charges toward a maximum voltage of $E - E_t$, and the voltage of point a rises exponentially toward zero. When the current reaches zero, tube 1 stops conducting and point a has attained a constant positive voltage of $E - E_t$ with respect to point c. Tube 2 may now be fired by a suitable control signal to its grid, since its cathode is negative with respect to its anode by $E - E_t$ volts. When tube 2 fires, the potential of point a suddenly rises to $E - 2E_t$ volts and then decays exponentially to zero, leaving terminal a of the capacitor

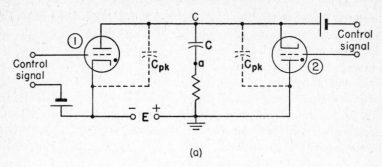

(a)

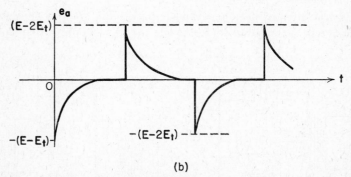

(b)

Fig. 2-6. (a) Series control circuit which is basis of series inverter. (b) Wave form of voltage e_a across the load resistor R_L.

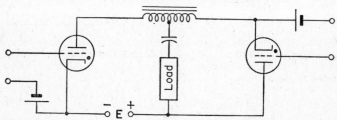

Fig. 2-7. Practical series control circuit.

charged positive to c by E_t volts. After the current in tube 2 has become zero, tube 1 may be fired again, thus driving point a negative to $-(E - 2E_t)$ volts. Thereafter the wave form of the voltage across the resistor R_L is symmetrical about the zero axis, the peak voltages being the same in either direction.

Although this circuit could be made to operate as described above, successful operation depends upon making sure that the current in one tube is completely extinguished before the other tube fires, for otherwise the d-c power supply could be short-circuited through the two tubes in series.   It is poor practice to try to operate a circuit in which such a possibility exists.   One way in which this difficulty can be avoided is to separate the anode of tube 1 from the cathode of tube 2 by inserting a center-tapped inductive reactance as is shown in Fig. 2-7.   This circuit is essentially a series inverter circuit, and since such circuits are discussed in detail in Chapter 3, no further discussion will be given here.

2.9   Alternating-current Thyratron Circuits

It has already been mentioned in Sec. 2.4 that in thyratron circuits where the power for the anode circuit is supplied from an a-c

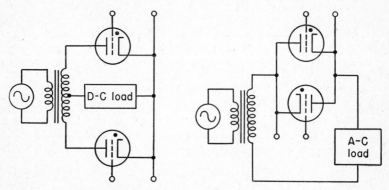

Fig. 2-8.   Basic rectifying and back-to-back thyratron circuits for controlling power from an a-c source.   (a) Thyratron-controlled rectifier circuit.   (b) Circuit for controlling alternating current to a load by means of a back-to-back connection of thyratrons.

source, extinction of the anode current is not usually a problem and that principal interest centers around the method of controlling the grid.   Before proceeding to detailed discussions of such circuits it is well to point out that thyratron circuits taking their power from an a-c source may be divided broadly into two groups, those which supply the load with rectified current, and those which supply the load with alternating current, which may or may not be sinusoidal.   For example, the rectifying type of circuit would be used to operate a d-c motor from an a-c line.   But the nonrectifying type of circuit is more suitable for applications involving only the accurately controlled production of heat, because then transformers can be used to advantage. This kind of circuit is used widely in resistance welding applications, some of which are discussed in Chapter 6 on timing circuits. Elementary circuit diagrams of these two basic circuit types are shown in Fig. 2-8. In part (a) is shown the basic full-wave rectifying circuit, and in part (b) is shown the basic non-rectifying circuit in which the tubes are connected in the so-called back-to-back connection.

2.10   Thyratron Control by D-C Bias

In Fig. 2-9 is shown one of the simplest rectifier type circuits in which some degree of control over the average current and power in the load resistor R_L is possible. In part (b) of the figure is shown the sinusoidal supply voltage e_{ba}, the voltage of point a with respect to point b, to which all voltages will be referred. Also the control characteristic curve of anode voltage e_b against critical grid voltage e_c is plotted so that the vertical anode voltage axis is used for both the control characteristic curve and the sinusoidal supply voltage curve. Negative grid voltage e_c is plotted to the left of the origin, and angular displacement ωt is plotted to the right of the origin. As long as no anode current flows, the voltage of the anode with respect to the cathode is the sinusoidal supply voltage e_{ba}. Therefore the critical grid voltage at which the tube fires must vary with time also. At a given time t_1, for example, the instantaneous anode voltage may be calculated or found from the curve of e_{ba}. This voltage and the control characteristic determine the critical grid voltage as shown at point y, which may then be plotted at time t_1 below the time axis. In the figure this point is marked x. Graphical determination of a number of such points determines a curve of critical grid voltage as a function of angular displacement of the supply voltage. This curve is called the *control locus* for this particular tube used with this particular sinusoidal supply voltage. For a different supply voltage or a different tube the control locus would, in general, be different. Suppose now that the grid bias voltage E_{cc} is adjusted to -4 volts. The point at which the tube fires is then given by the intersection of the control locus with the horizontal line $e_c = -4$. In Fig. 2-9 this intersection occurs at the angle α, and if tube drop is considered to be negligible, the voltage across the load suddenly jumps to the value $E_m \sin \alpha$, and it varies sinusoidally thereafter until the supply voltage goes to zero again. The grid then regains control.   It is apparent that variation of the d-c grid bias may be used to control the angle at which the tube fires within a range from about zero to 90°.   It is not possible to make the tube fire at a point between 90° and 180°, and this is

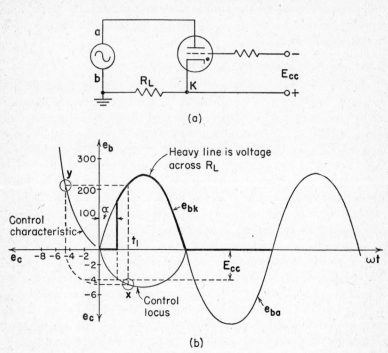

(a)

(b)

Fig. 2-9.   Thyratron control by means of an adjustable d-c bias.   In part (a) E_{cc} may be supplied from any adjustable d-c source, such as a battery and potentiometer, or a d-c amplifier.

one of the principal disadvantages of this circuit.   Another disadvantage is that for firing angles near 90° the firing angle is likely to shift slightly from cycle to cycle, because in this region a very slight vertical shift in either the control locus or the bias voltage causes a relatively large horizontal shift in the intersection of these two curves.   The advantage of the circuit is its simplicity.

The method described above for controlling the firing angle of a thyratron involves the variation of magnitude, and hence the verti-

cal shifting, of the grid voltage.   Therefore this method of control is
sometimes referred to as *vertical control*.

2.11   Thyratron Control with D-C and A-C Voltages

A circuit is shown in Fig. 2-10(a) in which the disadvantages of
the simple d-c bias type of control are removed.   The new feature of

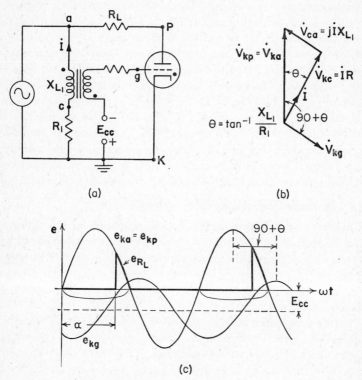

(a)   (b)

(c)

Fig. 2-10.   (a) Circuit for thyratron control with a-c and d-c voltages in the
grid circuit.   (b) Phasor diagram for the alternating voltages of the circuit.
(c) Instantaneous values of voltages showing firing angle α.

the circuit is that an alternating component of voltage has been
added to the d-c component of grid bias, and the phase of the alternating voltage has been shifted so that it lags the anode supply voltage by an angle $90 + \theta$, where θ is less than $90°$.   The phase shift is
accomplished by placing a resistor in series with the primary of the
transformer whose secondary supplies the a-c part of the grid volt-

age. The phasor[1] diagram, Fig. 2-10(b), shows the various voltage drops involved. In reading this diagram it is important to notice the order of the subscripts. Thus $\dot{V}_{ka}$ is the voltage drop from k to a, etc. The polarity of the transformer has been so selected that the a-c component of grid voltage *lags* $\dot{V}_{kp}$ instead of leading. If this is not so, the tube fires as soon as the anode becomes positive. The instantaneous voltages of the anode and grid with respect to the cathode are plotted in part (c) of the figure. It is apparent that the firing angle α can be shifted over a range very considerably greater than 90° in this circuit by variation of the d-c component of bias E_{cc}. Furthermore, since the angle of intersection between the grid voltage and the control locus is quite large, especially in the region near 90°, the firing angle does not tend to shift as much from cycle to cycle as in the circuit of Fig. 2-9. The circuit has the disadvantage that a greater change in E_{cc} is necessary to produce a given phase shift, the greater the a-c component of grid voltage is made. Since phase shift is accomplished here by variation of the d-c bias, this circuit may be classed as a vertical control circuit also.

2.12 Thyratron Control with Phase Shifting Circuits

In Fig 2-10 it is apparent that the firing angle of the thyratron could be shifted by shifting the phase of the a-c component of grid voltage with respect to the anode supply voltage instead of by changing the d-c bias voltage. In such a control system, which is sometimes called horizontal control, it is not even necessary to use a d-c component of bias.

Before proceeding with details of electronic circuits, a few phase shifting circuits will be discussed. As an introduction to the subject, the circuit of Fig. 2-11 will be analyzed. The transformer is center-tapped, so that the voltage drops V_{12} and V_{23} are equal. The current $\dot{I}$ lags the applied voltage by the angle θ, and so also does the voltage $\dot{V}_{14}$. The drop across L is $\dot{V}_{43}$, which leads $\dot{V}_{14}$ by 90°. The sum of these voltages must equal the constant voltage $\dot{V}_{13}$, which is the hypotenuse of the right triangle 1-4-3. As the resistance R is varied, $\dot{I}$ and $\dot{V}_{14}$ vary in magnitude and direction, but the

---

[1] The term *phasor* is used in this book to designate quantities with sinusoidal time variation, such as voltage, in order to avoid confusion with true *vector* quantities which have direction as well as magnitude. See Sec. 10.5 for a discussion of this terminology.

hypotenuse and the right angle do not change. Therefore the locus of point 4 is a semicircle of radius V_{12} with center at 2. The voltage $\dot{V}_{24}$ therefore has constant magnitude, but its phase with respect to $\dot{V}_{13}$ is continuously adjustable from 0 to 180° if R is varied from infinity to zero, respectively.

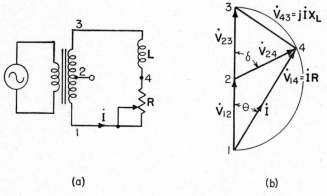

(a)   (b)

Fig. 2-11. Simple R-L phase shifting circuit.

The angle δ by which $\dot{V}_{24}$ lags $\dot{V}_{13}$ is very easily found. From the geometry of the phasor diagram,

$$\delta = 180 - (180 - 2\theta) = 2\theta, \tag{2.8}$$

where
$$\theta = \tan^{-1}\frac{X_L}{R}.$$

A similar phase shifting circuit can be made by replacing the inductance by a capacitance, and in many cases this is a more practical circuit, since it is very difficult to build low-resistance inductances, but it is easy to obtain almost perfect capacitances.

The phase of the voltage V_{24} of Fig. 2-11 may also be shifted by changing L, and this is sometimes done by using a saturable core reactor as the inductance. In this way the inductance may be changed over a wide range by a change of a few milliamperes of direct current in the saturating winding.

Thus one may use L-R circuits where either inductance or resistance is variable, or R-C circuits with resistance variable. The choice of which of these to use depends upon the kind of stimulus or signal which is to be used to produce the phase shift.

The analysis of the phase shifting circuit of Fig. 2-11 was very simple because it was assumed that there was no external circuit connected across terminals 2 and 4. There are many applications (see, for example, Sec. 6.12), where this is not so, and therefore an analysis of a more general circuit will be made. Reference will be made to Fig. 2-12. This circuit contains a general reactance X, which may be inductive or capacitive, and a general load impedance $\dot{Z}_L$.

Take point 1 as a reference and write Kirchhoff's current law equation at junction 4 in terms of voltage drops from points 2, 3, and

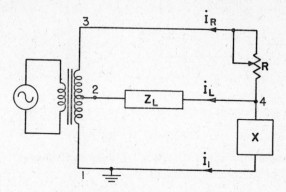

Fig. 2-12.   Resistance-reactance phase shifting circuit with a load.

4 to the reference point. Assume that $\dot{V}_{31} = 2\dot{V}_{21}$ and that these are known. Then at junction 4,

$$\dot{I}_1 + \dot{I}_L + \dot{I}_R = 0$$

$$\dot{V}_{41}\dot{Y} + (\dot{V}_{41} - \dot{V}_{21})\dot{Y}_L + (\dot{V}_{41} - \dot{V}_{31})\dot{Y}_R = 0$$

$$\frac{\dot{V}_{41}}{\dot{V}_{21}} = \frac{(\dot{Y}_L + 2\dot{Y}_R)}{\dot{Y} + \dot{Y}_L + \dot{Y}_R}$$

$$\frac{\dot{V}_{41} - \dot{V}_{21}}{\dot{V}_{21}} = \frac{\dot{V}_{42}}{\dot{V}_{21}} = \frac{\dot{Y}_L + 2\dot{Y}_R}{\dot{Y} + \dot{Y}_L + \dot{Y}_R} - 1 = \frac{\dot{Y}_R - \dot{Y}}{\dot{Y}_R + \dot{Y} + \dot{Y}_L}. \quad (2.9)$$

In many circuits, X is capacitive, so that $\dot{Y} = j(1/X_c)$, and $\dot{Z}_L$ may be a pure resistance R_L. Then Eq. (2.9) becomes

$$\frac{\dot{V}_{42}}{\dot{V}_{21}} = \frac{1/R - j(1/X_c)}{1/R_L + 1/R + j(1/X_c)}. \quad (2.10)$$

In Eq. 2.9 it will be noticed that if the load impedance is either infinite or very large compared to R and X, then $\dot{Y}_L$ can be neglected compared with $\dot{Y}$ and $\dot{Y}_R$. Then if $X = X_c$,

$$\frac{\dot{V}_{42}}{\dot{V}_{21}} = \frac{\dot{Y}_R - \dot{Y}}{\dot{Y}_R + \dot{Y}} = \frac{1/R - j(1/X_c)}{1/R + j(1/X_c)} = 1 \left/ -2 \tan^{-1} \frac{R}{X_c} \right. \quad (2.11)$$

Equation 2.11 states that $\dot{V}_{42}$ is a phasor of the same magnitude as $\dot{V}_{21}$ and lagging $\dot{V}_{21}$ by $2 \tan^{-1} (R/X_c)$. This is the case of the open-circuited phase shifting circuit. If $\dot{Y}_L$ is not negligible compared to $\dot{Y}_R$ and $\dot{Y}$, then $\dot{V}_{42}$ is not of the same magnitude as $\dot{V}_{21}$ and its phase with respect to $\dot{V}_{21}$ is not the simple relation given by Eq. 2.11. Then Eqs. 2.9 or 2.10 must be used.

In many applications the load, instead of being a pure resistance, may be an inductive reactance, such as the primary winding of a transformer whose secondary load is either zero or negligibly small. In many cases the transformer primary may be considered to be a pure inductance. Then in Eq. 2.9,

$$\dot{Y}_L = -j \frac{1}{X_L}.$$

$$\frac{\dot{V}_{42}}{\dot{V}_{21}} = \frac{1/R - j(1/X_c)}{1/R + j(1/X_c) - j(1/X_L)} = \frac{R + jX_c}{(X_c - X_L)R/X_L + jX_c}. \quad (2.12)$$

Examination of this result shows that certain combinations must be avoided. If $X_c = X_L$, Eq. 2.12 reduces to

$$\frac{\dot{V}_{42}}{\dot{V}_{21}} = 1 - j \frac{R}{X_c}. \quad (2.13)$$

Here variation of R can give only 90° of phase shift, and at 90°, the voltage $\dot{V}_{42}$ is infinite. If $X_c = 2X_L$, Eq. 2.12 becomes

$$\frac{\dot{V}_{42}}{\dot{V}_{21}} = \frac{R + jX_c}{R + jX_c} = 1, \quad (2.14)$$

and no phase shift is possible.

If phase shift with essentially constant amplitude is desired, X_c must be made small compared to X_L. If $X_c \leqq 0.1 X_L$, Eq. 2.12 becomes approximately

$$\frac{\dot{V}_{42}}{\dot{V}_{21}} \cong - \frac{R + jX_c}{R - jX_c} = -1 \left/ 2 \tan^{-1} \frac{X_c}{R} \right. \quad (2.15)$$

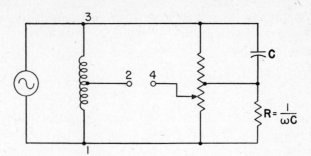

Fig. 2-13.   Phase shifting circuit which produces a continuous phase change of 180°.

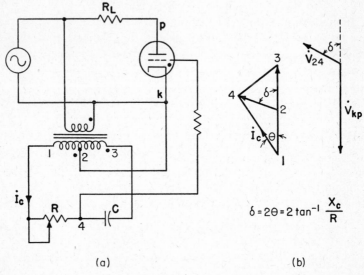

$$\delta = 2\theta = 2\tan^{-1}\frac{X_c}{R}$$

(a)   (b)

Fig. 2-14.   (a) Thyratron circuit controlled by means of an R-C phase shifting circuit. (b) Phasor diagram showing relative phases of various voltages. Note especially that the voltage from cathode to grid $\dot V_{24}$ lags the voltage from cathode to plate $\dot V_{kp}$ by an angle less than 180°. This is accomplished by arranging the transformer polarity so that $\dot V_{31}$ is in phase with $\dot V_{kp}$.

Obviously then, $\dot V_{42}$ is a phasor of constant magnitude whose phase with respect to $\dot V_{21}$ may vary from 0 to 180° as R varies from 0 to ∞.

In practice it is never possible to vary the phase shifting resistor continuously from zero to infinity, so that none of the circuits discussed can actually provide a phase shift of 180°. Figure 2-13 shows a circuit which gives a continuous phase shift over 180°, but

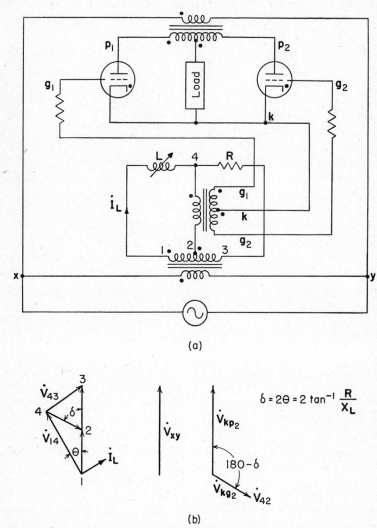

(a)

(b)

Fig. 2-15. (a) Full-wave grid-controlled rectifier with an R-L phase shifting circuit in which L is the variable inductance of a saturable reactor. (b) Phasor diagram showing relative phases of the voltages for half of the circuit.

the magnitude of the shifted voltage varies by a factor of $\sqrt{2}$ over this range.   In many applications this variation is not objectionable. It is left for the reader to satisfy himself that the statements about Fig. 2-13 are true.

Figure 2-14 shows a simple thyratron circuit in which the grid is controlled by an R-C phase shifting circuit.   The cathode and grid are connected directly to the output terminals of the phase shifting circuit.   Until the tube fires, the grid draws negligible current, and therefore the simple open-circuit theory can be applied in designing the phase shifting circuit.   Of course after the tube fires, the grid draws current.   However, we are not concerned with the performance of the phase shifting circuit after the tube fires, and furthermore the series grid resistor should be large enough to keep this current to a negligible value.

Figure 2-15 shows a full-wave grid controlled rectifier with an R-L phase shifting circuit in which the inductance is variable.   The variation of inductance is accomplished by the use of a saturable core reactor, the details of which are not shown in the figure. Saturable core reactors are discussed in Sec. 2.13.   In Fig. 2-15 the output of the phase shifting circuit is definitely loaded by the primary winding of the transformer used to couple to the two grids. Therefore either the exact relations for such a circuit must be used (Eq. 2.12), or else X_L and R must be made small enough compared to the transformer impedance so that the approximate theory will suffice.   The phasor diagrams are drawn on the basis of the latter assumption, and are included principally to emphasize the fact that correct transformer polarity relations must be maintained in order for the grids to control the firing angles of the tubes.   The phasor diagrams are drawn for only one-half of the full-wave circuit, and it will be well worth the reader's time to verify that the circuit is also correctly connected for the other half.

2.13   Saturable Reactors

Since saturable reactors are involved in numerous electronic circuits, a brief discussion of the principle of operation of this very useful device will be given here.   In Fig. 2-16(b) is shown the core and winding arrangement of a three-legged saturable reactor.   The middle leg contains the d-c winding, whose function is to produce an adjustable but constant component of flux in the two outer legs.

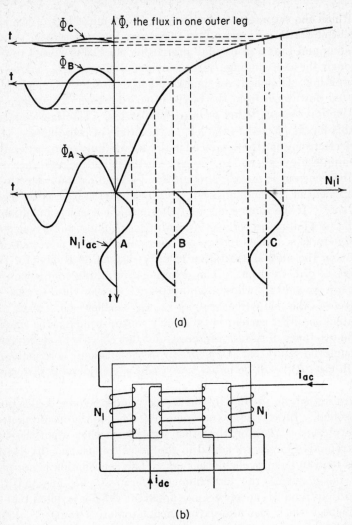

Fig. 2-16.   Saturable reactor.

The two outer legs contain the a-c windings, which are identical. In this circuit they are usually connected in series, but they may also be connected in parallel.   A small change in the amount of direct current in the d-c winding changes the reactance of the a-c windings over a wide range.   That this is true can be shown from Fig. 2-16(a), in which the saturation curve for one of the outer legs of the core has been drawn. Suppose first that there is no current in the d-c winding and that a sinusoidal alternating current is caused to flow through the a-c winding. This current, designated i_{ac}, causes an alternating component of magnetomotive force $N_1 i_{ac}$, which is plotted downward from the origin of coordinates. This magneto-motive force causes a flux Φ_A in each outer leg. The time variation of this flux is plotted to the left of the origin of coordinates. The back electromotive force induced in the a-c winding is proportional to the amplitude of Φ_A, and so, therefore, is the inductive reactance. If a direct current is passed through the d-c winding, a unidirectional component of magnetomotive force is produced in each outer leg of the core. If the same sinusoidal alternating current is maintained in the a-c windings as before, the resulting a-c component of magneto-motive force is applied to the core above and below a new quiescent point on the normal saturation curve as shown at B or C for two values of direct current. The resulting alternating components of flux are Φ_B and Φ_C, whose amplitudes are smaller than in case A. Therefore the inductive reactances are smaller too. Thus the greater the direct current in the d-c or control winding, the smaller is the reactance of the a-c windings, and this effect is brought about through the saturating characteristic of the magnetic core material.

In case B it will be noted that there is considerable distortion of the wave shape of the flux because of operation at the knee of the saturation curve, so that the back electromotive force is also non-sinusoidal. However the time phase of the induced electromotive force of the winding on the other leg is such that when the two electromotive forces are added in the series connection, the distortions tend to balance each other out. The cancellation is not perfect, but it reduces the distortion considerably. The fact that the distortions tend to cancel becomes apparent when it is noted that at an instant when the alternating magnetomotive force is adding to the constant magnetomotive force of the right leg, it is subtracting from the constant magnetomotive force of the left leg. This is one reason for using the three-legged construction of Fig. 2-16(b). Another and more important reason is that with this construction and winding arrangement there is no a-c component of voltage induced in the d-c winding due to the alternating currents. This is an important consideration, because usually the d-c winding has many more turns than the a-c windings, and the induced a-c voltage could be very large and troublesome.

There are other ways in which the results described above can be achieved, but the basic ideas are the same. Saturable reactors are built in many sizes and for many purposes. Small ones may be used as shown in Fig. 2-15, where the d-c requirement for the control winding may be small enough so that a conventional receiving type triode can control the direct current. There are many applications of larger saturable reactors where the direct current must be controlled by thyratrons. Applications of this type are control of electric furnaces and control of theater lights, where accurate and continuous control is necessary, but where sinusoidal current wave form is not important.

2.14 Peaking Transformers

It seems appropriate to discuss at this point another device whose operation also depends upon the nonlinear properties of magnetic circuits, namely the peaking transformer. A peaking transformer is a transformer whose output voltage wave form is sharply peaked, although the input voltage is sinusoidal. There are many applications for such transformers in thyratron grid circuits and other places, and it is therefore desirable for the industrial electronics engineer to understand their operation.

In Fig. 2-17(a) are shown the core and winding arrangement of one form of peaking transformer. The secondary coil is wound on a core of very small cross section compared to the cross sections of the other parts of the core. It is made of a special core material such as Nicaloi,[2] which saturates at a very low magnetomotive force, as shown in (b) of the figure. For purposes of the approximate analysis to follow, the actual saturation curve will be idealized to that shown in Fig. 2-17(c). The operation is as follows. A sinusoidal voltage e_1 is applied to the primary winding. A sinusoidal flux Φ_1 must result in the primary core, as shown in Fig. 2-17(d). As this flux increases from its zero value, the reluctance of the air gap is very large, whereas that of the idealized secondary core is zero. Hence all the primary flux flows through the secondary core and none flows through the air gap until the secondary core saturates. In the

---

[2] Nicaloi is the trade name used by the General Electric Co. for such material.

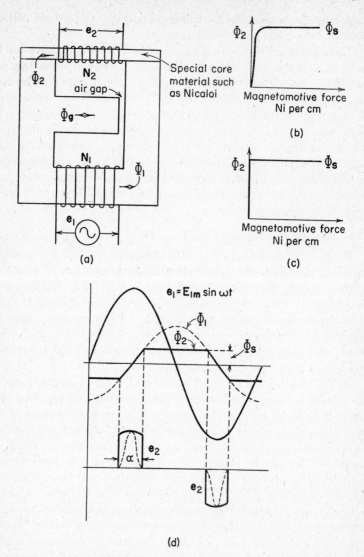

Fig. 2-17. Peaking transformer and wave forms. (b) Saturation curve for secondary core. (c) Idealized saturation curve for secondary core. (d) Voltage and flux wave forms in the idealized peaking transformer.

idealized case complete saturation occurs at a flux Φ_s, and thereafter the reluctance of the secondary core is infinite. All the additional flux from the primary core must now flow through the air gap. There is a relatively short period of time or angular displacement, designated by α in Fig. 2-17(d), when flux is changing in the secondary core, and during this time a voltage e_2 is induced in the secondary winding. The idealized wave form of the secondary voltage is shown in Fig. 2-17(d). Its amplitude E_{2m} can be calculated as follows:

$$e_1 = N_1 \frac{d\Phi_1}{dt} \times 10^{-8} = E_{1m} \sin \omega t$$

$$e_2 = N_2 \frac{d\Phi_1}{dt} \times 10^{-8}$$

$$\therefore \quad e_2 = \frac{N_2 \times 10^{-8} E_{1m}}{N_1 \times 10^{-8}} \sin \omega t, \qquad \frac{\pi - \alpha}{2} < \omega t < \frac{\pi + \alpha}{2}$$

$$\therefore \quad E_{2m} = \frac{N_2}{N_1} E_{1m} \tag{2.16}$$

The angular width α of the peak depends upon A_s, Φ_1, and the value of flux density at which the secondary saturates.

Let A_s = area of secondary core cross section,

        A_p = area of primary core cross section,

        ϕ_1 = flux density in primary, instantaneous,

        ϕ_2 = flux density in secondary, instantaneous,

        ϕ_s = flux density in secondary, at saturation.

In the interval when the secondary is not saturated,

$$A_s \phi_2 = \phi_{1m} A_p \cos \omega t, \qquad 90 - \frac{\alpha}{2} < \omega t < 90 + \frac{\alpha}{2}$$

The value of α may be determined by putting $\phi_2 = \phi_s$ and $\omega t = 90 \pm \frac{\alpha}{2}$. Therefore

$$A_s \phi_s = \phi_{1m} A_p \cos \left(90 + \frac{\alpha}{2} \right). \tag{2.17}$$

In Eq. 2.17, ϕ_{1m} may be determined from the applied voltage and the number of primary turns, N_1.

Thus
$$E_{1m} \sin \omega t = N_1 \frac{d\Phi_1}{dt} \times 10^{-8},$$

$$d\Phi_1 = \frac{E_{1m}}{N_1} \times 10^8 \sin \omega t \, dt,$$

$$\Phi_{1m} = + \frac{E_{1m} \times 10^8}{\omega N_1} = \phi_{1m} A_p.$$

$$\therefore \quad A_s \phi_s = \frac{E_{1m} \times 10^8}{\omega N_1} \cos \left(90 + \frac{\alpha}{2}\right) \cong \frac{E_{1m} \times 10^8}{\omega N_1} \frac{\alpha}{2}. \quad (2.18)$$

Equation 2.18 gives the value of α approximately. The primary current is determined mostly by the air gap. It can be calculated on the basis of finding the magnetomotive force required to force the primary flux $\phi_1 A_p$ across the air gap, and adding that to the magnetomotive force required to force the flux through the iron.

In many cases the magnetomotive force required to force the flux through the iron is negligible compared to that required for the air gap. A calculation will be made upon this assumption. Since the secondary circuit influences the primary only during the angle α, its effect can also be neglected. The instantaneous primary current can be found from the relation

$$\frac{0.4\pi N_1 i_1 \mu A_g}{g} = \Phi_g, \quad (2.19)$$

where i_1 = instantaneous primary current; $\mu = 1$; A_g = air gap area, sq cm; g = air gap, cm; Φ_g = total air gap flux. Then since Φ_g is assumed to equal Φ_1, in the intervals when the secondary is saturated,

$$i_1 = \frac{\Phi_1 g}{0.4\pi N_1 A_g}$$

To find Φ_1 notice that

$$e_1 = N_1 \frac{d\Phi_1}{dt} \times 10^{-8} = E_{1m} \sin \omega t,$$

$$\Phi_1 = - \frac{E_{1m}}{\omega N_1 \times 10^{-8}} \cos \omega t,$$

$$i_1 = \frac{-E_{1m} g}{0.4\pi \omega N_1{}^2 A_g \times 10^{-8}} \cos \omega t,$$

$$I_1 = \frac{g E_1}{0.4\pi \omega N_1{}^2 A_g \times 10^{-8}} \text{ amperes rms}, \quad (2.20)$$

where E_1 = rms primary voltage and $\omega = 2\pi f$. Such a transformer presents an impedance which is primarily a reactance, whose value can be computed from Eq. 2.20.

In the above analysis, several simplifying assumptions have been made. It was assumed that the secondary core had the idealized saturation curve shown in Fig. 2-17(c), that there was no leakage flux, that no magnetomotive force was required to force flux through the iron core except for the secondary, and that all losses were neglected. Also fringing at the air gap was neglected. Actually none of these assumptions is fulfilled in practice, and the above equations may be used only for a preliminary design. The actual wave form of the secondary voltage is more like that shown dotted in Fig. 2-17(d). In spite of the approximations involved, it is felt that the simple analysis given above is useful because it emphasizes the basic principles involved and promotes an understanding of the peaking transformer.

2.15 Thyratron Control by Nonsinusoidal Wave Forms

In the circuits discussed so far which contain a sinusoidal component of grid voltage, it is sometimes not possible to obtain sufficiently accurate control of the firing angle. Variations in line voltage, in circuit constants, or in tube characteristics may produce variations in the firing angle from cycle to cycle. The reason for this can be seen clearly in Fig. 2-10(c), for example. Here the slope of the grid voltage curve as it crosses the control locus curve is not very large, so that small vertical displacements of either curve can cause appreciable shifting of the firing angle, especially near the beginning or end of the half cycle. This difficulty may be partly overcome by making the a-c component of grid voltage very large, but this expedient causes other difficulties. In this particular circuit, for example, it would mean a greater change in the d-c component of grid voltage to produce a given phase shift. In certain automatic control circuits this would be highly undesirable.

These troubles may often be avoided by using a nonsinusoidal wave form in the grid circuit, so that the grid voltage is vertical, or nearly vertical, at the point where it crosses the control locus. Such a circuit is shown in Fig. 2-18(a), where a peaking transformer is used to provide the nonsinusoidal voltage for firing the thyratron. It is apparent from part (b) of the figure that the grid voltage is nearly vertical where it crosses the control locus, so that small vertical shifts in either curve make little difference in the firing angle. Control of the firing angle must be obtained in such a circuit by shifting the phase of the voltage applied to the primary of the peaking transformer. The peaking transformer is also easily

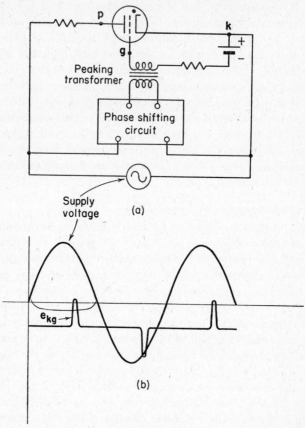

Fig. 2-18. Circuit showing the use of a peaking transformer in the grid circuit of a thyratron.

adaptable for use in a full-wave circuit by placing a center tap on the secondary winding.

The ideal voltage pulse for firing a thyratron would be one with a perfectly vertical wave front. This ideal may be approached in the circuit of Fig. 2-19. Here the output of a square wave generator is applied to a series R-C differentiating circuit in which the product

RC is much less than the period of the generator. The differentiated voltage is a series of sharp spikes of very steep wave front, and these are applied to the grid of the thyratron in the manner shown. Here the wave front of the triggering pulse is for all practical

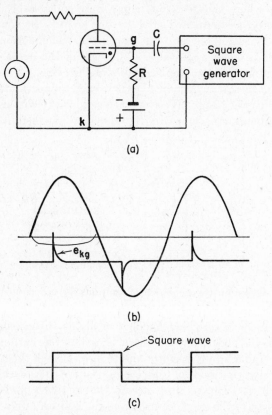

(a)

(b)

(c)

Fig. 2-19. Use of a square-wave generator and differentiating circuit to fire a thyratron.

purposes vertical. There are many ways to produce such pulses, but there is not space to discuss them here.

2.16 Ignitron Circuits

The principal difference between ignitrons and thyratrons, as far as circuitry is concerned, lies in the method of controlling the firing time. In thyratron circuits this is done by controlling the voltage of the grid with respect to the cathode, but in ignitron circuits conduction is initiated by passing a pulse of current through the ignitor.

Ignitrons are used very frequently in a back-to-back connection in circuits where they serve as a precisely controllable switch for controlling power to an a-c load.   In such circuits the ignitrons may be either "controlled" or "uncontrolled," which means that the firing angle is either adjustable at the will of the operator, or else the tubes always fire at the beginning of the cycle.

A circuit for an uncontrolled back-to-back connection of ignitrons is shown in Fig. 2-20.   The operation is very simple.   Let the controlling contactor or switch be closed at an instant when the

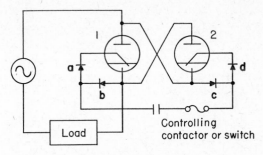

Fig. 2-20.   Back-to-back connection of ignitrons for use as an uncontrolled switch.

supply voltage is zero and anode 1 is about to become positive. As the anode goes positive, there is a flow of current through rectifiers c and a into the ignitor and thence through the load.   During this period the anode of tube 1 goes positive to its cathode by the amount of the voltage drop across the rectifiers and ignitor in series.   Most of the drop occurs across the ignitor.   In a very short time the ignitor current becomes large enough to cause the ignition of tube 1.   When ignition occurs, the ignitor current drops to a very low value, because the only voltage available to cause ignitor current is the tube drop, which is of the order of 15 volts.   On the next half cycle tube 2 is fired in a similar way by ignitor current flow through rectifiers b and d.   The tubes continue to conduct in their respective half cycles as long as the controlling switch is kept closed.   Therefore the accuracy of timing of the conduction period in this circuit depends upon how accurately the controlling switch can be closed and opened. The purpose of the rectifiers a, b, c, and d is to prevent flow of current through the ignitors in the reverse direction, for if this happens the life of the ignitors is greatly shortened. The reader can easily confirm from the circuit that if the rectifiers were not present there would be reverse current through ignitor 2 when anode 1 is positive.

In practical circuits a fuse is usually inserted in the ignitor circuit, because if the ignitor is allowed to carry too large an average current in the forward direction it will be overheated and damaged. If for some reason one of the ignitrons should fail to fire when it should, the full supply voltage would be applied to the ignitor in

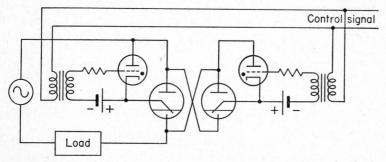

Fig. 2-21.   Circuit showing a method of controlled firing of ignitrons.

series with the load for a complete half cycle, and a very large ignitor current would flow. The fuse is designed to protect the ignitors in case of such a failure.

The rectifiers of the ignitor circuits are usually copper oxide or selenium rectifiers, which are discussed in detail in Chapter 4.

Wherever it is necessary to control accurately either the firing angle or the number of cycles of conduction, or both, the ignitor currents are usually controlled by auxiliary thyratrons, whose firing angles may be controlled by one of the methods discussed previously in this chapter. Such a circuit is suggested in Fig. 2-21.

PROBLEMS

2.1. A type FG-57 thyratron (see Fig. 1-12) is to be used in the relaxation oscillator circuit shown. The grid bias is adjusted to -4 v, $R_1 = 75,000$ ohms, $C = 1$ μf, and E_{dc} is 600 v. The condensed mercury temperature is 40°C.

What is the frequency of oscillation? Assume an extinction voltage of 10 v.
What is the average thyratron anode current?

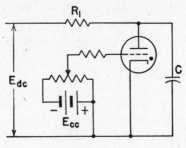

Prob. 2.1

2.2. If the grid of the thyratron in problem 2.1 has applied to it, in addition
to the negative bias, a sequence of large positive voltage pulses occurring at the
rate of 60 per second, what will be the peak-to-peak amplitude of the voltage
across C?

2.3. Show that the wave form of Fig. 2-5(b) is correct by sketching the
wave forms of the voltages of points p_1 and p_2 and subtracting one from the
other.

2.4. Show by drawing the phasor diagram of voltages in Fig. 2-13 that the
voltage $\dot{V}_{24}$ can be shifted through 180° with respect to $\dot{V}_{13}$.

2.5. The accompanying circuit is useful for producing a phase shift of less
than 180°, the limits of phase shift being adjustable by taps at 5 and 7. Draw
the phasor diagram to show the range of angles and amplitudes of voltage $\dot{V}_{26}$.

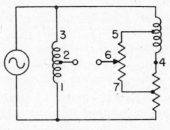

Prob. 2.5

CHAPTER 3

RECTIFIERS AND INVERTERS

The term "rectifier" or "inverter" has several connotations depending upon the person involved. Most electronic equipment, whether it is classified in communications, power, control, or some other phase of electrical work, usually includes at least one application of rectification. Inversion is not quite as commonly known since a great majority of low-power applications find it more desirable to perform this function by the use of oscillators. Strictly speaking, inversion is the transfer of power from a d-c source to an a-c sink by means of some commutating device that provides the necessary change in electric connections. This may be mechanical or electrical. Here we are interested only in the electrical possibilities.

A third application of electronics that fits well in this section is that of conversion. It is often desirable to convert power from one frequency to another, and the circuits involved are often combinations of rectifiers and inverters or modified simplifications.

The application, particularly of rectifiers, is as wide as the gap between the d-c source for your table radio and the rectifier necessary for proposed d-c transmission where several hundred thousand kilowatts may be involved.

An attempt will be made to touch on the fundamental method of approach to these applications, along with a few of the more common circuits.

For convenience, the two subjects will be treated separately, although, as already mentioned, many applications include both.

3.1 Rectifier Components

The rectifier is centered around some unilateral device that is capable of conducting current much more readily in one direction than the other.   We are primarily interested in the electron tube as this component, and upon the ratings and limitations that it may have in various applications.   There are almost hundreds of types of tubes, different in some small or large detail, that may find use in this field.   Certainly the first component of an electronic rectifier would be an electron tube, whether it be a thyratron, a phanatron, an ignitron, or a mercury pool.   From the definition of rectification there must be an a-c source.   This is usually in the form of a transformer since this is the most economical method of matching a particular power load to the country's electric supply system.

There must also be a general load for which the d-c power is to be produced.   This will have certain electrical characteristics of its own, and their effect on the rectifier's performance must be known.

The various switching and controlling elements must also be included, since many of the rectifiers depend upon direct control of the tube's firing point for control of the d-c output.

It is also often necessary to better the first product of the rectifier so that it will more nearly meet the requirements of a specific load. The reduction of ripple is accomplished by a combination of circuit components in conjunction with the load known as the filter. When needed, this is always considered as part of the rectifier and thus is listed here as an essential component.

3.2 Perfect Rectifier Analysis

The electron tube which is the chief component of the electronic rectifier is unilateral and in general nonlinear.   This is most easily seen for any particular tube by a study of its volt-ampere characteristic.   These volt-ampere characteristics are usually classified as to whether the tube is gas or vacuum.   If gas, the plate voltage is almost constant as a function of current, requiring only the ionization voltage irrespective of current so long as the conventional flow of current is from anode to cathode.   Such a curve is shown in Fig. 3-1.

In comparison, the vacuum tube requires an increasing plate voltage as the current requirement goes up.   This is, of course, due to the fact that such a tube is space-charge-limited, and the relation is approximately specified by the familiar Child's law, $i = KE^{3/2}$.   A typical relation is shown in Fig. 3-2.

The purpose of this chapter is to show the effect on current, voltage, power, and wave form of these and other electronic devices on electric circuits made up of such usual linear components as resistance, inductance, and capacitance. The task is appreciably easier if some assumptions be made concerning the rectifier that are in keeping with its actual performance. To do this a fictitious element known as a perfect rectifier will be defined.

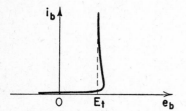

Fig. 3-1. Typical volt-ampere characteristic of a gas-filled thermionic tube.

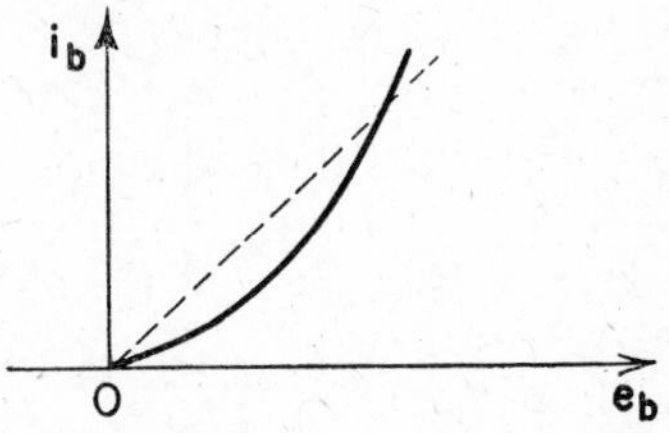

Fig. 3-2. Typical volt-ampere characteristic of a vacuum thermionic tube.

A perfect rectifier will be considered to be a perfect unilateral device, carrying any amount of current in the forward direction with no self-impedance drop of any kind, but refusing to carry any current whatsoever in the reverse direction, regardless of the applied voltage. The volt-ampere characteristic thus specified is shown in Fig. 3-3.

The actual rectifiers having such characteristics as those shown in Fig. 3-1 and Fig. 3-2 will be replaced in the electric circuit by this

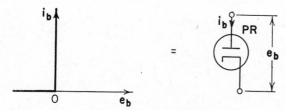

Fig. 3-3.   Volt-ampere characteristic of a perfect rectifier.

perfect rectifier. It is sometimes helpful to think of this new component as an automatic switch with zero resistance that conveniently opens or closes with the direction of proposed current flow. To make this substitution it is necessary to determine the magnitude of the error which is being introduced into the solution.

If the voltages in the circuit, such as supply voltage and load voltage, are large compared to the voltage drop across the actual tube when it carries the required current, little error results from calling this tube drop zero. If it is felt that such an assumption is too erratic, it is often possible to add some linear component to the perfect rectifier substitution that is more nearly correct, but still not

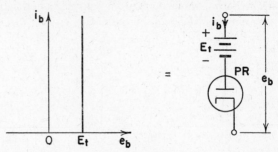

Fig. 3-4.   Volt-ampere characteristic of a series combination of perfect rectifier and constant voltage.

as difficult to handle as the actual component. For example, the characteristic of Fig. 3-1 is much more closely approximated by the dotted line than by the zero axis for positive currents. Such an equivalent characteristic is shown in Fig. 3-4, and would be the result

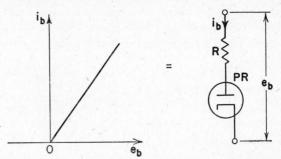

Fig. 3-5.   Second approximation to a vacuum rectifier.

of the series combination of a perfect rectifier and a battery or constant voltage of value E_t.

In the same manner the vacuum characteristic of Fig. 3-2 is better represented by the dotted line than by the zero axis for positive currents. This combined characteristic is easily obtained by the series combination of a perfect rectifier and a resistance.

More elaborate approximations can be utilized, such as curve matching, or if the situation warrants, an actual graphical solution can often be carried out from the tube's actual characteristics.

Most of the work to follow will make use of the perfect rectifier and one or more of the approximations mentioned, depending upon the error and the circuit involved.

3.3 Single-phase Half-wave Rectifier with Resistance Load

The first application of electronic rectifiers to be considered will be a single tube placed in series with a resistive load and a single-phase a-c supply. Although the actual tube may be either vacuum or gas, the analysis will assume a perfect rectifier.

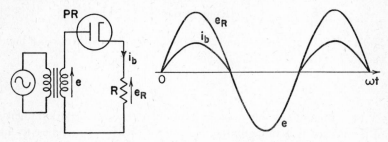

Fig. 3-6. Single-phase half-wave rectifier with resistance load.

It is apparent from Fig. 3-6 that both the current through and the voltage across the load are unidirectional. Contrary to the normal connotation of direct current, they are pulsating with appreciable periods of zero conduction. Although this single circuit would not be adequate for many applications, it does find use and is basic in understanding the action of the rectifying element.

It is usually necessary that certain facts be known or calculated for a rectifier. Some of the most important are:

(1) Average voltage and current, E_{dc}, I_{dc}.
(2) Effective voltage and current, E_{rms}, I_{rms}.
(3) Average load power, P_{avg}.
(4) Peak tube current, I_p.
(5) Average tube current, I_b.
(6) Peak inverse tube voltage, E_{pi}.
(7) Ripple factor at the load, γ.

The first six of these are self-explanatory, but the seventh should be defined to eliminate confusion arising from several common interpretations.

This text will define ripple factor as the per cent ratio of the rms value of the a-c component to the d-c or average value. Thus

$$\gamma = \frac{\text{rms of the a-c component} \times 100}{\text{d-c}}. \tag{3.1}$$

Calculation of the seven factors for the simple rectifier of Fig. 3-6 follows:

(1) Average load voltage. From the curves of Fig. 3-6 it is apparent that the load voltage is the supplied sine wave during the conduction period and is zero the remaining half cycle. Thus

$$E_{dc} = \frac{1}{2\pi} \left(\int_0^\pi E_m \sin \omega t \, d\omega t + \int_\pi^{2\pi} 0 \right) = \frac{E_m}{\pi}. \tag{3.2}$$

Since the load is resistive and thus the load voltage and current have the same form, it is obvious that

$$I_{dc} = \frac{I_m}{\pi} = \frac{E_m}{\pi R}. \tag{3.3}$$

(4) and (5) Peak and average tube current. From the simplicity of the circuit it is immediately apparent that the peak tube current is equal to the peak load current. Thus

$$I_p = \frac{E_m}{R}. \tag{3.4}$$

The average tube current is of necessity equal to the average load current, and was already expressed by Eq. 3.3.

(2) Effective load voltage. From the definition of rms value

$$E_{rms} = \sqrt{\frac{1}{2\pi} \left(\int_0^\pi E_m^2 \sin^2 \omega t \, d\omega t + \int_\pi^{2\pi} 0 \right)} = \frac{E_m}{2}. \tag{3.5}$$

Since the forms are similar the effective current can be immediately written as

$$I_{rms} = \frac{I_m}{2}. \tag{3.6}$$

(3) Average load power. The average power dissipated in R can be found either by integrating the expression for instantaneous power or from the value of effective current.

$$P_{avg} = I_{rms}^2 R = \frac{I_m^2 R}{4} = \frac{E_m^2}{4R}. \tag{3.7}$$

(6) Peak inverse tube voltage. The peak inverse tube voltage appears across the tube at the center of the nonconduction period and is obviously equal to E_m.

$$E_{pi} = E_m. \tag{3.8}$$

(7) Ripple factor at the load. As defined

$$\gamma = \frac{\text{rms a-c component} \times 100}{\text{d-c}}.$$

The denominator has already been given as E_m/π. The numerator is most easily found by use of the Fourier series. The load voltage may be expressed as follows:

$$E_{rms}^2 = E_{dc}^2 + \left(\frac{E_{m1}^2 + E_{m2}^2 + E_{m3}^2 + \cdots}{2}. \right) \tag{3.9}$$

$$E_{rms}^2 = E_{dc}^2 + E_{ac}^2. \tag{3.10}$$

Thus the numerator of the ripple factor is the square root of the last term.

Substituting in the known values for the first two terms of this last equation:

$$E_{ac} = \left(\frac{E_m^2}{4} - \frac{E_m^2}{\pi^2} \right)^{1/2} = E_m \left(\frac{1}{4} - \frac{1}{\pi^2} \right)^{1/2}. \tag{3.11}$$

The evaluation of the ripple factor is then

$$\gamma = \frac{100 E_m (\frac{1}{4} - (1/\pi^2))^{1/2}}{E_m/\pi} = 100 \frac{(\pi^2 - 4)^{1/2}}{2} = 100 \sqrt{\frac{\pi^2}{4} - 1} \%. \tag{3.12}$$

$$\gamma \equiv 122.0\%. \tag{3.13}$$

If a constant voltage such as that from a battery is the measure of quality, it is apparent that γ should be as small as possible.

3.4 Full-wave Single-phase Rectifier with Resistance Load

A second type of rectifier which is even more widely used than the half-wave type is the full-wave rectifier. This is essentially two half-wave rectifiers operating alternately on the same load. The circuit is shown in Fig. 3-7.

It is obvious that each tube and its half of the transformer operate half the time. This is rather poor utilization as far as the transformer is concerned, although no worse than the half-wave circuit, and the end result is appreciably better. When vacuum tubes are used it is often convenient to use one tube with a common cathode and two anodes. This is not possible with gas tubes since the circuit requires that one plate to cathode sustain an inverse voltage while the other pair is conducting.

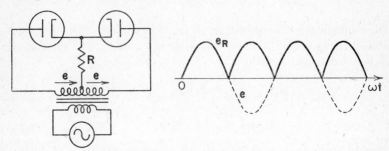

Fig. 3-7. Full-wave rectifier with resistive load.

The same list of important factors could be calculated for this rectifier. The average voltage and current of the load is twice its previous value, or

$$E_{dc} = \frac{2}{\pi} E_m \tag{3.14}$$

and

$$I_{dc} = \frac{2}{\pi} I_m. \tag{3.15}$$

The peak and average tube currents are still E_m/R and $2/\pi I_m$ as before.

The effective load voltage and current, being proportional to the square of the current, are the same as for a full sine wave, their squares being identical. Thus

$$I_{rms} = 0.707 I_m \tag{3.16}$$

and

$$E_{rms} = 0.707 E_m. \tag{3.17}$$

The average load power is expressed by

$$P_{avg} = I_{rms}{}^2 R = \frac{I_m{}^2 R}{2} = \frac{E_m{}^2}{2R}. \tag{3.18}$$

One of the chief disadvantages of the circuit is the required inverse voltage. It is this quantity that often determines the maximum output voltage that can be obtained with a particular tube.

From the circuit of Fig. 3-7 it follows that the inverse voltage on a tube will be the sum of its own instantaneous transformer voltage and the load voltage. Both of these values have their maximum simultaneously, and thus

$$E_{pi} = 2E_m. \tag{3.19}$$

This is twice as large as for the half-wave rectifier with similar supply per tube, but of course the output voltage is twice also.

Since the repetition rate is greater it is to be expected that the ripple factor will be smaller. Thus

$$\gamma = \frac{(E_m{}^2/2 - 4E_m{}^2/\pi^2)^{1/2}}{(2/\pi)E_m} = \frac{(\frac{1}{2} - 4/\pi^2)^{1/2}}{(4/\pi^2)^{1/2}}$$

$$\gamma = 100(\pi^2/8 - 1)^{1/2} = 49.0\%. \tag{3.20}$$

This is appreciably smaller than for the half-wave case and thus would be more desirable even for similar output voltages. It should be noted that the same transformer with a center tap produces the same output voltage with either circuit, but the full-wave circuit has less ripple, equal inverse tube voltage, half the average and peak tube current, and half the average power dissipation in the load. These factors must all be considered when the circuit is chosen for a particular application.

3.5 Full-wave Bridge Rectifier with Resistance Load

A third common rectifier circuit that has some advantages over either of the first two is the bridge rectifier. The name comes from the similarity of connection to that used in the fundamental bridge circuit. The two chief advantages are the reduction in peak inverse voltage per tube and the improved utilization factor of the supply transformer. A simplified circuit is shown in Fig. 3-8.

Each half cycle the circuit provides a path for current flow in alternate directions through the supply, but in the same direction through R_L. Current flowing in either direction from the source must flow through two tubes in series as shown by the arrow. If the voltage of the conducting tube is considered to be zero, it is obvious that the inverse voltage across a tube is equal to the load voltage and thus has a maximum value of E_m. Thus

$$E_{pi} = E_m. \tag{3.21}$$

From the curves of Fig. 3-8 it is clear that with a supply half as large the average and effective values of current and voltage, the average power and the ripple factor are the same as for the full-wave rectifier of Sec. 3.4.

Since the entire transformer is used each half cycle, the total voltage of the secondary need only be half as great as for the center-tapped full-wave rectifier for the same output voltage. This is

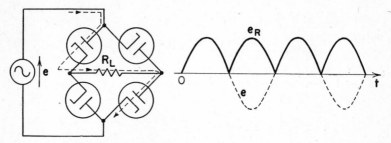

Fig. 3-8.   Single-phase bridge rectifier with resistance load.

very desirable since the transformer may be smaller for a particular application, both in voltage and kva rating.

It will be noticed in Fig. 3-8 that the two tubes on the left have a common cathode connection, and often may be a single tube with two anodes if the vacuum type is used.   If gas tubes are chosen they of course must be separate.   The two tubes on the right have a common anode connection.   This is not particularly desirable since no tube is built with two cathodes and one anode.   It also requires that the heaters for these two tubes operate with a maximum potential difference of line voltage.   Thus three separate heater supplies are required, and they must be sufficiently insulated from each other to withstand the peak supply voltage.   The additional heater supplies and tubes are disadvantages as far as cost is concerned.   When large voltages are involved the lower peak inverse requirement more than compensates by decreasing the tube cost.

3.6 Power Transformer Rating

When any appreciable power is involved it is apparent that the circuit designer must have some knowledge of the rating of the transformer that the application and circuit require. Since transformers are usually rated in kva it is desirable to convert a knowledge of the circuit and load into this unit.

The basis for volt-ampere design is essentially that the voltage must be sufficient to produce the desired voltage, and the current rating must be such as to allow an equivalent amount of heating. This demands an equality of rms currents. Also to be considered is the fact that the primary side cannot have an average value of current other than zero, since it is connected to the a-c line.

Consider first the simple circuit of Sec. 3.3. The average secondary current equals I_m/π, and has an rms value of $I_m/2$. Therefore

$$I_{rms} = \frac{I_m}{2} = \frac{I_{dc}\pi}{2}. \tag{3.22}$$

The voltage produced equals E_m/π. Thus the rms value required to provide E_m is

$$E_{rms} = \frac{E_m}{\sqrt{2}} = \frac{E_{dc}\pi}{\sqrt{2}}. \tag{3.23}$$

Consequently the volt-ampere rating of the secondary of a half-wave rectifier with resistance load is

$$VA_s = E_{rms}I_{rms} = 3.5E_{dc}I_{dc}. \tag{3.24}$$

Although the secondary carries an average current of I_m/π, the primary cannot. It is usually assumed that the primary carries about as much exciting current during the secondary's nonconducting half cycle as during the secondary's conducting half cycle. Thus, in the primary winding

$$I_{rms} = \frac{I_m}{\sqrt{2}} \times \frac{N_s}{N_p} = \frac{I_{dc}\pi}{\sqrt{2}} \times \frac{N_s}{N_p} \tag{3.25}$$

and

$$E_{rms} = \frac{E_m}{\sqrt{2}} \times \frac{N_p}{N_s} = \frac{E_{dc}\pi}{\sqrt{2}} \times \frac{N_p}{N_s}. \tag{3.26}$$

Therefore the volt-ampere rating of the primary of a half-wave rectifier with resistance load is

$$VA_p = E_{rms}I_{rms} = 4.95E_{dc}I_{dc}. \tag{3.27}$$

On the same basis the calculation for the full-wave center-tapped circuit of Sec. 3.4 may be calculated. The rms current and voltage in each half of the secondary winding are

$$I_{rms} = \frac{I_m}{2} = \frac{I_{dc}\pi}{4},$$ (3.28)

and
$$E_{rms} = \frac{E_m}{\sqrt{2}} = \frac{E_{dc}\pi}{2\sqrt{2}}.$$ (3.29)

Thus the volt-amperes for one-half the secondary winding of a full-wave rectifier with center-tapped transformer and resistance load are

$$\frac{VA_s}{\frac{1}{2}} = 0.875 E_{dc}I_{dc}.$$ (3.30)

Or the volt-amperes for the entire secondary are

$$VA_s = 1.75 E_{dc}I_{dc}.$$ (3.31)

The primary winding carries current during both half cycles, and thus for the primary

$$I_{rms} = \frac{I_m}{\sqrt{2}}\left(\frac{N_s}{2N_p}\right) = \frac{I_{dc}\pi}{2\sqrt{2}}\left(\frac{N_s}{2N_p}\right).$$ (3.32)

The primary voltage is

$$E_{rms} = \frac{E_m}{\sqrt{2}}\left(\frac{2N_p}{N_s}\right) = \frac{E_{dc}\pi}{2\sqrt{2}}\left(\frac{2N_p}{N_s}\right).$$ (3.33)

Therefore the volt-amperes of the primary are

$$VA_p = 1.24 E_{dc}I_{dc}.$$ (3.34)

The bridge circuit of Sec. 3.5 is most economical from the transformer point of view, using the entire primary and secondary both half cycles. For the secondary,

$$I_{rms} = \frac{I_m}{\sqrt{2}} = \frac{I_{dc}\pi}{2\sqrt{2}}$$ (3.35)

$$E_{rms} = \frac{E_m}{\sqrt{2}} = \frac{E_{dc}\pi}{2\sqrt{2}}.$$ (3.36)

Thus the volt-amperes of the secondary of a bridge rectifier with resistance load are

$$VA_s = 1.24 E_{dc} I_{dc}. \tag{3.37}$$

It follows that this is also the value for the primary.

3.7 Resistance-capacitance Load

The discussion to this point has been limited to circuits using only pure resistance as the power-dissipating load. This is not always the case. The first variation to be considered will be that of a resistance and a capacitance in parallel. As will be seen, the addition of a capacitor is often desirable for no other reason than to reduce the ripple factor, γ. At other times the load involved requires the capacitor, or behaves as if it were already a resistance and capacitor in parallel. The last example is particularly true of a d-c motor. Thus the generality of the application warrants the study of such a circuit.

Consider the simple circuit of Fig. 3-9.

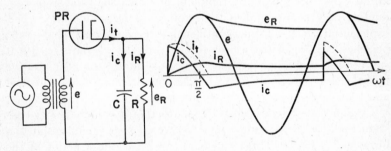

Fig. 3-9.   Half-wave rectifier with R-C load.

From Kirchhoff's law,

$$i_t = i_c + i_R.$$

If

$$i_t = 0, \quad i_c = -i_R.$$

Consider the circuit from a time when the supply voltage is passing through zero with a positive derivative. Assume the capacitor to be initially uncharged. The voltage is building up in such a direction that the rectifier may conduct, and thus its voltage drop may be neglected so long as i_t is positive.

From fundamentals,

$$i_c = C \frac{de}{dt}, \tag{3.38}$$

and
$$i_R = \frac{e}{R}. \tag{3.39}$$

The three currents, i_c, i_R, and i_t are shown in Fig. 3-9. During the first quarter cycle all three are positive, the tube conducts, and the voltage across the resistor and capacitor builds up along with the sine wave supply.

At $\omega t = \pi/2$, the current i_c passes through zero and becomes negative. As soon as it has reached a negative value equal to i_R, the value of i_t becomes zero. If the tube were to continue conduction so that the sinusoidal supply appeared across R and C, then i_t would of necessity become negative. Since this is impossible, the tube stops conduction, $i_t = 0$, and the capacitor continues to discharge through R. This is, of course, an exponential decay with the initial value determined by the point at which the tube stops conducting, and the rate of decay determined by the product RC. This exponential decay continues until such time as the plate of the tube becomes positive with respect to the cathode. From Fig. 3-9 it can be seen that this occurs at some time during the next positive half cycle of the supply voltage. The capacitor is then recharged and the cycle repeats.

A glance at the variation of e_R shows that it is more nearly constant than for the resistance load alone, and thus should result in a lower value for γ. This effect is referred to as filter action of the capacitor. Although the load voltage and thus the resistor current are much more constant, the tube conduction time has been appreciably shortened. Since the tube must still carry the same average current as the load, the peak tube current has definitely increased. In fact, this is the chief difficulty of this circuit. The tube is required to pass short spurts of current, and thus is usually prohibited from carrying its normal average current because of its peak current rating. A second disadvantage is that the peak inverse tube voltage approaches $2E_m$ as a limit.

As before it is desirable to be able to calculate some of the important values from a knowledge of the circuit components.

Since the assumption of a perfect rectifier and perfect supply transformer is an approximation at best, it seems permissible to make a further simplifying approximation with respect to the output voltage wave form.

The actual curve from Fig. 3-9 and the proposed approximation are shown in Fig. 3-10.

Although some deviation from the actual curve is obvious, the error decreases as the amount of capacitor discharge per cycle decreases, and in most practical circuits this is kept small.

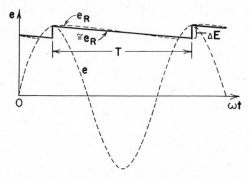

Fig. 3-10.   Actual and approximate variation of e_R.

The approximation is essentially that the capacitor is recharged instantaneously and discharges linearly. Thus the capacitor current and hence the average load current are assumed constant. From Fig. 3-10 and Eq. 3.38,

$$I_{dc} = C \frac{\Delta E}{\Delta t} = C \frac{\Delta E}{T}. \tag{3.40}$$

Solution for ΔE results in

$$\Delta E = \frac{I_{dc}T}{C}. \tag{3.41}$$

Since T is assumed to be one complete cycle,

$$T = \frac{1}{f},$$

and

$$\Delta E = \frac{I_{dc}}{fC} = \frac{E_{dc}}{fRC}. \tag{3.42}$$

From Fig. 3-10 it can be seen that

$$E_{dc} = E_m - \frac{\Delta E}{2}. \tag{3.43}$$

Therefore, from Eq. 3.42,

$$E_{dc} = E_m - \frac{E_{dc}}{2fRC},$$

or

$$E_{dc} = E_m \left(\frac{2fRC}{2fRC + 1} \right). \tag{3.44}$$

If the reasoning of Fig. 3-10 is applied to a full-wave rectifier circuit, it can be seen that the only change is that $T = 1/2f$. Thus

$$\Delta E = \frac{I_{dc}}{2fC} = \frac{E_{dc}}{2fRC}, \tag{3.45}$$

and

$$E_{dc} = E_m \left(\frac{4fRC}{4fRC + 1} \right). \tag{3.46}$$

It is apparent from Eq. 3.42 and Eq. 3.43 that the value of E_{dc} depends upon the load current, and thus the circuit has appreciable voltage regulation.

The peak inverse tube voltage approaches $2E_m$ for both cases as C becomes very large.

Since the peak tube current is usually the limiting factor in such a circuit, it is important to have some idea of its magnitude. Under normal operation the peak current would occur at the beginning of each conduction period. One approximate method of obtaining this point is to assume the load voltage at the start of tube conduction to be $E_m - \Delta E$. Thus

$$\theta_f = \sin^{-1} \frac{E_m - \Delta E}{E_m}. \tag{3.47}$$

The tube current is $i_t = i_c + i_R$. Thus

$$I_p = CE_m\omega \cos \theta_f + \frac{E_m}{R} \sin \theta_f. \tag{3.48}$$

The distinct advantage of the circuit is the reduction in ripple factor γ.

Since the a-c component of the voltage is assumed triangular in form, it is easily shown that

$$\gamma = \frac{\text{rms of a-c component}}{\text{d-c}} = \frac{0.58(\Delta E/2)}{E_{dc}} = 0.29 \frac{\Delta E}{E_{dc}}. \quad (3.49)$$

Since ΔE is a function of either E_{dc} or I_{dc},

$$\gamma = \frac{0.29}{fRC} \text{ for half-wave rectification,}$$

and

$$\gamma = \frac{0.29}{2fRC} \text{ for full-wave rectification.} \quad (3.50)$$

The transformer rating may be calculated approximately by assuming that the secondary carries the same rms current as the load.

$$I_{rms} = \left[I_{dc}^2 + \left(0.29 \frac{\Delta E}{R} \right)^2 \right]^{1/2} \quad (3.51)$$

and

$$E_{rms} = \frac{E_m}{\sqrt{2}} = \frac{E_{dc} + \dfrac{\Delta E}{2}}{\sqrt{2}}. \quad (3.52)$$

Again since ΔE is a function of the load current or voltage and the type of rectifier, the volt-ampere rating becomes a complex function of the circuit components, and is best calculated from Eqs. 3.51 and 3.52.

3.8 Resistance-inductance Load

It is often necessary to consider a load consisting of a resistance and a inductance in series. Although seldom used in this manner, let us first consider this type of load with the single-phase half-wave rectifier. The simplified circuit is shown in Fig. 3-11.

Consider the time marked zero when the voltage e is passing through zero and building up positively. Just previous to this the current has been zero and thus the voltage e_{RL} is also zero. Since the polarity of the voltage as it builds up is such that the tube conducts, current flows in the direction indicated. This flow of current continues as long as it is in the positive direction.

The relation that must always be satisfied is

$$e = e_{tube} + i_R + L \frac{di}{dt}. \quad (3.53)$$

If the tube drop is neglected during the conduction,

$$e = iR + L\frac{di}{dt} = E_m \sin \omega t. \tag{3.54}$$

From differential equations,

$$i = K_1 \epsilon^{-Rt/L} + \frac{E_m}{(R^2 + \omega^2 L^2)^{1/2}} \sin (\omega t - \theta). \tag{3.55}$$

$$\theta = \tan^{-1}\frac{\omega L}{R}.$$

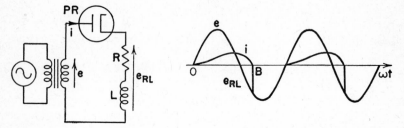

Fig. 3-11.   Half-wave rectifier with resistance and inductance load.

The constant K_1 may be evaluated from the boundary condition that at $t = 0$, $i = 0$. Therefore,

$$i = +\frac{E_m}{Z}\epsilon^{-Rt/L} \sin \theta + \frac{E_m}{Z} \sin (\omega t - \theta), \tag{3.56}$$

where $Z = (R^2 + X_L^2)^{1/2}$.

Equation 3.56 expresses the current as a function of time measured from the beginning of any particular half cycle as long as its solution is positive or zero. However, since the tube is incapable of conducting negative current, Eq. 3.56 is invalid once the solution is negative. The current then remains at zero until the beginning of the next half cycle, at which time Eq. 3.56 again expresses the current if time is considered to start from that particular half cycle.

Since no average voltage can exist across the pure inductance in the steady state, the average value of the voltage across R and L must exist entirely across R. Therefore

$$E_{dc} = \frac{1}{2\pi}\int_0^\beta E_m \sin \omega t \, d\omega t = \frac{E_m}{2\pi}(1 - \cos \beta). \tag{3.57}$$

It can be seen from Eq. 3.57 that as $\beta \rightarrow 2\pi$, $E_{R\,avg} \rightarrow 0$.

Since the effect of adding inductance into the circuit is to increase β toward 2π, it also results in approaching an average load voltage of zero.

Small values of inductance do increase the conduction period beyond the 180 degrees of a pure resistive load, but the smoother current is seldom worth the reduction in average voltage.

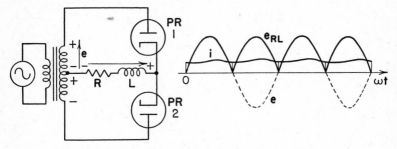

Fig. 3-12.   Full-wave rectifier with resistance-inductance load.

However, the series resistance and inductance load is practical when used with a full-wave rectifier, either of the center-tapped or bridge variety.   Consider the circuit of Fig. 3-12.   ·Here the relation

$$e = iR + L\frac{di}{dt}$$

must again be satisfied, but we will find that it is satisfied continually by the loop through one tube or the other with no periods of zero current through the load.

Several methods of analysis are possible, but for reasons of understanding a descriptive approach will be used.   Consider the analysis of the circuit of Fig. 3-11.   If the supply voltage were to start building up at $t = 0$ as shown in Fig. 3-12, tube 2 could not conduct, and the analysis would be identical with that of Fig. 3-11 for the first half cycle.   At the end of 180 degrees the current through tube 1 would not be zero even though the supply voltage is zero.   The current would have a negative slope and the negative value of $L(di/dt)$ would be exactly equal to iR.   Since the current is still positive and tube 2 is not conducting, tube 1 continues to conduct.   If this takes place, the supply voltage and the voltage across the load must build up to a polarity opposite to that shown in Fig. 3-12.   It is apparent that the voltage building up positively on tube 2 is $2E_m \sin \omega t$. If tube 2 is a perfect rectifier, it conducts immediately. Thus tube 2 has been started by the continuing conduction of tube 1. However, if tube 2 is conducting, Kirchhoff's law must be satisfied around the loop of tube 2, and thus the polarity of voltage across the load must be as shown in Fig. 3-12. If this is satisfied, the voltage on tube 1 is reduced to zero and it goes out. Thus tube 1 has stopped conduction due to the starting of tube 2. This process of current shifting from tube 1 to tube 2 is known as commutation; it reverses in sequence every half cycle.

The important facts are that the transition takes place just as the supply voltage goes through zero, and that the current through the load is not necessarily ever zero.

If the inductance is large, the actual variation in current is small, as indicated by Fig. 3-12. The variation in voltage across the total load is a full rectified sine wave, and thus the average voltage and current of the resistance are

$$E_{dc} = \frac{2}{\pi} E_m, \qquad (3.58)$$

and

$$I_{dc} = \frac{E_{dc}}{R} = \frac{2E_m}{\pi R}, \qquad (3.59)$$

both independent of current.

It is generally assumed that the current is nearly constant, and thus

$$P_{avg} \cong E_{dc} I_{dc} = \frac{4E_m{}^2}{\pi^2 R}. \qquad (3.60)$$

In order that this assumption be approximately true, it is necessary that the ripple factor across R be small. The value may be found from the ratio of the rms value of the alternating component of current to the average value of current given in Eq. 3.59.

The form of the voltage across the R-L load is known and may be expressed by the following Fourier series

$$e_{RL} = \frac{2}{\pi} E_m + \frac{2}{3} \left(\frac{2}{\pi} E_m \right) \cos \omega t + \cdots, \qquad (3.61)$$

where ω = twice the supply frequency.

Since the series converges very rapidly, it is permissible to use only the first two terms as a good approximation. Thus

$$i_{ac} \cong \frac{\frac{2}{3}((2/\pi)E_m)}{\sqrt{R_L{}^2 + \omega^2 L^2}} \cos (\omega t - \theta). \tag{3.62}$$

Therefore,

$$\gamma = \frac{I_{ac}}{I_{dc}} \cong \frac{0.707 \times \frac{2}{3}R_L}{\sqrt{R_L{}^2 + \omega^2 L^2}} = \frac{0.48R_L}{\sqrt{R_L{}^2 + \omega^2 L^2}}.$$

$$\gamma = \frac{0.48}{\sqrt{1 + Q^2}}, \tag{3.63}$$

where

$$Q = \frac{X_L}{R_L}.$$

If γ is to be less than 0.01,

$$0.01 \geqq \frac{0.48}{\sqrt{1 + Q^2}},$$

and

$$Q \geqq 48. \tag{3.64}$$

Thus for a resistance load of 1000 ohms, at 60 cycles, $X_L = 48,000$ and $L_{min} = 64$ henries. This condition of almost constant current is of course ideal for the tubes since there are no severe peaks to limit their average rating. Thus

$$I_p \cong \frac{I_{dc}}{2}. \tag{3.65}$$

The transformer secondary utilization is also improved, since the effective current in each secondary coil is

$$I_{rms} = 0.707 I_{dc}.$$

Thus the volt amperes of the secondary with R-L load will be

$$VA_s = 0.707 \times \frac{\pi}{2} \times \sqrt{2}\, I_{dc}E_{dc} = 1.57 I_{dc}E_{dc}. \tag{3.66}$$

All considerations made of this circuit are identical for the bridge circuit except the transformer utilization, which results in the volt-amperes of the secondary being

$$VA_s = 1.11 I_{dc}E_{dc}. \tag{3.67}$$

3.9 Voltage Doublers and Triplers

The voltage doubler or tripler circuits are particularly useful types of rectifiers that make possible the production of large d-c voltages with relatively small transformers if the current demand is small.

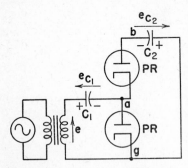

Fig. 3-13.   Voltage doubler circuit, positive terminal grounded.

Most of the circuits depend upon the same basic principle. During one half cycle a simple half-wave rectifier circuit charges a capacitor to E_{max} of the supply. Then during the next half cycle both the charge accumulated on the capacitor and the supply voltage are used in series to charge a second capacitor. If desired, the third half cycle may make use of the charge on the second capacitor plus the supply voltage and so on.

The basic doubler circuit is shown in Fig. 3-13. Assuming perfect rectifiers and no load, the voltage variations are shown in

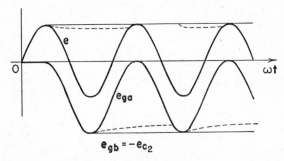

Fig. 3-14.   Voltage variations in doubler circuit of Fig. 3-13.

Fig. 3-14.   If a resistive load is placed in parallel with C_2, the voltage e_{gb} does not remain constant but decays exponentially until recharged once each cycle. This variation is shown dotted. It must also be remembered that the charge on C_1 is used to charge C_2, and therefore the voltage e_{c1} is decreased by this charging action. It is obviously desirable that C_1 be somewhat larger than C_2 in order to minimize this effect, and that the charge per cycle removed from C_2 by the load be a small percentage of its total charge.

Although large voltages can be produced in this manner, it can be seen from Fig. 3-13 or 3-14 that the maximum inverse voltage on any tube is $2E_m$. This relation is also apparent for any order of multiplier circuit of this type.

Consider the general circuit of Fig. 3-15. Additional tubes and capacitors can be added to the circuit at will, with each pair increasing the output voltage by E_m.

The circuits of both Fig. 3-13 and Fig. 3-15 have their positive output terminals grounded. It is just as easy to have the negative

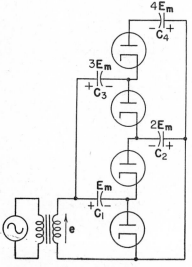

Fig. 3-15. Voltage quadrupler.

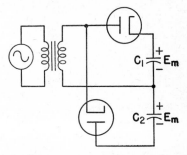

Fig. 3-16. Center grounded doubler circuit.

terminals grounded and requires only that the tube connections, plate and cathode, be reversed. The circuit of Fig. 3-16 shows a doubler circuit with the center point grounded.

Probably the chief problem in the design of doubler or higher circuits is insulation. It will be noticed that all circuits mentioned have one side of the transformer secondary carefully grounded. However, the filament supplies are isolated and must be sufficiently insulated to withstand the voltage of the particular stage to ground.

One of the most important uses of such circuits is the d-c supply for x-ray tubes, as will be discussed in a later chapter.

3.10 Practical Rectifier Consideration

So far the analyses of the rectifier circuits have assumed perfect rectifiers and supply transformers. At best this is only a good approximation. The tubes do require a certain potential drop and the supply transformers have some internal impedance.

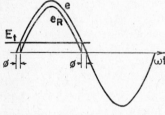

If gas tubes are used, as is often the case, it is possible to consider their effect to a good degree by assuming the drop across them during conduction to be a constant, E_t. Consider this as applied to the simple half-wave rectifier with resistance load. First of all, the cut-in and cut-out angles of the tube are no longer

Fig. 3-17. Half-wave rectifier output with resistance load assuming constant tube drop.

0 and π radians, but are later and earlier, respectively, by the angle ϕ, where

$$\phi = \sin^{-1} \frac{E_t}{E_m}. \tag{3.68}$$

This is shown in Fig. 3-17. Also, the voltage across the load is reduced during tube conduction by the tube drop E_t. Thus

$$E_{dc} = \frac{1}{2\pi} \int_\phi^{\pi-\phi} [E_m \sin \omega t - E_t]\, d\omega t. \tag{3.69}$$

If $\qquad\qquad E_m \gg E_t, \quad \phi \cong 0, \quad \text{and} \quad \pi - \phi \cong \pi.$

This again is an approximation and its use results in an answer only partially correct. The extent to which such factors must be considered is always a question that must be answered upon the merits of the individual problem. The method is obvious from Eq. 3.69 and can be applied to the calculation of average power, peak current, or any other desired quantity.

Occasionally the demand is such that a vacuum rectifier may be approximated more closely by the series combination of a perfect rectifier and a resistance. This may or may not complicate the results depending upon the circuit.

It is possible to account to some degree for the impedance of the power transformer by assuming a series R-L circuit for it in series with a perfect supply.

In almost all cases the addition of the corrective terms merely adds one or more circuit components to the basic circuits considered in the previous sections. The additional work thus introduced must be weighed against the results obtained for each problem. It is felt that the reader now has sufficient background to carry out these calculations for himself.

Another practical form of correction, often useful to the engineer, is the plotting by the manufacturer of load characteristics of certain rectifier tubes when utilized in certain specified circuits. Examples of such curves are shown in Fig. 3–18.

These curves take into account the average drop due to tube impedance, transformer drop, etc. They are very useful when conventional circuits are being used and the engineer is interested only in the output characteristics.

In order to place full emphasis on the circuit operation with as little added complexity as possible, the circuits yet to be studied will be approached from the perfect rectifier point of view, even though it may often be desirable to make one or more corrections in the calculations in practice.

3.11 Controlled Gas Tube Rectifiers

The rectifier circuits considered up to this point have all made use of rectifying elements of the diode type. Any circuit element that has the property of passing current in only one direction and conducting whenever the voltage across it is of the correct polarity could be used in these circuits. There is another large field of circuit components having these properties in addition to the added factor of control, that permits them to be used also as switches to determine the exact times at which the conduction starts. Thyratrons, ignitrons, and mercury pool tanks are probably the most important of these elements, depending somewhat upon the desired power rating. They are particularly well adapted to the regulated or variable type rectifier when the change can best come from an electric signal to the grid or ignitor.

A few basic circuits will be considered, chiefly to determine the effect of firing point control on wave shape, power, and peak voltages.

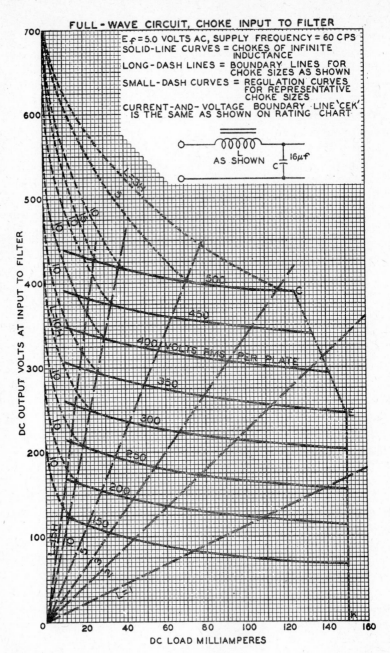

Fig. 3-18.

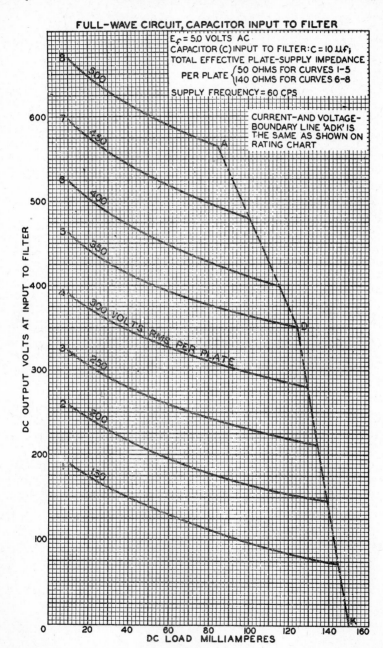

Fig. 3-18. (*Continued*)

3.12 Controlled Gas Tubes with Resistance Load

First consider a full-wave center-tapped rectifier of the type discussed in Sec. 3.4. The only difference is the substitution of controlled gas tubes for the perfect rectifiers. With this substitution it is still assumed for simplicity that the tube is a perfect rectifier to which has been added a switch that can be closed at any time while the plate voltage is positive, but once closed, cannot be opened until the current has gone to zero, at which time it opens automatically. A simplified circuit is shown in Fig. 3-19.

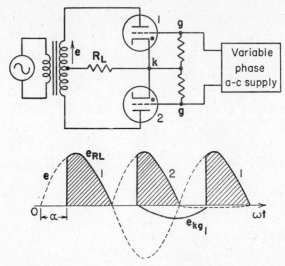

Fig. 3-19. Full-wave controlled rectifier with resistance load.

It can be seen from Fig. 3-19 that the wave form of the voltage across the resistance is very similar to that when the circuit used diodes, except that part of each cycle is missing because the tubes are prevented from firing during this portion of the cycle.

The average voltage may be calculated in the same general manner as before.

$$E_{dc} = \frac{1}{\pi} \int_{\alpha}^{\pi} E_m \sin \omega t \, d\omega t \qquad (3.70)$$

$$= \frac{E_m}{\pi} (1 + \cos \alpha). \qquad (3.71)$$

Here α is the angle in each half cycle at which the tubes are permitted to fire. It has been assumed that both tubes are delayed by the same amount.

If the tube drop during conduction is to be considered a constant E_t,

$$E_{dc} = \frac{1}{\pi} \int_{\alpha}^{\pi - \phi} (E_m \sin \omega t - E_t) \, d\omega t. \qquad (3.72)$$

If $\pi - \phi \cong \pi$,

$$E_{dc} = \frac{E_m(1 + \cos \alpha) - E_t(\pi - \alpha)}{\pi}. \qquad (3.73)$$

The power dissipated in the load cannot be correctly found from the d-c value, but must be calculated from the effective voltage and current. Thus

$$P_{avg} = \frac{E_m{}^2}{\pi R_L} \int_{\alpha}^{\pi} \sin^2 \omega t \, d\omega t. \qquad (3.74)$$

$$P_{avg} = \frac{E_m{}^2}{2\pi R_L} \left(\pi - \alpha + \frac{1}{2} \sin 2\alpha \right). \qquad (3.75)$$

It is apparent that Eq. 3.75 reduces to the value for diode rectifiers if $\alpha = 0$. The other important factors such as ripple factor, transformer utilization, and peak values may be calculated from their fundamental definitions, if desired.

3.13 Controlled Tubes with R-C Load

The application of controlled gas tubes to loads of the parallel resistance-capacitance type is quite different from that of Sec. 3.12 with only resistance. Consider first the characteristics of such a load when used with conventional diodes as in Sec. 3.7. Here the tubes conducted whenever their plate was positive, but this period was reduced to a fraction of a half cycle and was one of the chief disadvantages of such a circuit. It is likewise necessary for the plate of the controlled gas tube to be positive during conduction. Since the function of the grid is to delay the firing time for some period after the plate goes positive, this results only in firing the tube even later in the half cycle and allowing a still shorter conduction period. This is shown by the curves of Fig. 3-20.

If the assumption is made that there is no series inductance so that the voltage across the load rises to the line voltage as soon as the tube fires, the conduction period is reduced to a value $\beta - \alpha$, since the extinction angle is approximately the same in either case. The output voltage and ripple are then even more nearly equal to the approximation of Sec. 3.7, and independent of α.

The reasoning here is true only if the controlled tube is still permitted to fire at some time previous to $\alpha \cong \pi/2$. If the firing point is delayed until some point between $\pi/2$ and π, the maximum value of the output voltage is no longer E_{max} but is reduced to $E_{max} \sin \alpha$. The assumptions made then result, of course, in a zero

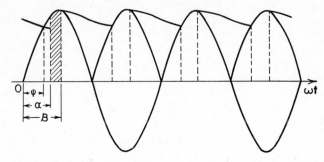

Fig. 3-20. Comparison of wave forms for diode and controlled gas tube full-wave rectifiers with R-C load.

ψ = normal diode firing angle
β = normal diode extinction angle
α = controlled firing angle

conduction period of infinite current in each tube. Although this is not physically possible, it certainly is the worst possible use of the tube and usually requires enough series resistance and inductance to limit the tube current to a safe value.

A continuation of the curves of Fig. 3-20 is shown in Fig. 3-21, with the firing angle suddenly delayed into the second half of the half cycle.

As can be seen from Fig. 3-21, the first result of delaying the firing angle is for one or more half cycles of conduction to be missed until the voltage has decayed to a value equal to or less than the supply voltage at the permitted firing angle. The time of transition is a function of the R-C time constant and is a factor of sluggishness in reducing output voltage in this manner.

The calculations of voltage and ripple factor are similar to those of Sec. 3.7, with slight changes if $\alpha > \pi/2$.

Thus, if $\alpha \leqq \pi/2$,

$$E_{dc} \cong E_m - \frac{\Delta E}{2},$$

and

$$\Delta E = \frac{E_{dc}}{2fRC},$$

Thus

$$E_{dc} = E_m \left(\frac{4fRC}{4fRC + 1} \right), \qquad (3.76)$$

and

$$\gamma \cong \frac{0.58(\Delta E/2)}{E_{dc}} = \frac{0.29}{2fRC}. \qquad (3.77)$$

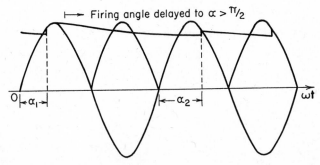

Fig. 3-21.   Result of delaying firing angle α to the second half of each half cycle in an R-C load.

If $\alpha > \pi/2$,

$$E_{dc} = E_m \sin \alpha - \frac{\Delta E}{2},$$

and

$$\Delta E = \frac{E_{dc}}{2fRC}.$$

Thus

$$E_{dc} = E_m \sin \alpha \left(\frac{4fRC}{4fRC + 1} \right), \qquad (3.78)$$

and

$$\gamma = \frac{0.58(\Delta E/2)}{E_{dc}} = \frac{0.29}{2fRC}. \qquad (3.79)$$

It is interesting to note that although the load voltage is reduced by delayed firing, the ripple factor remains constant, still only a function of the load resistance and capacitance.

A good example of this type of circuit is its application to the driving of a d-c motor from the a-c line.   As will be shown in a later chapter, a d-c shunt motor appears as a resistance and a capacitance in parallel.   The back electromotive force, which is a function of speed, produces the opposing voltage similar in polarity to the charge on the capacitor and allows tube conduction only during those periods when the supply voltage is greater than this value. Thus the average back electromotive force is controlled just as is the average voltage across the capacitor in the R-C circuit.   Since speed control is desired, operation normally takes place in the last half of the half cycle with $\pi/2 \leq \alpha \leq \pi$.   Chapter 9 is devoted to the consideration of this type of drive and thus it will not be discussed further at this time.

3.14   Controlled Tubes with R-L Load

A third type of load often encountered with controlled tubes is one that appears similar to a resistance and inductance in series.

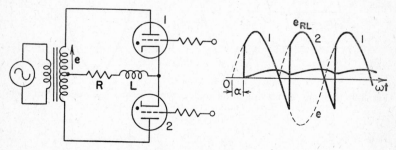

Fig. 3-22.   Full-wave controlled rectifier with R-L load.

Since the average value of the output voltage tends toward zero if half-wave rectification is used, the full-wave circuit is more common. A simplified circuit is shown in Fig. 3-22.

Review for a moment the circuit of Sec. 3.8.   The only difference in Fig. 3-22 is the substitution of controlled tubes.   With diodes it will be remembered that commutation from one tube to the other took place as the supply voltage went through zero.   Now this is not necessarily true.   Although the conditions determining plate voltage are similar, the tube "coming in" may be prevented from firing by a sufficiently negative grid voltage.   Since the current through the conducting tube is not yet zero, sufficient induced volt-

age is produced across the inductance by a negative current derivative to continue conduction.   This conduction is possible only until
the current reaches zero, when conduction through this tube must
stop.

During this period of conduction in the second half cycle of the
supply voltage, the plate voltage on the nonconducting tube is
equal to the sum of the load and supply voltages and is
approximately

$$e_b \cong 2E_m \sin \omega t. \tag{3.80}$$

If the grid voltage of the nonconducting tube permits it to fire
before the conducting tube ceases, commutation takes place immediately, and the voltage and current wave forms are similar to those
of Fig. 3-22.

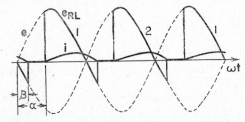

Fig. 3-23.   Wave form of controlled rectifier in discontinuous operation.

If, however, the conducting tube has already extinguished before
the second tube fires, there is a period each half cycle when neither
tube conducts and the voltage across the load is zero.   This condition is shown in Fig. 3-23.

It will be noticed in Fig. 3-23 that two angles are required to
specify the operation.   The angle α is still reserved as the angle,
measured in a particular half cycle, at which the tube starts conduction.   A new angle β is introduced to specify the point in the same
half cycle at which the preceding tube ceases conduction.   It is
possible and quite probable that α may be greater than β.   However,
it is not possible for β to be larger than α since the preceding tube
is forced to stop conduction when a new tube starts if it has not
done so already.

The values of average voltage, current, and power will be calculated for the general case of Fig. 3-23 and then the relation of
Fig. 3-22 will become a special case of $\alpha = \beta$.

Since no average voltage can exist across a pure inductance in the steady state, the average value of the voltage across the resistance becomes equal to the average value of the curve e_{RL} in Fig. 3-23. Thus, the average voltage across R_L is

$$E_{dc} = \frac{1}{\pi} \int_{\alpha}^{\pi+\beta} E_m \sin \omega t \, d\omega t$$

$$= \frac{E_m}{\pi} (\cos \alpha + \cos \beta), \tag{3.81}$$

and

$$I_{dc} = \frac{E_m}{\pi R_L} (\cos \alpha + \cos \beta). \tag{3.82}$$

From Eq. 3.81 and Eq. 3.82 it is apparent that if $\alpha = \beta$,

$$E_{dc} = \frac{2E_m}{\pi} \cos \alpha \tag{3.83}$$

and

$$I_{dc} = \frac{2E_m}{\pi R_L} \cos \alpha. \tag{3.84}$$

Before the average power is calculated, a word should be said concerning ripple. It is quite common practice in the literature to consider only the d-c component of voltage and current as contributing to the average power. Thus

$$P_{avg} \cong E_{dc} I_{dc} = \frac{E_m{}^2}{\pi^2 R_L} (\cos \alpha + \cos \beta)^2, \tag{3.85}$$

or if $\alpha = \beta$,

$$P_{avg} \cong \frac{4E_m{}^2}{\pi^2 R_L} \cos^2 \alpha. \tag{3.86}$$

The error involved in this approximation depends almost directly upon the ripple factor of the output voltage across R_L.

Consider the ripple factor for the case where $\alpha = \beta$. The total load voltage may be represented by a Fourier series of the form:

$$e_{RL} = \frac{2E_m}{\pi} \cos \alpha + \frac{2E_m}{\pi} \left(\frac{10}{9} + \frac{2}{3} \cos 4\alpha \right)^{\frac{1}{2}} \cos (2\omega t + \phi) + \cdots \tag{3.87}$$

Here α is measured in radians at the supply frequency ω.

If it is permissible to neglect all terms of the series beyond the first two,

$$i = \frac{2E_m}{\pi R_L} \cos \alpha$$

$$+ \frac{\sqrt{2}\left[\frac{\sqrt{2}E_m}{\pi}\left(\frac{10}{9} + \frac{2}{3}\cos 4\alpha\right)^{\frac{1}{2}}\right]}{(R_L{}^2 + 4\omega^2 L^2)^{\frac{1}{2}}} \cos (2\omega t + \phi') + \cdots \quad (3.88)$$

From Eq. 3.88,

$$e_R = \frac{2E_m}{\pi} \cos \alpha + \frac{\sqrt{2}\left[\frac{\sqrt{2}E_m}{\pi}\left(\frac{10}{9} + \frac{2}{3}\cos 4\alpha\right)^{\frac{1}{2}}\right] R_L}{(R_L{}^2 + 4\omega^2 L^2)^{\frac{1}{2}}}$$
$$\cos (2\omega t + \phi') + \cdots . \quad (3.89)$$

Thus
$$\gamma = \frac{(\frac{10}{9} + \frac{2}{3}\cos 4\alpha)^{\frac{1}{2}} R_L}{\sqrt{2}\,(R_L{}^2 + 4\omega^2 L^2)^{\frac{1}{2}} \cos \alpha}. \quad (3.90)$$

Since γ is the ratio of the rms a-c voltage across R_L to the d-c voltage, the general relation for the rms voltage across R_L becomes

$$E_{rms} = \left[\left(\frac{2E_m}{\pi}\cos \alpha\right)^2 (1 + \gamma^2)\right]^{\frac{1}{2}}. \quad (3.91)$$

Thus
$$P_{avg} = \frac{E_{rms}{}^2}{R_L} = \frac{4E_m{}^2}{\pi^2 R_L} \cos^2 \alpha (1 + \gamma^2). \quad (3.92)$$

$$\alpha = \beta$$

From Eq. 3.92 it can be seen that the average power is more correctly given as the d-c power times $(1 + \gamma^2)$. The need for a small ripple factor in order that Eq. 3.86 shall hold is obvious.

More elaborate solutions for γ may be made if the problem justifies it, by including still more of the current harmonics.

Equation 3.92 may also be expanded to include the case of $\alpha \neq \beta$ by similar reasoning, and thus

$$P_{avg} = \frac{E_m{}^2}{\pi^2 R_L} (\cos \alpha + \cos \beta)^2 (1 + \gamma^2). \quad (3.93)$$

Another circuit which is finding use where large inductances are involved, such as the fields of d-c machines, is shown in Fig. 3-24. The circuit is basically a half-wave controlled rectifier with a gas diode placed across the load. Consider that the controlled tube is allowed to fire at the angle α as shown in Fig. 3-24. If the tube drop is neglected, the supply voltage appears across the R-L load, and the current must have such a magnitude and derivative that

$$e = iR_L + L\frac{di}{dt}. \tag{3.94}$$

The polarity of the voltage is such that the diode cannot fire. Conduction takes place exactly as in the half-wave case until the time when the supply voltage passes through zero. Since the current is not normally zero, an induced voltage builds up across L sufficient to still satisfy Eq. 3.94 even though e has changed polarities. It is now apparent that the net voltage across R and L, which

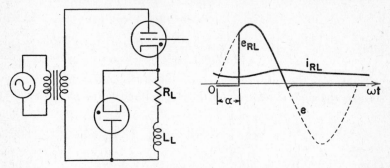

Fig. 3-24.   Follow-up circuit for R-L loads.

is also the voltage across the diode, is building up with the plate of the diode positive. As soon as this voltage has built up to a value sufficient to cause breakdown of the diode it provides a discharge path for the R-L circuit, and the controlled tube ceases conduction, since its net plate voltage must now be negative.

This R-L discharge continues, independent of either the supply or the controlled tube, until such time as the supply again makes the plate of the controlled tube positive and its grid voltage permits conduction.

If all tube drops are neglected, the average voltage and current are easily calculated.

$$E_{dc} = \frac{1}{2\pi}\int_{\alpha}^{\pi} E_m \sin \omega t \, d\omega t$$

$$= \frac{E_m}{2\pi}[1 + \cos \alpha]. \tag{3.95}$$

For loads such as fields of d-c machines, this circuit has several advantages over the full-wave circuit.

First, it utilizes the full secondary winding of the supply transformer.

Second, it requires only one relatively expensive controlled tube.

Third, the variation of voltage with firing angle is more gradual.

Fourth, it does not have a discontinuance of operation in going from continuous to pulse conduction since the plate voltage and thus the control locus of the controlled tube are not different for the two cases.

There are naturally disadvantages that also must be considered.

First, since the one controlled tube must now carry the total average current of the load and yet conduct for only a portion of the half cycle, both its average and peak ratings must be larger.

Second, it will be noticed from Fig. 3-24 that the diode is asked to go from a condition of ionization and conduction in one direction to a blocking condition of the opposite polarity in the time required for ionization of the controlled tube. This is impossible for many tubes, and at least hard on those capable of such a transition, since the blocking voltage may be the maximum of the supply. Occasionally some type of "cushion" circuit is devised by use of resistors and capacitors to give the diode more time to deionize.

3.15 Filters

So far the rectifiers studied have had certain ripple factors dependent upon the particular load and type of circuit. As long as these are satisfactory for a particular application, there is no need of further complicating the rectifier. However, if the requirements of the load require a smaller ripple factor than can be obtained with the circuits available, the circuit must be altered in some manner.

Since the rectifier is built, first of all, to produce a d-c voltage, and the magnitudes available are determined by the circuits as studied, the ripple factor is best reduced by eliminating part of the a-c component. This involves a change in wave form without appreciably affecting the d-c or average value.

The device for accomplishing this is known as a filter, and is usually inserted as a unit between the rectifier proper and the load. As mentioned, this filter must have the basic property of reducing the a-c component of the output, while not appreciably affecting

the d-c.   From the standpoint of efficiency it is also desirable that
the filter consume as little power as possible and still have comparatively small initial cost.

If the elements are to be passive, they must be resistance, inductance, or capacitance.   If they are to consume little or no average
power, the resistance is probably eliminated.   As will be found
later, two of the three elements are necessary.   The combination of
inductance and capacitance gives the best filter, but the combination
of resistance and capacitance provides the cheapest filter.

Consider a *full-wave* circuit similar to the type shown in Fig. 3-9,
whose average voltage is given in Eq. 3.46.   This circuit is shown
with the addition of a filter in Fig. 3-25.   It will first be noticed that

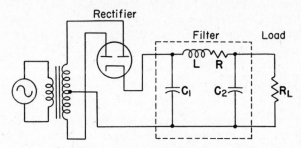

Fig. 3-25.   Full-wave rectifier with L-C filter.

the capacitor C_2, which is in parallel with the load R_L, is included
as part of the filter.   It will be remembered that it was mentioned in
Sec. 3.7 that this capacitor was often added for the express purpose
of reducing the ripple factor and thus was actually a simple filter in
its own right.   It is also included as part of the filter here along with
the inductance and the capacitor C_1.   It must be understood that
the load R_L is not necessarily a pure passive resistance.   The only
requirement is that the load in the range being considered shall
behave as if it were a resistance of value R_L.

The analysis carried out in Sec. 3.7 depended only upon the load
in parallel with the capacitor drawing a certain average current.
If C_1 in Fig. 3-25 is considered as this same capacitor, the voltage
across C_1 would have the same form and average value as found in
Sec. 3.7 if the rest of the circuit demands the same average current.

Thus, using the same approximation as before, the voltage across
C_1 is represented by a sawtooth wave where

$$E_{dc} = E_m \left(\frac{4fR_tC_1}{4fR_tC_1 + 1} \right), \tag{3.96}$$

and the amplitude of the voltage variation is

$$\Delta E = \frac{I_{dc}}{2fC_1}. \tag{3.97}$$

It should be noticed that Eq. 3.96 and Eq. 3.97 are similar to Eq. 3.45 and Eq. 3.46, except the value of capacitance is C_1 and the resistance is R_t, the total series resistance in the d-c path.

The average voltage across R_L is now reduced from the total average value of Eq. 3.96 to a fraction of this, depending upon the ratio of R_L to R. Thus across R_L

$$E_{dc} = E_m \left(\frac{4fR_tC_1}{4fR_tC_1 + 1} \right) \left(\frac{R_L}{R_t} \right)$$

$$= E_m \left(\frac{4fR_LC_1}{4fR_tC_1 + 1} \right). \tag{3.98}$$

If R is small compared to R_L, there is little difference between the values at the two points. This is of course desirable.

Since the wave form of the voltage across C_1 is being considered identical to that without L, R, and C_2, the a-c component of voltage at C_1 is identical and has an effective value of

$$E_{ac} = 0.58 \frac{\Delta E}{2}. \tag{3.99}$$

For analysis here it is more convenient to express this variation by a Fourier series. Thus

$$e(t) - E_{dc} = \frac{2}{\pi} \frac{\Delta E}{2} \sin(\omega't - \theta_1) + \frac{\Delta E}{2\pi} \sin(2\omega't - \theta_2) \tag{3.100}$$

The first term of Eq. 3.100 is the fundamental and has an angular frequency of ω'. Note that ω' is not necessarily equal to ω of the supply, but is the frequency of periodic repetition of the a-c ripple.

As a first approximation, consider that the a-c ripple is expressed entirely by the first term of Eq. 3.100. Thus the total voltage appearing across C_1 in Fig. 3-25 is

$$e_{C1} \cong E_m \left(\frac{4fR_tC_1}{4fR_tC_1 + 1} \right) + \frac{\Delta E}{\pi} \sin(\omega't - \theta_1). \tag{3.101}$$

With this assumption, C_1 and the parts of the circuit to the left of C_1 in Fig. 3-25 may be replaced by a special generator with an output voltage expressed by Eq. 3.101.

The part of the d-c component appearing across R_L has already been expressed by Eq. 3.98. It now remains to determine what portion of the a-c term appears across R_L and upon what this value depends.

A glance at Fig. 3-25 indicates that the ratio of a-c voltage across C_1 to that across R_L is equal to the ratio of the impedances seen at these two points. Thus

$$\frac{E_{acC1}}{E_{acRL}} = \frac{R + j\omega'L - \dfrac{jR_L/(\omega'C_2)}{R_L - j/(\omega'C_2)}}{-\dfrac{jR_L/(\omega'C_2)}{R_L - j/(\omega'C_2)}} \qquad (3.102)$$

Two simplifying assumptions may be made.

First, at the frequency involved $R \ll \omega'L$. It is generally true that the choke used has a high Q at the frequency ω'.

Second, in most practical filters the value of C_2 would be so chosen that $R_L \gg \dfrac{1}{\omega'C_2}$, perhaps a ratio of 10 to 1 or greater.

With these assumptions Eq. 3.102 reduces to

$$\frac{E_{acC1}}{E_{acRL}} = \frac{j\omega'L - jL/(\omega'C_2)}{-j/(\omega C_2)} = (\omega')^2 LC_2 - 1 = \zeta \qquad (3.103)$$

Equation 3.103 is the smoothing factor, and expresses the ratio by which the fundamental a-c component of voltage is reduced by one filter section consisting of a choke and capacitor. If only the fundamental a-c component is considered, Eq. 3.103 is also the approximate ratio by which the ripple factor is reduced from C_1 to R_L. Thus for full-wave capacitor input,

$$\gamma_{RL} \cong \frac{0.707}{\pi \zeta 2fR_LC_1} \qquad (3.104)$$

If need be several filter sections, each consisting of a choke and a capacitor, may be used in tandem so that the output of one becomes the input to the second, and so on. Thus the combined smoothing factor of such a series becomes the product of the individual smoothing factors.

In the analysis of this filter, use was made of only the fundamental a-c component of the Fourier series. This is acceptable for two reasons.

First, the results of such an analysis indicate that the effectiveness of such a filter is almost proportional to the square of the frequency of the a-c component. Thus if the fundamental is satisfactorily eliminated, the second and higher harmonics are reduced to a much smaller fraction of their original size.

Second, both this series and others that are usually encountered converge rather rapidly, making the magnitudes of the higher harmonics usually negligible compared to the fundamental.

Mention was made of using a combination of resistance and capacitance as a comparatively cheap substitute for the filter just discussed. This assumes an appreciable cost differential between a satisfactory choke and resistance.

Consider the circuit of Fig. 3-25 with L removed and R no longer negligible.

Using the same approach, the d-c voltage across R_L is again

$$E_{dc} = E_m \left(\frac{4fR_LC_1}{4fR_tC_1 + 1} \right). \tag{3.98}$$

The a-c component of the voltage across C_1 is now divided between the series resistance and the parallel combination of R_L and C_2. If R_L is again large enough so that C_2 furnishes an effective by-pass,

$$\frac{E_{acC1}}{E_{acRL}} \cong \frac{R - j/(\omega'C_2)}{-j/(\omega'C_2)}. \tag{3.105}$$

Since we are not interested in phase relations, but only absolute values,

$$\frac{E_{acC1}}{E_{acRL}} \cong \sqrt{R^2\omega'^2C_2^2 + 1} = \zeta. \tag{3.106}$$

It is apparent from Eq. 3.106 that the smoothing factor of an R-C filter is roughly proportional to the frequency rather than the square of the frequency as was true of the L-C filter.

It is also apparent that the filtering action should come from large values of $\omega'C$ rather than large resistances, since this affects the d-c voltage least. This type of filter is very common in applications where two or more values of d-c voltage are required, and thus the dropping resistors can serve double duty.

It should be clear to the reader that although these filters have so far been discussed in connection with reducing the a-c component of voltage across an input capacitor, the general filter theory is not dependent upon the source of this a-c component.   Circuits of this type in which a parallel capacitor is the first element out of the rectifier are known as "capacitor input filters."   This is true regardless of the number of L-C or R-C filter sections that follow.

In comparison, consider the R-L circuit of Fig. 3-12.   This circuit is redrawn with the addition of a capacitor across R_L and a separation of choke and load resistance in Fig. 3-26.

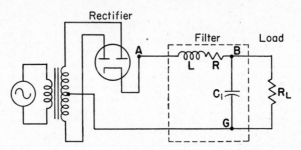

Fig. 3-26.   Full-wave rectifier with choke input filter.

Except for the capacitor C_1 the analysis of this circuit is the same as for the previous circuit of Fig. 3-12.   One of the important factors in this analysis was the fact that one plate or the other of the rectifier conducted at all times.   In other words, the current through L never went to zero.

Without C_1 this was of course an obvious necessity if L were anything greater than zero.   However, the addition of C_1 makes this condition dependent upon the relative values of L, C_1, and R_L. Consider the following approach to the limiting values.

Assume first of all that one plate or the other is conducting at all times and that commutation takes place when the supply voltage passes through zero.   The voltage wave form across A to G is a full rectified sine wave and has the following Fourier expression:

$$e_{AG} = \frac{2}{\pi}E_m + \frac{4}{3\pi}E_m \sin\ (\omega't - \theta) + \cdots \tag{3.107}$$

Again only the d-c and fundamental terms are considered. If this is to result in a current through L that never goes to zero, the amplitude of the a-c component of current must never be greater than the d-c. Thus the limiting condition of the two just being equal is

$$\frac{2E_m}{\pi R_t} = \frac{4E_m}{3\pi\left(R + j\omega'L - \dfrac{jR_L/\omega'C_1}{R_L - j/\omega'C}\right)}. \qquad (3.108)$$

If it assumed that the smoothing factor ζ is large enough to be approximately $\omega'^2 LC_1$, and R is neglected, for a 60-c supply, Eq. 3.108 reduces to

$$L_{min} = \frac{R_L}{1132}. \qquad (3.109)$$

Thus

$$L_{min} \cong \frac{R_L}{1000}, \qquad (3.110)$$

and if $\omega'^2 LC_1 \geqq 10$,

$$C_1 \geqq \frac{10^4}{\omega'^2 R_L} = \frac{0.0176}{R_L} \text{ using } L_{min}. \qquad (3.111)$$

Having met these conditions, the effect of the filter is the same on the respective d-c and a-c components as calculated before.

Thus

$$E_{dc} = \frac{2}{\pi} E_m \frac{R_L}{R + R_L}, \qquad (3.112)$$

and

$$E_{ac} \cong \frac{0.707 \times 2 \times 2E_m}{3\pi\zeta}. \qquad (3.113)$$

Therefore, across R_L

$$\gamma = \frac{1.414(R + R_L)}{3\zeta R_L}. \qquad (3.114)$$

From Eq. 3.114 if $R \ll R_L$, γ is independent of either R_L or E_m, but is a constant over the operating range. This is a definite advantage of this type of circuit over the capacitor input type whose ripple factor is expressed by Eq. 3.104 and definitely does depend upon R_L. The chief advantage of the capacitor input filter is the attempt to produce and average output voltage equal to the peak of the supply.   All other factors, such as regulation, tube utilization, peak tube current, etc., seem to favor the choke input circuit.

3.16   Polyphase Rectifiers

Although the single-phase rectifier in its various forms, as already discussed, probably accounts numerically for 90 per cent of the rectifier applications, there are situations which demand outputs that cannot be met by them.   For example, it may be necessary to have a much smaller ripple factor without the use of a filter than single-phase circuits can produce.   Or the load may demand a much larger average current than can be handled by two tubes. These are two of the chief reasons for considering polyphase rectifiers.

In general, polyphase rectifiers result in lower ripple factors, less average current per tube, and a more even flow of power than is possible with any of the single-phase circuits studied.   Since the three-phase system is most common, the text will limit itself to these, realizing that the same principles might be applied to any particular system.

It is general practice in the three-phase systems to connect the power transformer with its primaries in delta and its secondaries in wye.   This gives a voltage step-up across the transformer and provides the neutral of the secondary as the common return which is required in so many of the polyphase circuits.

3.17   Three-phase Star, Resistance Load

Perhaps the simplest three-phase rectifier is that shown in Fig. 3-27.

The operation of such a circuit is quite simple.   Each of the three phase voltages E_{NA}, E_{NB}, and E_{NC} is connected to the resistance load through a diode rectifier.   Conduction takes place through whichever tube has the largest plate supply voltage with respect to the neutral point N.   Thus from Fig. 3-28 each phase conducts for $2\pi/3$ radians or 120° of each cycle.   The fundamental ripple frequency is three times the supply frequency or 180-c for a 60-c source. It is also apparent that neither the voltage nor the current ever goes to zero in the load.

The average load voltage may be calculated by

$$E_{dc} = \frac{1}{2\pi/3} \int_{\pi/6}^{5\pi/6} E_{sm} \sin \omega t \, d\omega t. \qquad (3.115)$$

Thus
$$E_{dc} = \frac{3\sqrt{3}}{2\pi} E_{sm} = 0.827 E_{sm}. \qquad (3.116)$$

Since the load is pure resistance,

$$I_{dc} = \frac{E_{dc}}{R_L} = 0.827 \frac{E_{sm}}{R_L}. \qquad (3.117)$$

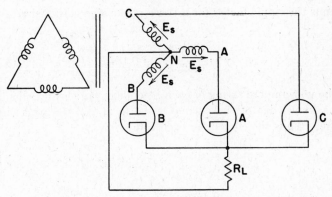

Fig. 3-27.　Three-phase star rectifier with resistance load.

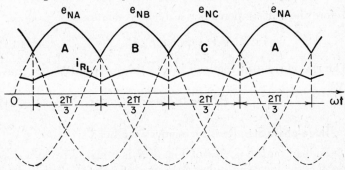

Fig. 3-28.　Voltage and current variations in a three-phase star rectifier with resistance load.

From the curves it can be seen that the peak inverse voltage on the two nonconducting tubes does not occur simultaneously with the peak of any single phase.　For example, the inverse voltage on tube C is expressed for the period $\pi/6 \leqq \omega t \leqq 5\pi/6$ by

$$e_{c\ inverse} = E_{sm} \sin(\omega t - 60°) + E_{sm} \sin \omega t. \qquad (3.118)$$

Equation 3.118 reduces to

$$e_{c\ inverse} = 1.732 E_{sm} \sin(\omega t - 30°). \qquad (3.119)$$

Thus the peak inverse voltage on tube C is $1.732E_{sm}$ and occurs $120°$ after e_{NA} passes through zero.

The ripple factor may be evaluated from its fundamental definition.

$$(E_{ac})^2 = 0.024E_m{}^2,$$

and thus the ripple factor for a three-phase star with resistive load is

$$\gamma = \frac{0.155E_m}{0.827E_m} = 0.187. \qquad (3.120)$$

The volt-ampere rating of each secondary can also be calculated from a knowledge of the current wave form and the peak supply voltage. Thus the current in each coil is

$$I_{rms} = \sqrt{\frac{1}{2\pi} \int_{30}^{150} I_m{}^2 \sin^2 \omega t \, d\omega t}. \qquad (3.121)$$

$$= 0.486 I_m. \qquad (3.122)$$

Therefore the volt-amperes per secondary coil are

$$VA_s = 0.502 E_{dc} I_{dc}. \qquad (3.123)$$

The rms current of the load is $\sqrt{3}$ times Eq. 3.122 and thus

$$P_{avg} = 0.706 \frac{E_{sm}{}^2}{R_L}. \qquad (3.124)$$

3.18 Three-phase Star, Resistance-inductance Load

If the load on the circuit of Fig. 3-27 is replaced by a load consisting of resistance and inductance in series, the analysis is fundamentally the same.

It is still true that the tube with the largest plate supply voltage with respect to N conducts, and thus both the voltage wave form and average value are identical with those for the resistance load. However, the current is no longer a direct replica of the load voltage, but is appreciably smoothed out by the inductance. As discussed in Sec. 3.8, the effect of the series inductance and resistance is to decrease the a-c component of voltage across the resistance and thus divide the ripple factor for a series resistance and inductance by the smoothing factor which is

$$\zeta = \sqrt{1 + Q^2}.\qquad(3.125)$$

Thus the ripple factor across R_L with R-L load is

$$\gamma_{RL} = \frac{0.187}{\sqrt{1 + Q^2}}.\qquad(3.126)$$

It is apparent that if the load is appreciably reactive, it is a fairly good assumption to assume the load current constant at its average value. With this assumption

$$P_{avg} \cong E_{dc}I_{dc} = 0.684\,\frac{E_{sm}^{\;2}}{R_L}.\qquad(3.127)$$

Also, assuming the current in each secondary coil constant during the conduction period,

$$I_{rms/coil} = \frac{I_{dc}}{\sqrt{3}}.\qquad(3.128)$$

Thus the volt-amperes per secondary coil are

$$VA_s = 0.494E_{dc}I_{dc}.\qquad(3.129)$$

3.19 Three-phase Bridge, Resistance Load

A second popular three-phase rectifier is the three-phase bridge circuit shown in Fig. 3-29. Similar to the single-phase bridge cir-

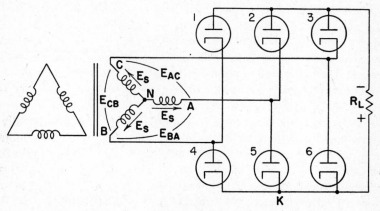

Fig. 3-29. Three-phase bridge rectifier, resistance load.

cuit, each conduction path through the supply transformer and load passes through two rectifiers in series and thus reduces the peak inverse voltage per tube approximately one-half. A second characteristic, equally important, is the fact that commutation takes place every 60 degrees, or six times per cycle, thus reducing the ripple factor and increasing the ripple frequency.

For purposes of analysis, assume E_{BA} is at its positive peak at time t_1. Conduction is taking place through tube 5 since point A is positive with respect to both points B and C. The conduction is completed through R_L and back through tube 1, since point B is more negative with respect to A than is point C. Thus one tube out

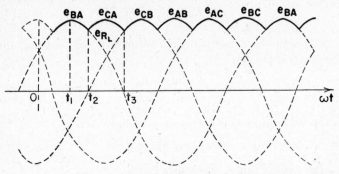

Fig. 3-30. Voltage and current variation in three-phase bridge rectifier with resistance load.

of each set of three is conducting at t_1. If the rectifiers are considered perfect, point K the cathodes of tubes 4, 5, and 6 are all at the potential of point A. Thus tubes 4 and 6 do not conduct so long as their plates, which are points B and C, respectively, are negative with respect to A. Likewise, the plates of tubes 1, 2, and 3 are all at the potential of point B, and tubes 2 and 3 do not conduct so long as point B is negative with respect to their cathodes, which are points A and C, respectively.

Progressing on from time t_1, points B and C become equally negative with respect to A at time t_2, and from there B is more negative than C, so conduction is transferred from tube 1 to tube 3, and thus the voltage E_{CA} rather than E_{BA} appears across R_L. This continues until time t_3, at which points B and A become equally positive with respect to C. Since from here on B is more positive than A, conduction is transferred to tube 4 from tube 5, and the voltage E_{CB} appears across R_L. Thus commutation takes place every 60 degrees in such a manner as to maintain the maximum possible voltage across R_L. This load voltage variation is shown in Fig. 3-30.

The average value of this voltage is easily calculated from the curve.

$$E_{dc} = \frac{3}{\pi} \int_{\pi/3}^{2\pi/3} \sqrt{3}\ E_{sm} \sin \omega t\ d\omega t. \tag{3.130}$$

$$= 1.65 E_{sm}. \tag{3.131}$$

Study of the circuit reveals that since the operation of the circuit requires that the most negative cathode of tubes 1, 2, and 3 conduct, and the most positive plate of tubes 4, 5, and 6 conduct, the peak inverse voltage across any tube is the peak voltage across R_L, and thus

$$E_{pi} = \sqrt{3}\ E_{sm}. \tag{3.132}$$

As already mentioned, the fundamental frequency of the ripple voltage is six times the supply voltage. It can also be seen from the curves that the a-c variation is less than for the star rectifier, and the d-c voltage is greater. Thus the ripple factor should be less. It will now be calculated.

$$(E_{rms})^2 = E_{dc}^2 + E_{ac}^2 \tag{3.133}$$

$$= \frac{3}{\pi} \int_{\pi/3}^{2\pi/3} (\sqrt{3}\ E_{sm} \sin \omega t)^2\ d\omega t. \tag{3.134}$$

$$= 2.74 E_{sm}^2. \tag{3.135}$$

Thus
$$2.74 E_{sm}^2 = 2.73 E_{sm}^2 + E_{ac}^2 \tag{3.136}$$

Therefore
$$E_{ac}^2 = 0.01 E_{sm}^2. \tag{3.137}$$

Thus the ripple factor is

$$\gamma = \frac{0.1 E_{sm}}{1.65 E_{sm}} = 0.0606 \cong 6.0\%. \tag{3.138}$$

The volt-ampere rating of the secondary coils may be found from the fact that each coil carries the effective load current for four periods of 60 degrees each cycle.

From Eq. 3.135 the effective load current is

$$I_{rms}{}^2 = 2.74 \frac{E_{sm}{}^2}{R_L{}^2}.\tag{3.139}$$

Thus $\qquad I_{rms/coil}{}^2 = \dfrac{2 \times 2.74}{3} \dfrac{E_{sm}{}^2}{R_L{}^2} = 1.828 \dfrac{E_{sm}{}^2}{R_L{}^2},\tag{3.140}$

or $\qquad\qquad\qquad I_{rms/coil} = 1.351 \dfrac{E_{sm}}{R_L}.\tag{3.141}$

From Eq. 3.131

$$I_{dc} = 1.65 \frac{E_{sm}}{R_L}.\tag{3.142}$$

Thus the volt-ampere rating for each secondary coil is

$$VA_s = 0.351 E_{dc} I_{dc}.\tag{3.143}$$

The analysis of inductive load is similar, as was true of the star rectifier, and will be left as an exercise for the reader.

3.20   Six-phase Rectifier

Occasionally the six-phase rectifier is used in place of the star, when less ripple is required.   Such a circuit is shown in Fig. 3-31.

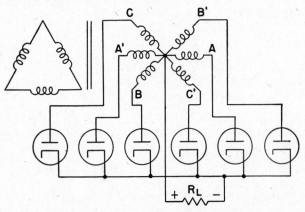

Fig. 3-31.   Six-phase rectifier with resistance load.

It is apparent from the circuit that the maximum voltage across the load is E_{sm} and that each tube conducts for approximately 60 degrees each cycle.   Thus both the tube utilization and the output voltage per volt of secondary coil voltage is less than for the bridge circuit of the preceding section.   For this reason the circuit finds limited practical application.   However, one aspect is that it applies conveniently to a mercury pool type of rectifier with one common cathode and six anodes.

The analysis of this circuit will be left to the reader since it follows exactly the method already applied.

3.21 Double Wye Rectifier with Interphase Winding and Resistance and Inductance Load

Probably the most used polyphase rectifier circuit is the double wye with interphase winding, since it results in the best combination

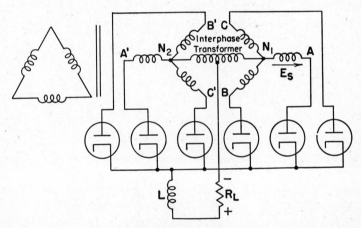

Fig. 3-32.   Double wye rectifier with interphase transformer and resistance, inductance load.

of good transformer utilization, primary and secondary, low ripple factor, low peak inverse voltage, and good tube utilization.   The basic circuit is shown in Fig. 3-32.

Since it is almost universal to use a smoothing reactor in series with the load, if it is not already inductive, only such a combination will be considered.   It might be mentioned that this is also very common practice in the other circuits already discussed.

The analysis of this circuit is perhaps the most easily approached by considering it to be two three-phase star systems operating together with separate loads.   The instantaneous curves for such an

analogy appear in Fig. 3-33. The dotted set represents system 1
with phases A, B, and C, and neutral N_1. The solid set represents
system 2 with phases A', B', and C', and neutral N_2.

The shaded areas indicate the difference in the potentials of
points N_1 and N_2. It is the job of the interphase transformer to
withstand this difference of potential, since its terminals are connected to N_1 and N_2, respectively. If this interphase transformer
were a perfect reactor, it could maintain this voltage gradient with
zero current, but since it is not perfect, its operation fails at very
small currents and the circuit reverts to the 6-phase star.

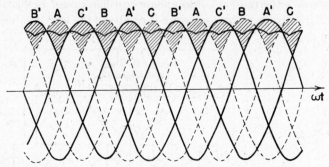

Fig. 3-33. Voltage variation for double wye rectifier.

Assuming the interphase transformer is successful in maintaining
each neutral at the same potential as if that set operated alone,
connection of the load to the center tap makes it possible for both
systems to work into one load. The voltage across the load becomes
the instantaneous average value of the two supplies, and is shown in
heavy line in Fig. 3-33. It is quite apparent that the ripple frequency is twice that of either star alone, or six times the supply
frequency.

A brief consideration will be given to the operation of the interphase transformer. Since each half of the transformer carries
separate components of load current, it is of interest to consider
their magnetic effect on the core.

If the load inductance is sufficient to decrease the load current
ripple to a negligible value, then the current in each half is d-c and
the magnetic effects obviously cancel. If ripple current exists then
for set number 1, it is of the form

$$i_1 = I_{dc} + I_{m3} \sin (3\omega t + \theta_3) + I_{m6} \sin (6\omega t + \theta_6) + \cdots \quad (3.144)$$

Likewise for set number 2, since it is displaced 60 degrees along the fundamental axis,

$$i_2 = I_{dc} + I_{m3} \sin 3 \left(\omega t + \frac{\theta_3}{3} - 60° \right)$$

$$+ I_{m6} \sin 6 \left(\omega t + \frac{\theta_6}{6} - 60° \right) + \cdots. \qquad (3.145)$$

Thus the net magnetizing effect is due to their difference, and is proportional to

$$i_{net} = i_1 - i_2 = 2I_{m3} \sin (3\omega t + \theta_3) + 0 + \cdots. \qquad (3.146)$$

Thus only those harmonics which are not multiples of 6 have any net magnetizing effects. Therefore the reactor must depend primarily for its excitation current upon circulating currents through the conducting coils and rectifiers. The major part of the excitation current does not pass through the load.

The volt-ampere rating of this reactor is arrived at by assuming that each half carries one-half of the average load current, and thus the current rating for the interphase transformer is approximately

$$I_{rms} \cong \frac{I_{dc}}{2}. \qquad (3.147)$$

On the other hand the reactor must be able to withstand the peak difference voltage between N_1 and N_2 without saturation and thus the peak voltage for the interphase transformer

$$E_{peak} = 0.5E_{sm}. \qquad (3.148)$$

The average voltage across the load will now be calculated.

$$E_{dc} = \frac{6}{2\pi} \int_{60}^{90} E_{sm}[\sin \omega t + \sin (\omega t + 60°)] \, d\omega t. \qquad (3.149)$$

Thus $\qquad E_{dc} = \frac{3E_{sm}}{\pi} \left[- \cos \omega t - \cos (\omega t + 60°) \right]_{60°}^{90°}$

and $\qquad E_{dc} = 0.825E_{sm}. \qquad (3.150)$

It is now possible to calculate the volt-ampere rating of the reactor in terms of the d-c output. Thus from Eqs. 3.147, 3.148, and 3.150, the volt-amperes of the reactor are

$$VA = 0.214E_{dc}I_{dc}. \tag{3.151}$$

Since one tube of each set conducts at all times, the average load current is equally divided between the two tubes, and therefore the average current per tube is

$$I_{dc/tube} = \frac{I_{dc}}{6} = 0.167I_{dc}. \tag{3.152}$$

For comparison it is essential to calculate the ripple factor of this preferred circuit. As has been shown before, the series load reactor serves to reduce the ripple across the resistive part of the load by a factor of at least $\sqrt{1 + Q^2}$. Thus calculation will be made of the inherent ripple across the entire rectifier load. As before, the total rms value of the load voltage squared is expressed as

$$E_{rms}{}^2 = E_{dc}{}^2 + E_{ac}{}^2. \tag{3.153}$$

This value can be calculated directly from the curves of Fig. 3-33. From such a calculation

$$E_{rms}{}^2 = 0.685E_{sm}{}^2. \tag{3.154}$$

Thus $$E_{ac}{}^2 = 0.685E_{sm}{}^2 - 0.680E_{sm}{}^2$$

$$= 0.005E_{sm}{}^2. \tag{3.155}$$

From Eq. 3.155,

$$E_{ac} = 0.070E_{sm}$$

and $$\gamma = \frac{0.070E_{sm}}{0.825E_{sm}}$$

$$\gamma = 0.083. \tag{3.156}$$

The peak inverse voltage is approximately given by

$$E_{pi} = E_{sm} + E_{dc}. \tag{3.157}$$

Thus from Eq. 3.150

$$E_{pi} = \left(1 + \frac{1}{0.825}\right) E_{dc} = 2.212E_{dc}. \tag{3.158}$$

This value is not exact, but the calculated value would not be much closer practically unless such things as tube drop, leakage reactance, and overlap are considered.

The volt-ampere rating of the primaries and secondaries can be found from the knowledge of the current wave form. In each secondary the current for R-L load is a block of current equal to $I_{dc}/2$ and existing for $\frac{2}{3}\pi$ radians per cycle. The primary current, since one primary serves two secondaries 180° out of phase, consists of two such block currents oppositely directed and equally spaced. The turns ratio from primary to secondary, N_p/N_s, also enters the calculation of the primary current. Thus the effective values for the secondary may be found to be

$$I_{rms} = 0.29 I_{dc}, \tag{3.159}$$

and for the primary,

$$I_{rms} = 0.408 \frac{N_s}{N_p} I_{dc}. \tag{3.160}$$

Using Eq. 3.159 and Eq. 3.160, it is now easy to calculate the required volt-ampere rating of each coil.

Thus the volt-amperes of each secondary coil are

$$VA_s = 0.248 E_{dc} I_{dc}, \tag{3.161}$$

and the volt-amperes of each primary coil are

$$VA_p = 0.35 E_{dc} I_{dc}. \tag{3.162}$$

3.22　Utility Factor of Polyphase Rectifiers

A very common method of comparing the relative quality of rectifier circuits is to evaluate the ratio of d-c power output $E_{dc} I_{dc}$ to the total volt-ampere rating of the primary or secondary coils. Thus

$$\text{Utility Factor} = U.F. = \frac{E_{dc} I_{dc}}{\text{volt-amperes of coils}}. \tag{3.163}$$

One of the best utility factors obtainable is for the double wye circuit of Sec. 3.21. Calculated for the primary of a double wye,

$$U.F. = 0.952. \tag{3.164}$$

For convenience most of the results of the previous circuits have been grouped together for comparison in Table 3.1.

Table 3.1 Polyphase Rectifiers

	E_{dc}	E_{pi}	γ	VA_s per sec coil	P_{avg}
3Φ star, R load	$0.827E_{sm}$	$1.732E_{sm}$	0.187	$0.502E_{dc}I_{dc}$	$\dfrac{0.706E_{sm}{}^2}{R_L}$
3Φ star, R-L load	$0.827E_{sm}$	$1.732E_{sm}$	$\dfrac{0.187}{\sqrt{1+Q^2}}$	$0.494E_{dc}I_{dc}$	$\dfrac{0.684E_{sm}{}^2}{R_L}$
3Φ bridge, R load	$1.65E_{sm}$	$1.732E_{sm}$	0.0606	$0.351E_{dc}I_{dc}$	$\dfrac{2.74E_{sm}{}^2}{R_L}$
Double wye with interphase, R-L load	$0.825E_{sm}$	$2.212E_{dc}$	0.083	$0.248E_{dc}I_{dc}$	$\dfrac{0.685E_{sm}{}^2}{R_L}$

3.23 Grid Controlled Three-phase Rectifiers

The previous analysis of polyphase rectifiers has been carried out for the case of straight rectifying elements such as diodes. This is undoubtedly the one most important application, but not the only one. For some special purpose, such as a variable voltage output, it is sometimes desirable to use grid controlled rectifiers. Thus a brief mention of grid control's effect should be made.

First consider the simple three-phase star system. The circuit will be remembered from Fig. 3-27, Sec. 3.17. The only change is the substitution of grid controlled gas tubes for the diodes shown, and the load will be considered to consist of both resistance and inductance.

Two conditions of operation must be distinguished when grid controlled tubes are used. These are pulse conduction and continuous conduction. The terms refer to the current in the load and are self-explanatory.

Two conditions must be satisfied in order that the tubes fire. First, the voltage rise from cathode to plate must be positive, and the grid voltage, cathode to grid, must be less negative than the critical value determined by the tube characteristics and the plate voltage. Thus by properly controlling the grid voltage, the firing of any tube may be delayed or prevented during the period it would normally conduct as a diode. It is not possible to fire the tube sooner by this grid action.

Figure 3-34 shows the voltage and current wave form of such a rectifier. The curves shown in Fig. 3-34 are for pulse conduction since there are periods of zero conduction. Although the firing angle α can be controlled at will, the extinction angle β is a function of α, E_m, and the load. The relation between these parameters is taken up in detail in the chapter on motor control. For the moment it is sufficient to indicate such a relation exists.

It can be seen from Fig. 3-34 that conduction becomes continuous when each tube conducts for 120°, or when $\beta = \alpha + 120 - 180 = \alpha - 60$. Since each tube can conduct at most for 120 degrees, the

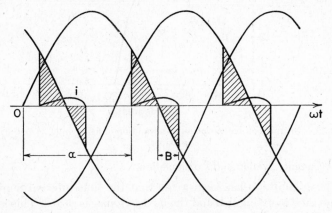

Fig. 3-34.   Three-phase star rectifier with controlled grid tubes.

place that conduction takes place in the half cycle can be varied from a maximum output voltage condition corresponding to operation similar to diodes to a minimum voltage of zero as $\alpha \to 180°$.

The average load voltage will now be calculated for the continuous conduction operation as a function of the firing angle.

$$E_{dc} = \frac{3E_{sm}}{2\pi} \int_{\alpha}^{\alpha + 2\pi/3} \sin \omega t \, d\omega t. \qquad (3.165)$$

$$E_{dc} = 0.83 E_{sm} \sin \left(\alpha + \frac{\pi}{3} \right). \qquad (3.166)$$

Equation 3.166 is plotted in Fig. 3-35. The point at which the dotted curve breaks away from the solid curve is the point at which pulse conduction starts, and depends upon the factors already mentioned.

A similar method of analysis would hold for the other rectifier circuits and thus will not be considered here.

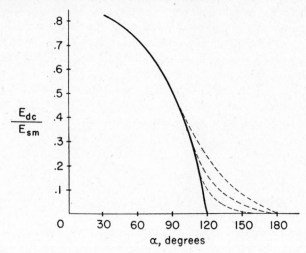

Fig. 3-35. Output voltage variation as a function of firing angle in a controlled rectifier.

3.24 Current Overlap and Commutation

The assumption has been made that the time interval required for one tube to extinguish and the next to ionize is zero. This is not true in a practical application. From the time the second tube starts to ionize until it has completely relieved the first tube of

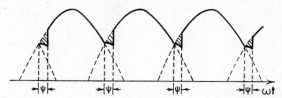

Fig. 3-36. Effect of deionization time and commutation.

current is a finite period. Let this mutual conduction period be expressed by ψ. During this time both tubes are conducting, and the load voltage is something between the two values if either tube alone conducted. A reasonable approximation might be to assume the load voltage to be the average of the two values during this time. The relations are shown in Fig. 3-36.

The average value of load voltage is apparently decreased by an amount proportional to the shaded areas. The best method of calculating this effect is to consider the amount which it decreases the average value calculated without it. In this manner it can be applied to any of the previous calculation. Thus

$$\Delta E_{dc} = -\frac{3E_m}{2\pi} \int_{\pi/6}^{\pi/6+\psi} \left[\sin \omega t - \sin\left(\omega t + \frac{2}{3}\pi\right)\right] d\omega t. \quad (3.167)$$

$$= -\frac{3E_m}{2\pi} \sqrt{3}\,(1 - \cos \psi). \quad (3.168)$$

Equation 3.168 is calculated for the particular condition shown in Fig. 3-36. The method is apparent for other rectifier circuits with different tube conduction periods.

3.25 Inverters

The basic circuits for series and parallel single-phase inversion were mentioned in Chapter 2. They are repeated here in Fig. 3-37.

Consider the operation of the parallel circuit of Fig. 3-37(a). Before either tube fires, the current is zero in all parts of the circuit and the capacitor C is uncharged. Assume now that tube 1 is permitted to fire as the result of the proper grid signal. Conduction starts around the loop consisting of the d-c supply, the choke L, and the upper half of the transformer. This flow of current results in an induced voltage of the polarity shown across the transformer. Since the primary is a center-tapped winding on one core, an equal voltage appears across the lower half. The result of this voltage is to charge C to a voltage equal to the sum of the transformer voltage and to produce a voltage across the load impedance Z_L. This continues until tube 2 is allowed to fire as a result of its grid action, since its plate is positive. When tube 2 fires, the loop including tube 2, C, and tube 1 is completed. Since the voltage on C cannot be changed instantaneously, the plate of tube 1 goes negative and it extinguishes. The process thus reverses, charging C up to the opposite polarity in preparation for the extinction of tube 2 when tube 1 is again fired. Thus an alternating voltage appears across the primary of the output transformer and thus a similar voltage across the load. The effect of load power factor and load current on wave form and stability will be discussed later.

The operation of the series circuit of Fig. 3-37(b) is similar, but the center-tapped inductance rather than the capacitor is used to extinguish the conducting tube.

As before, assume neither tube has been conducting and then allow tube 1 to start. Conduction takes place through L', C, and the left side of the center-tapped choke L, and produces voltages of

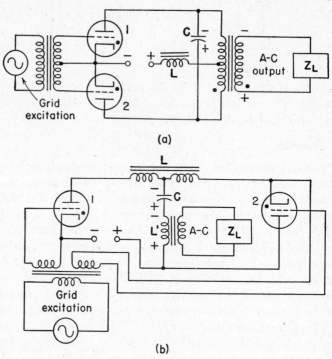

(a)

(b)

Fig. 3-37. (a) Parallel separately excited inverter. (b) Series separately excited inverter.

the polarity marked. This conduction is limited to the time necessary to charge C up to the supply voltage minus the tube drop. Tube 2 may be fired at any time after its plate voltage becomes positive. Its path of conduction is through the right half of the center-tapped choke, the capacitor C, and the choke L'. It can also be seen that if both tubes 1 and 2 conduct simultaneously, they provide a short-circuit loop through the supply and the choke L. Thus it is apparent that the purpose of L is to produce a voltage in the plate circuit of either tube that tends to extinguish it when the other tube fires.   This is easily accomplished if the period of the grid excitation is long enough to permit the plate current of one tube to become small before the other tube fires.

A third important industrial inverter is the controlled polyphase rectifier with the d-c source supplied and the firing angle delayed into the negative half of the a-c cycle.

For simplicity, consider the three-phase star rectifier with resistance load.   A simplified circuit is shown in Fig. 3-38, where the curves are shown assuming the firing angle of each tube is delayed 180° after the sinusoidal component of its plate voltage goes through

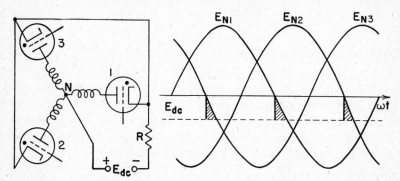

Fig. 3-38.   Three-phase star rectifier connected for use as an inverter.

zero.   Since the d-c supply has its polarity *reversed* from that as a rectifier, it is adding to the plate voltage of each tube and is shown as a shift of the zero axis.   Thus the plates are actually positive during a portion of the negative half cycle of the a-c supply.   Operation in this manner must be controlled very carefully since both supply voltages tend to encourage large current flow during a large percentage of the cycle.   In actual operation the resistance is usually replaced by a choke since it consumes less power.

This last circuit is used extensively in all systems where large amounts of d-c power must be pumped into the a-c line.

3.26 Operational Characteristics of Single-phase Inverters

Consider first the single-phase parallel type inverter of Fig. 3-37(a).   For purposes of analysis each half cycle of operation will be considered separately.   If the output transformer is closely coupled, as it usually is, the load, with correction for turns ratio, may be considered to exist directly across the capacitor. An equivalent circuit for a half cycle of operation is shown in Fig. 3-39.

The voltage E_c is the voltage on the commutating capacitor at the time that tube 1 of Fig. 3-37(a) starts conduction, and is the voltage required to extinguish the other thyratron.

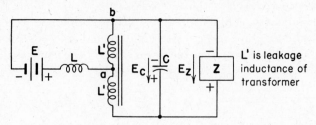

Fig. 3-39.   Equivalent circuit of single-phase parallel type inverter for one-half cycle.

For purposes of analysis, it will also be assumed that the two coils L' behave as an autotransformer, and that they require negligible excitation current. Thus, within reason, the circuit of Fig. 3-39 may be simplified to assume that Z and C are directly across points a and b. This is shown in Fig. 3-40.

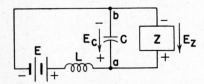

Fig. 3-40.   Simplified equivalent circuit of Fig. 3-39.

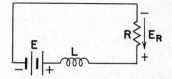

Fig. 3-41.   Simplified circuit for small R load.

The analysis of the wave shape of voltage across Z as a function of Z is now quite elementary. As a first possibility, assume that $Z = R + j0$ and that R is relatively small (large load). The R-C time constant of the load and capacitor is then small, and may usually be neglected in comparison with L/R as far as its effect on the transient output is concerned. The circuit is then further simplified as shown in Fig. 3-41.

The voltage across R is obviously of the form

$$E_R = K_1\epsilon^{-Rt/L} + K_2.\qquad(3.169)$$

The boundary conditions require that at $t = 0$, $E_R = -E_{c0}$ and at $t = \infty$, $E_R = E$. Thus

$$E_R = (E - [E + E_{c0}]\epsilon^{-Rt/L}). \tag{3.170}$$

Plotted as a function of time Eq. 3.170 appears in Fig. 3-42.

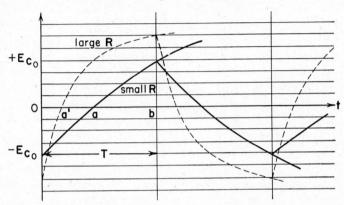

Fig. 3-42.   Output wave form of parallel inverter with a large resistive load.

After the period T, the second thyratron is fired and the transient is repeated except for the reversal of relative polarities.   The dotted curve of Fig. 3-42 indicates a decrease in the ratio L/R with the accompanying wave shape.   Both the period T and the supply voltage E remain constant.   Thus the period is determined by the excitation, and the wave shape is a series of R-L transients with L and R determining the rate of rise of E_R.

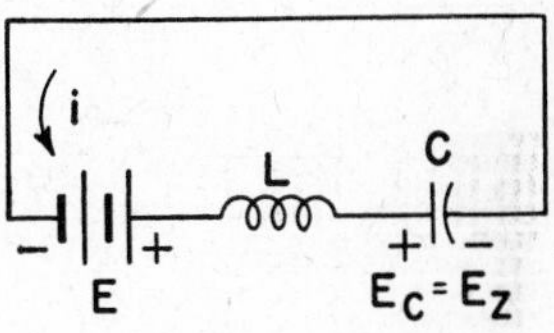

Consider again the circuits of Fig. 3-40.   Assume that Z is still resistive, but is allowed to become quite large, so that RC is appreciable.   This is merely an extension of the trend indicated in Fig. 3-42; thus consider for convenience that $R \rightarrow \infty$.

Fig. 3-43.   Equivalent circuit as $R \rightarrow$ infinity.

It is now possible to neglect Z in comparison with C, and the circuit of Fig. 3-40 simplifies to that shown in Fig. 3-43.   Kirchhoff's loop equation in operational form becomes

$$E = \left(Lp + \frac{1}{Cp}\right) i. \tag{3.171}$$

Solution for E_c results in

$$E_c = E_z = E_R = K_1 \cos (\omega t + \theta) + K_2. \qquad (3.172)$$

where $\omega = 1/\sqrt{LC}$.

Without evaluating the constants it is apparent that the form of the output voltage is sinusoidal. Thus as R increases, the output wave form more nearly approaches a sine wave. However, it is necessary that the excitation be carefully adjusted as to frequency and phase with regard to L and C as this sinusoidal operation is approached. It is helpful, however, that this frequency is relatively independent of R as long as it is large.

As a third possibility, assume Z is reactive in nature. From the last case it should be apparent that the form of E_C or E_Z approaches a sinusoid and now also is a function of Z, since its reactive component combines with L and C.

Therefore, in general, for large resistive loads the wave form approaches a series of R-L transients, while for small resistive loads or reactive loads, the wave form approaches a sine wave.

On the same basis, consider the single-phase series type separately excited inverter. The equivalent circuit during the charging half cycle is shown in Fig. 3-44.

A simple analysis of this circuit shows the form of the current and of E_Z to be a constant plus a transient that is either a damped sinusoidal oscillation or an exponential decay depending upon the

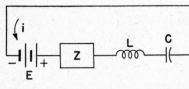

values of Z, L, and C. This results from the writing of Kirchhoff's loop equation, which results in a second-order equation. A complete discussion of the solution to such an equation is carried out in Chapter 7.

Fig. 3-44. Equivalent circuit of series type inverter during charging half cycle.

During the discharge half cycle, the circuit is identical with that of Fig. 3-44 except for the omission of E. Thus the form of the transient voltages and currents is the same, since they are not dependent upon the driving function E, but are entirely a function of the circuit components L, C, and Z.

Since Z definitely enters into the form of the transient, it is apparent that the load Z always plays an important part in determining the wave form of the series inverter. It is also apparent that the frequency of the excitation must be critically adjusted to fit the output wave form each half cycle, and thus the operating frequency is critically dependent upon Z.

3.27 Deionization Time

One very practical limitation of all power inverters is the maximum frequency that is permitted by the deionization time of their thyratrons.

It will be remembered that it was the negative value of E_R or E_C at $t = 0$ that caused the previously conducting tube to extinguish. From Fig. 3-42 it is apparent that this voltage remains negative for the time interval from $t = 0$ to $t = a$. At $t = a$ this voltage passes through zero and rises positively. Therefore, the available deionization time or period during which the tube's plate voltage is negative is from $0 \leqq t \leqq a$. The time allotted varies considerably with wave form, being maximum for very large unity power factor loads.

PROBLEMS

3.1. A battery charger is to be built in accordance with the circuit of Fig. 3-6. However, the battery will comprise an equivalent load consisting of a d-c source and a resistance in series. (a) Draw a typical set of curves showing currents and voltages as a function of time. (b) Calculate the peak, average, and rms current through the battery in terms of the circuit components.

3.2. A certain power transformer has a center-tapped secondary with a voltage of 220 rms from center tap to each end. It is to be used to supply a resistance load of 1000 ohms with d-c power.

If the half-wave circuit of Fig. 3-6 is used, calculate the seven factors relative to rectifier operation.

Recalculate and compare the same values if the full-wave circuit of Fig. 3-7 is used.

3.3. Calculate the effect on peak inverse voltage of considering constant tube drops E_t in the circuit of Fig. 3-8.

3.4. Calculate the peak voltage to ground that the filament transformers must be insulated to withstand in the circuits of Figs. 3-6, 3-7, and 3-8.

3.5. A certain resistance load of 100 ohms is to be supplied with d-c power at 500 v d-c.

Calculate the volt-ampere ratings of both the primary and secondary windings of the power transformer required for each of the three rectifier circuits of Figs. 3-6, 3-7, and 3-8 if a-c power is supplied at 220 v.

3.6. The following circuit is being used to supply d-c power to a resistance and a capacitance in parallel. (a) What transformer ratio is necessary to

produce an output voltage of 300 v d-c? (b) What are the peak and average
tube currents? (c) What is the ripple factor across the load?

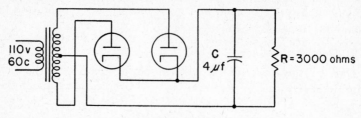

Prob. 3.6

3.7. Consider the circuit in Fig. 3-12. For a resistance of 100 ohms calculate the transformer kva rating, the inductance required for a current ripple
of 0.001, and the peak inverse voltage for a power dissipation of 1000 w.

3.8. In the circuit of Fig. 3-11 what ratio of L/R is required to make the
extinction angle β equal to 270°?

3.9. Consider a portion of the basic voltage doubler circuit. C_1 has just
been charged to the peak value E_m as indicated, and C_2 is completely uncharged,
S having been opened just as C_1 reached full charge. The voltage e is just

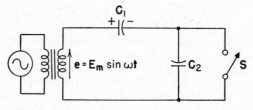

Prob. 3.9

starting to decrease from its peak positive value. Calculate the difference
between $2E_m$ an the voltage which C_2 reaches after the next half cycle, in terms
of C_1 and C_2.

3.10. Calculate and compare the results obtained for the circuit of problem
3.6: (a) Using the curves of Fig. 3.18; (b) By assuming the rectifiers to be
gas tubes with a constant tube drop of 15 v and calculating the values mathematically; (c) Assuming the tubes to be perfect rectifiers.

3.11. A full-wave rectifier using a pair of mercury thyratrons is to operate
from the 220-V, 60-c mains through a four to one transformer, plate to plate.
(a) What power range is available to a resistive load of 1000 ohms if the grid
circuit used permits grid delay angles of 20° to 180°? Assume tube control
characteristic to be zero. (b) Plot power variation versus α and comment
on form of variation.

3.12. A 140-μf capacitor is placed in parallel with the load of problem 3.11.
(a) Calculate the average voltage, the ripple factor, and the power dissipated
if $\alpha = 135°$. Compare power with similar delay angle from curve b of problem

3.11. (b) Approximately how long would be required for the load voltage to reach a new steady state value if α were suddenly reduced to $\alpha = 60°$? (c) How long would be required if α then returned to 135°?

3.13. Consider again the circuit of problem 3.11 with a 5-h coil added in series rather than a capacitor in parallel.   (a) Calculate the average load voltage if $\alpha = 30°$. (Assume $\alpha = \beta$.)   (b) Calculate the ripple factor across R_L and the average power dissipated.

3.14. Consider the circuit shown in Fig. 3.24.   What ratio of L/R is required to keep the ripple across R_L less than 1 per cent for the maximum d-c voltage obtainable?

CHAPTER 4

SEMICONDUCTOR RECTIFIERS

The linear Ohm's law of solids is well known and includes most conductors and insulators. There is, however, another class of solids known as semiconductors, which exhibit nonlinear relationships. These nonlinear relations may be between temperature and resistance or between current and voltage. Some semiconductors also exhibit the property of polarization, and thus may be used as rectifiers.[1]

Two semiconductors exhibiting this rectifying property are germanium and silicon crystals. Although early communication sets made use of this type of rectifier for detection, they fell into disuse when replaced by the vacuum diode. However, during World War II the demand for low-capacitance, high-frequency rectifiers brought about their further development. They are now available for many applications.

As will be seen later, it is desirable to use the crystal in an impure state rather than as an intrinsic semiconductor. It is general practice in the preparation of the crystal to add small amounts of tin by melting. This tin acts as the necessary impurity by changing slightly the lattice structure of the crystal.

4.1 Construction and Operation

The basic components of the crystal rectifier are the crystal and a tungsten wire with a hook shape and sharp point which presses on the crystal. The wire is usually referred to as a "cat whisker." External connections are made to the "whisker" and the crystal, as shown in Fig. 4-1(a). Metal, such as tungsten, which is used

---

[1] Kloeffler, R. G., *Industrial Electronics and Control*, John Wiley & Sons, Inc., New York, 1949.

for the "whisker" must be strong, absorb shock, and be a good conductor of both heat and electricity.   The crystal is also critical, requiring grinding and polishing as well as lattice imperfections caused by introduced impurities.   A small amount of current flows through a circuit comprised of a low resistance and the rectifier even if no external electromotive force is applied.   This electron flow from crystal to metal increases if the wire is made positive with respect to the crystal.   However, if the wire is made negative with respect to the crystal only relatively few electrons move from

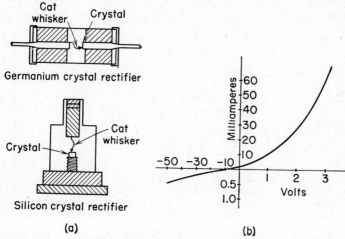

Fig. 4-1.   Construction and characteristics of semiconductor rectifier.

metal to crystal.   Thus, with current flowing more easily one way than the other, rectification is possible.   This relation is plotted in Fig. 4-1(b).

4.2   Theory of Metal-to-crystal Rectification

Several explanations of the rectifying property of a metal-to-crystal point contact have been made, but probably the most valid is that based on the energy level concept.[2]

It is well established that the electrons of an atom are limited to certain energy levels or orbits about the nucleus.   The innermost levels are tightly bound and are not available for conduction, but in

[2] Mott, N. F. and R. W. Gurney, *Electronic Processes in Ionic Crystals*, Oxford University Press, London, 1946.

metals the outer levels are more loosely attached and are usually thought of as free electrons. This may be shown for a simple two-dimensional case by use of Fig. 4-2. The dotted lines ① and ② indicate the loci of the *potential* energy an electron would have as it approached the atom nucleus α, due to the charges on α and the electron only. Lines ③ and ④ are similar for the atom β. The sum of these energies represents the minimum positive potential energy or the maximum negative potential energy that an electron could have and be at that position relative to the nuclei. Any additional (positive) potential energy would place the electron nearer the top or zero energy level. Consider the electron I. Its total energy is

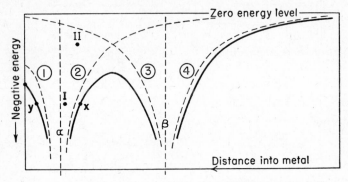

Fig. 4-2.   Energy barriers of electrons in a metal.

more than the minimum required potential energy, but it still finds itself between two energy hills that limit its travel to the space between x and y. However, the higher-energy electron II is not limited by these hills, and is considered to be a "free electron." It is free, however, only within the metal, since the energy wall near the surface is not brought back down by another atom, but approaches zero energy. The free electrons thus defined may have various energies, and are distributed according to the Fermi-Dirac energy distribution. At absolute zero all allowed energy levels up to a certain maximum, called the *normal maximum*, are occupied, and there are no electrons with energies above this. The work function ϕ_m of a metal is the additional energy above the normal maximum which an electron must acquire in order to be emitted. See Fig. 4-3. At temperatures above absolute zero the Fermi-Dirac distribution requires that a few electrons leave the lower levels and exist

just above the normal maximum.　In Fig. 4-3 the various energy
levels of the free electrons at $T = 0°K$ are shown as normal energy
levels with the maximum corresponding to E'.　The dotted line
just above E' represents the slight increase in energy of a few electrons at room temperature.

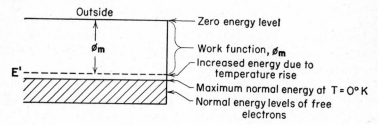

Fig. 4-3.　Energy level diagram of a metal at room temperature.

While the energy relations shown in Fig. 4-3 are true for a metal,
the energy level diagram of an intrinsic semiconductor such as silicon
or germanium is slightly different, as shown in Fig. 4-4.　Here the
electrons find themselves in a normal energy level region again, but
they are not free to absorb certain amounts of energy.　There is a
so-called forbidden band directly above the normally filled band
into which they cannot go.　If they leave the normal band their

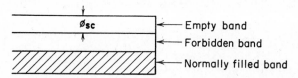

Fig. 4-4.　Energy level diagram of an intrinsic semiconductor at $T = 0°K$.

change of energy must be sufficient to take them into the normally
empty band where they will be available for conduction.

Occasionally the highest-energy electrons jump the forbidden
band into the empty band, making some conduction possible.
Theoretically, at absolute zero, no electrons would jump this forbidden band and no conduction would be possible, making a perfect
insulator.　As the temperature increases some electrons reach this
normally empty level and conduction is possible.　This explains the
inherent characteristic of all semiconductors of having a negative
temperature coefficient of resistance.

If certain semiconductors contain traces of an impurity, the energy level diagram is different than that of a pure semiconductor, as shown in Fig. 4-5. The impurity introduces positions or "holes" for electrons in the forbidden band near the conduction level. These "holes" may or may not be filled. If all these holes are normally occupied by electrons, the semiconductor is of the "excess" type. The work function of these electrons is usually considered to be the same as that of the semiconductor, ϕ_{sc}. At room temperature it is comparatively easy for some of these electrons to jump into the lower edge of the conduction band.

It is desirable to study the effect of bringing into contact a metal and an impure semiconductor under several conditions. Use will be made of the energy level diagrams, and the following facts should be remembered concerning them.

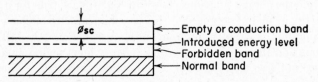

Fig. 4-5.   Energy level diagram of an impure semiconductor.

1. The vertical scale of energy *in the material* represents the equivalent potential energy of an electron if it had no kinetic energy, and it must be realized that its energy is being continually converted back and forth between the two forms.

2. A potential difference between two materials refers to a potential difference between their zero energy levels rather than between the energy levels of their respective free electrons or conduction levels.

3. A circuit potential *drop*, plus to minus, represents an increase in potential energy for the electron and therefore is plotted upward. This is obvious when it is realized that it is necessary to do work on the electron to take it through the potential drop.

4. An electron may move through a voltage rise, minus to plus, and thus decrease its potential energy. However, in so doing, the change in potential energy either appears as an increase in kinetic energy or is lost as heat.

Consider first the result of bringing into contact a metal and an impure semiconductor with an external circuit such that the potential difference between them is always zero, as shown in Fig. 4-6.

It is apparent that the conduction electrons of the semiconductor have greater energies than those of the metal. Thus there are more electrons crossing the boundary from semiconductor to metal than

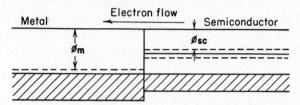

Fig. 4-6.   Energy level diagram of a metal and impure semiconductor in contact, with zero potential difference across the junction.

from metal to semiconductor, and a net flow results in the direction of the arrow. This conclusion is substantiated by the actual volt-ampere characteristic, in that some current flows at zero voltage.

Consider next the effect of changing the external circuit such that the metal is maintained positive with respect to the semiconductor.

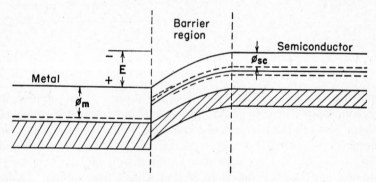

Fig. 4-7.   Energy level diagram of a metal and impure semiconductor in contact, with metal maintained positive.

This condition is shown in Fig. 4-7. Some of the electrons in the barrier region of the semiconductor are now accelerated to kinetic energies greater than normal as they move through the potential rise across the barrier region. Thus the net random flow of electrons from semiconductor to metal is increased. Most of the converted potential energy is lost as heat and tends to raise the temperature of the barrier material as well as that of the surrounding semiconductor. The electron flow under these conditions is limited for all voltages above a small value by the ability of the semiconductor to furnish electrons to the small contact area. This limitation gives rise to the so-called bulk resistance. Since the ability to supply electrons increases with temperature increase, it is to be expected that this resistance would decrease with increased current. This fact is also verified by the characteristic curves to the extent that the dynamic resistance actually becomes negative at higher currents.

Suppose now that the external circuit is adjusted so that it maintains the metal negative with respect to the semiconductor. This

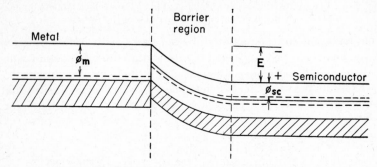

Fig. 4-8.   Energy level diagram for metal and semiconductor in contact, with metal maintained negative with respect to the semiconductor.

condition is shown in Fig. 4-8. Here the process of acceleration in the semiconductor is negative. Electrons moving in the semiconductor through the barrier are decelerated, converting their kinetic energies into potential energy. As the voltage increases, fewer and fewer have energies equal to that required to reach the boundary, and the net flow is reduced to zero at a very low voltage. Note that the barrier layer is considered to exist entirely in the semiconductor and that its thickness depends upon the applied voltage. This is the result of the comparative difficulty of maintaining a voltage gradient in a good conductor. Thus the same voltage drop that decelerates the electrons in the semiconductor cannot serve equally well to accelerate electrons in the metal. Since the field is external to the metal, the process of increasing the energies of electrons in the metal is similar to that of field emission and is not appreciable. Study of Fig. 4-8 would indicate that no electron would be permitted to go from metal to semiconductor unless its energy is greater than its normal maximum in the metal by the difference of ϕ_m and ϕ_{sc}. Few can ever satisfy this requirement. However, it is known that as the voltage increases in the sense of Fig. 4-8, current flow increases, and the volt-ampere characteristic folds back as does the forward characteristic, except at much higher voltages and much lower currents.

One fairly reasonable explanation of this phenomenon is that of "holes." This explanation reasons that the impurities in the semiconductor introduce an energy band in the forbidden region that may have only a definite number of electrons. This is normally filled, and is one of the chief sources of electrons for forward conduc-

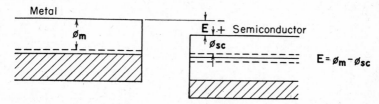

Fig. 4-9. Metal and semiconductor just before contact at zero current.

tion. However, with the negative voltage across the barrier and the resulting decrease in the number of electrons available for conduction in the semiconductor near the contact, some of these positions are left vacant. The greater the voltage the greater the number of vacancies. Quantum theory now proposes that an electron from the metal may cross the boundary into one of these "holes" without acquiring additional energy equal to the work function. Thus at higher voltages, conduction of electrons is possible from metal to semiconductor.

The conditions of zero current may be thought of as being the same as the conditions existing just before the materials are brought into contact, when the current is obviously zero. See Fig. 4-9. If the external circuit is adjusted so that the energy levels of the conduction electrons in both materials are equal and thus would result in no net flow even if brought in contact, it is obvious that the metal is negative with respect to the semiconductor by a value equal to the difference of their work functions. This is known as the "contact potential" difference and is equal to

$$\phi_m - \phi_{sc}. \tag{4.1}$$

Whether or not these explanations are valid will only be known as a greater knowledge of solid-state physics is accumulated. For practical purposes the volt-ampere characteristic may be found experimentally and used wherever desirable.

4.3 Volt-ampere Characteristics and Equivalent Circuit[3]

Much useful information can be obtained about a crystal rectifier from its volt-ampere characteristic, a technique already familiar

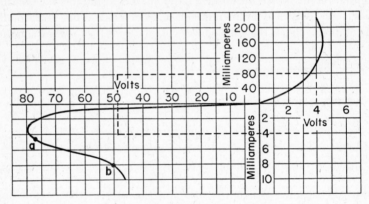

Fig. 4-10. Volt-ampere characteristic of crystal rectifier.

from thermionic rectifier theory. A typical curve for a crystal rectifier is shown in Fig. 4-10. The area within the dotted rectangle is the region normally used for rectification, although the other parts of the curve find application, as discussed in Secs. 4.4 to 4.7. If a positive voltage is applied to the rectifier, the current increases non-linearly much as it does in a vacuum diode, the main difference being the small forward voltage. If the forward voltage is increased, for the example of Fig. 4-10 to about 4.5 volts, the curve becomes vertical and then folds back, with the derivative de/di, the dynamic resistance, becoming zero and then negative. Note that the curve for negative applied voltage is very similar in form to that of forward voltage except for a scale factor of about 2000, differing for various

[3] Condensed from the article, "Germanium Crystal Diodes," by E. C. Cornelius, appearing in *Electronics*, February, 1946.

crystal rectifiers. The workable inverse voltage can easily be determined from such a curve as well as the forward current and voltage relations.

It is of interest to study some of the reasons for this peculiar volt-ampere characteristic in terms of an equivalent circuit. For frequencies below 100 megacycles the equivalent circuit has the form shown in Fig. 4-11. It consists of a bulk resistance R_b, which is determined by the ability of the semiconductor to furnish electrons from the impurity level; and a parallel R-C combination known as the barrier impedance. Here R varies with the magnitude and the

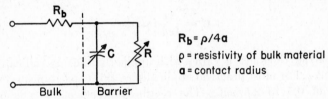

$R_b = \rho/4a$
$\rho =$ resistivity of bulk material
$a =$ contact radius

Fig. 4-11.   Equivalent circuit of crystal rectifier for frequencies below 100 megacycles.

polarity of the applied voltage, and C is the barrier contact capacitance. The bulk resistance R_b is given by the following relation,

$$R_b = \rho/4a \text{ ohms} \tag{4.2}$$

where ρ is the resistivity in ohm-meters of the bulk material and a is the contact radius in meters. However, since ρ varies greatly with temperature for a particular semiconductor, as indicated by Eq. 4.3, it is possible at high temperature, perhaps because of excessive currents, to have a decrease in bulk resistance and a dynamic resistance equal to or less than zero.

$$\text{Log } \rho = \gamma(1/T), \tag{4.3}$$

where γ is a constant for the material and T is the temperature in degrees K.

It is reasonable to expect a decrease in forward voltage for high currents. This bulk resistance is small, of the order of 20 to 35 ohms, and is not a function of applied voltage at any frequency. Since it is small, it is usually of little importance in operation because its effect is negligible compared to the resistance of most loads. It does help to explain the shape of the volt-ampere characteristic.

On the other hand, the barrier impedance, which is made up of the parallel combination of R and C, is a function of the applied voltage and the frequency. For low frequencies this resistance is large for back voltages and for forward voltages up to about 1 volt. For forward voltages above 1 volt it is reduced to a very small value. At higher frequencies the forward resistance also decreases with increased voltage, but not as much as for low frequencies.

The capacitance can be expressed in terms of the cross-sectional area A of the contact, the dielectric constant ϵ of the material, and the barrier thickness d, the same as for two parallel plates. Thus,

$$C = \frac{A\epsilon}{4\pi d} \text{ farads} \tag{4.4}$$

The barrier thickness d varies with applied voltage as indicated in Sec. 4.2. For most practical applications, this capacitance is of the order of 0.5 to 2.5 $\mu\mu$f. The rectification efficiency η is often expressed as the ratio of back to forward impedance.

$$\eta = \frac{Z_{back}}{Z_{forward}}. \tag{4.5}$$

Thus

$$Z_{back} = R_b + Z_{barrier},$$
$$Z_{forward} \cong R_b,$$

and

$$\eta = \frac{R_b + \dfrac{1}{1/R + j\omega C}}{R_b} = \left(1 + \frac{1}{R_b/R + jR_b\omega C}\right). \tag{4.6}$$

For good rectification, the term $R_b/R + jR_b\omega C$ must be as small as possible. The value of R here is the large contact resistance offered to back voltages.

Example. The rectification efficiency for the rectifier whose volt-ampere characteristic is shown in Fig. 4-10 will be approximated.

$$R_b \cong \frac{2}{65 \times 10^{-3}} = \frac{20}{0.65} \cong 31.$$

$$R \cong \frac{50}{0.5 \times 10^{-3}} = 100,000.$$

Thus

$$R_b/R = 31 \times 10^{-5} = .31 \times 10^{-3}.$$

If
$$C = 2.5\mu\mu\text{f},$$

$$R_b\omega C = 31 \times 6.28 \times 10^6 \times 2.5 \times 10^{-12}$$

$$\cong 500 \times 10^{-6} = 0.5 \times 10^{-3}$$

for a frequency of 1 megacycle.

The term $R_b/R + jR_b\omega C$ equals

$$0.31 \times 10^{-3} + j0.5 \times 10^{-3} \cong 0.6 \times 10^{-3}\underline{/60°},$$

and
$$\eta = \left(1 + \frac{1}{0.6 \times 10^{-3}\underline{/60°}}\right)$$

$$= (1 + 1667\underline{/-60°})$$

$$|\eta| \cong 1667.$$

4.4 Applications

As is true of any nonlinear device, its applications are limited only by the number of circuits which can make use of its volt-ampere characteristic. Only a few of the possible applications of the so-called "crystal rectifier" will be mentioned here. It is hoped that an understanding of its operation together with its characteristics will make possible its proper use by the development and design engineer.

4.5 Rectifier

The use of the unsymmetrical characteristics of a crystal and a metal in contact as a rectifier has already been mentioned. However, as the frequencies involved in electronic applications have increased, the demand for rectifiers with small interelectrode capacitance has become greater. It is also becoming more important for the rectifiers to work into a small load resistance. This, of course, requires a small dynamic resistance in the rectifier. Fortunately, both of these characteristics are properties of the crystal rectifier.

Use can also be made of the rectifier's properties in meters, where rectification makes metering possible with a d'Arsonval movement. The top frequency is determined by the rectifier's shunt capacitance. The crystal rectifier has the added advantages that no filament supply is required and that it is small.

A typical metering circuit for measuring high or low frequency a-c voltages with a d-c meter movement is shown in Fig. 4-12.

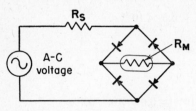

Fig. 4-12.   Metering Circuit.

It should be noticed that the series limiting resistor is in series with the entire bridge combination, rather than just the meter movement. This reduces the back voltage on the rectifiers, thus maintaining a large back impedance.   In a bridge rectifier the peak inverse voltage per rectifier is equal to the peak voltage across the load.   In the circuit of Fig. 4-12 this peak voltage E_{pi} would be

$$E_{pi} = E_m \left(\frac{R_M}{R_S + R_M} \right). \qquad (4.7)$$

If the limiting resistor were directly in series with the movement, the peak inverse voltage would be

$$E_{pi} = E_m.$$

When a metering circuit is designed, the following information is usually known:

E_m, the peak of the maximum voltage to be measured,

R_M, the meter movement resistance,

I_{FS}, the full scale current of the movement.

Using the bridge circuit of Fig. 4-12, and assuming the voltage to be measured is sinusoidal, the design might proceed as follows.   If the voltage to be measured is large compared to the 3- or 4-volt drop across the rectifiers, the rectifier drop may be neglected.   Thus the maximum average current is approximately

$$I_{dc\ max} = \frac{2E_m}{\pi(R_M + R_S)}.$$

This of course must be equal to I_{FS}.   Thus,

$$I_{FS} = \frac{2E_m}{\pi(R_M + R_S)}$$

or

$$R_S = \frac{2}{\pi} \frac{E_m}{I_{FS}} - R_M. \qquad (4.8)$$

This solution of R_S must then be checked in Eq. 4.7 to determine if E_{pi} is too great.

Since the current through R_S is a full rectified sine wave, the *maximum* power dissipation in R_S is

$$P_{avg} = I_{rms}{}^2 R_S = \left(\frac{\pi I_{FS}}{2\sqrt{2}}\right)^2 R_S.$$

Thus
$$P_{avg} = 1.24 I_{FS}{}^2 R_S \text{ watts.} \tag{4.9}$$

If the voltage to be measured is not large compared with the rectifier drop, the approximate solution just discussed may not be sufficiently accurate. A more exact solution for R_S may be found by use of a load line plotted on the combined volt-ampere characteristic of the two rectifiers in series. This method is similar to that used for thermionic tubes with resistance loads.

Again assume that the three values E_m, R_M, and I_{FS} are known. It is necessary to find the value of R_S. If the supply voltage is sinusoidal, it may be assumed as a first approximation that the current is sinusoidal. This is not exactly true since the rectifier characteristic is not linear. On this assumption, the maximum possible instantaneous current through the meter would be

$$I_m = \frac{\pi I_{FS}}{2}. \tag{4.10}$$

This would be simultaneous with the peak voltage E_m.

Referring to the equivalent volt-ampere characteristic of the rectifiers, plot a load line from the value E_m on the voltage scale such that the intersection of the two curves occurs at I_m on the current scale. The slope of the load line thus found is $-1/R_t$, where

$$R_t = R_M + R_S. \tag{4.11}$$

This gives a close approximation to R_S. Actually this assumes the rectifier characteristic to be a straight line from the origin through this point of intersection. It is easy to see by referring to Fig. 4-10 that as the voltage decreases, the successive replotting of the same load line would always result in slightly smaller currents than if the characteristic were straight. Thus this value of R_S is slightly greater than is necessary, and could be rounded off to a slightly smaller, more convenient size.

The power rating may still be approximated by Eq. 4.9, and should always be taken as the next largest standard value. It is possible in all rectifier applications to use crystals in parallel to increase the current rating or in series to increase the inverse voltage rating. Other simple rectifier circuits may be used equally well for metering purposes.

4.6   Oscillators

The volt-ampere characteristic of the crystal rectifier may also be utilized in electric oscillators of both the sinusoidal and the relaxation type. Application is made in the oscillators of the rapid foldback of the reverse characteristic. One oscillator of each type will be considered briefly.

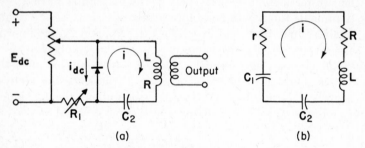

Fig. 4-13.   (a) Sinusoidal oscillator using a crystal rectifier.   (b) Equivalent a-c circuit.

A circuit for a sinusoidal oscillator is shown in Fig. 4-13. To produce sinusoidal oscillations, use is made of the large negative, *dynamic* resistance r, of the reverse characteristic. The d-c supply produces the negative voltage required to give this negative dynamic resistance. It also supplies the energy consumed in the circuit.

The property of oscillation is evident from the differential equation written for the loop current i in Fig. 4-13. It is assumed that operation is between points a and b on the characteristic curve of Fig. 4-10. The a-c drop across the rectifier due to i is the product of the current i, and the dynamic resistance r, at that point. Thus, writing the loop equation in operational form and neglecting the d-c biasing current gives

$$0 = ir + iR + Lpi + \frac{i}{Cp},\qquad(4.12)$$

where $1/C = 1/C_1 + 1/C_2$.   Rearrange and multiply by p/L.

$$0 = \left[p^2 + \left(\frac{r+R}{L} \right) p + \frac{1}{LC} \right] i. \tag{4.13}$$

Equation 4.13 is a second-order differential equation in i.   The solution for i has the form

$$i = i_{steady\ state} + i_{transient}. \tag{4.14}$$

It is obvious from the circuit that i_{ss} is zero; therefore

$$i = i_t. \tag{4.15}$$

The solution for i_t, and thus i, has the form

$$i = i_t = K_1 \epsilon^{m_1 t} + K_2 \epsilon^{m_2 t} \tag{4.16}$$

where m_1 and m_2 are the two roots of p in the characteristic equation 4.17.

$$\left[p^2 + \left(\frac{r+R}{L} \right) p + \frac{1}{LC} \right] = 0. \tag{4.17}$$

This solution for p gives

$$p = -\frac{(r+R)}{2L} \pm \frac{1}{2} \sqrt{\frac{(r+R)^2}{L^2} - \frac{4}{LC}}. \tag{4.18}$$

If in this particular application $r = -R$, the solution for p is simplified to

$$p = -0 \pm j\omega_n \tag{4.19}$$

where
$$\omega_n = \frac{1}{\sqrt{LC}}. \tag{4.20}$$

Substituting Eq. 4.19 into the general form of the solution for i, Eq. 4.16, gives

$$i = K_1 \epsilon^{j\omega_n t} + K_2 \epsilon^{-j\omega_n t}. \tag{4.21}$$

Equation 4.21 may be rewritten in the form

$$i = K_1(\cos \omega_n t + j \sin \omega_n t) + K_2(\cos \omega_n t - j \sin \omega_n t)$$

or
$$i = (K_1 + K_2) \cos \omega_n t + j(K_1 - K_2) \sin \omega_n t. \tag{4.22}$$

If desirable, this may be expressed as either a sine or cosine function with phase angle, such as

$$i = K_3 \cos (\omega_n t - \theta), \tag{4.23}$$

where

$$K_3 = \sqrt{(K_1 + K_2)^2 + [j(K_1 - K_2)]^2}$$

and

$$\theta = \tan^{-1} \frac{j(K_1 - K_2)}{K_1 + K_2}.$$

For our purpose, the phase angle θ is a means of referring the current function to some arbitrary reference, and it is sufficient to say that the current i is sinusoidal in nature, as is the output voltage.

It is interesting to consider the general form of the solution of Eq. 4.18. The solution for p may result in one of three types of answers:

1. Two real, unequal roots.
2. Two equal, real roots.
3. Two conjugate, complex roots.

The first two types of solution are undesirable if an oscillator is wanted, since they do not give an oscillatory function. However, the third type of solution may result in a damped oscillation of the form

$$i = K_3 \epsilon^{-\alpha t} \cos (\omega t - \theta), \tag{4.24}$$

or an undamped oscillation of the form

$$i = K_3 \cos (\omega t - \theta). \tag{4.25}$$

Equation 4.25 is really a special case of Eq. 4.24 with $\alpha = 0$. For this circuit

$$\alpha = \frac{r + R}{2L}$$

and

$$\omega = \sqrt{\frac{1}{LC} - \frac{(r + R)^2}{4L^2}} = \sqrt{\omega_n^2 - \alpha^2}.$$

$$\omega_n = \frac{1}{\sqrt{LC}}. \tag{4.20}$$

It is clear that if the value of r is exactly the negative of R, α is 0 and $\omega = \omega_n$.

The value of R is determined in part by the load being reflected through the transformer, and thus the d-c operating point of the crystal must be adjustable with load change. The frequency of oscillation is, however, the natural resonant frequency of the series L-C circuit, since α must be zero for steady-state oscillation.

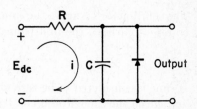

A simple relaxation oscillator is shown in Fig. 4-14. The nega-tive volt-ampere characteristic of the crystal is similar to the char-

FIG. 4-14. A simple relaxation oscillator using a crystal.

acteristic of a cold-cathode gas tube. They are shown for com-parison in Fig. 4-15. If the d-c voltage is suddenly applied to the circuit, the capacitor charges exponentially through R to the voltage E', at which point the crystal impedance suddenly decreases. See Fig. 4-15. The resulting surge of current discharges the capacitor to

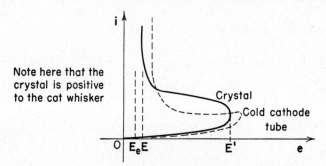

Fig. 4-15.   Comparison of characteristics of a crystal rectifier and a cold cathode gas tube.

a value E_e. The fact that E_e is less than the minimum maintaining voltage E may be attributed to the effect of the loop inductance and the resulting overshoot in voltage decay. At the potential E_e, the crystal impedance has returned to its original large value and the capacitor charging cycle repeats. The form of the voltage variation across the crystal is shown in Fig. 4-16. The period T of the saw-tooth oscillation may be found as follows.

Referring to Fig 4-14, write the loop equation during charging, neglecting the small crystal current.

$$E_{dc} = \left(R + \frac{1}{Cp}\right) i. \tag{4.26}$$

The solution for i is again the sum of the steady-state current and the transient current, the first being zero.   Thus

$$i = i_t = K_1 \epsilon^{-t/RC}. \tag{4.27}$$

If time is considered to be zero at the beginning of the period T, the voltage on the capacitor at $t = 0$ is E_e.   Therefore at $t = 0$, neglect-

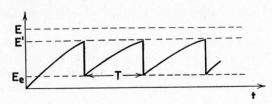

Fig. 4-16. Wave form of the voltage output for the circuit of Fig. 4-14.

ing the crystal current,

$$i = \frac{E_{dc} - E_e}{R}. \tag{4.28}$$

Thus

$$K_1 = \frac{E_{dc} - E_e}{R},$$

and

$$i = \frac{E_{dc} - E_e}{R} \epsilon^{-t/RC}. \tag{4.29}$$

After the period T, the capacitor voltage has reached the value E', and

$$i = \frac{E_{dc} - E'}{R}. \tag{4.30}$$

Thus

$$\frac{E_{dc} - E'}{R} = \frac{E_{dc} - E_e}{R} \epsilon^{-T/RC}. \tag{4.31}$$

Rewriting Eq. 4.31 gives

$$\frac{E_{dc} - E_e}{E_{dc} - E'} = \epsilon^{+T/RC}. \tag{4.32}$$

Take the natural logarithm of each side and multiply by RC.

$$T = RC \ln \frac{E_{dc} - E_e}{E_{dc} - E'}. \tag{4.33}$$

The frequency is of course the reciprocal of T.

It is easy to determine from Eq. 4.33 the effect on the frequency of varying any of the circuit values. It should be obvious from Fig. 4-14 that this circuit must work into a large impedance. Otherwise the capacitor and crystal are effectively shorted. If the load impedance is low, the circuit of Fig. 4-17 is more practical.

The circuit of Fig. 4-17 is similar to that of Fig. 4-14 with the addition of the coupled circuit output. It can be seen from the circuit that the output voltage is proportional to the derivative of the current i. The in-

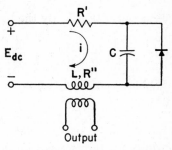

Fig. 4-17. Relaxation oscillator for low-impedance load.

ductance introduced into the loop is L, and R'' is the additional resistance both of the primary coil and the reflected load. The total resistance of the loop is

$$R = R' + R''.$$

It is proposed to show that if L is small, the current has approximately the same form as in the circuit of Fig. 4-14, and that the output voltage is a sawtooth with a period T, where

$$T = RC \ln \frac{E_{dc} - E_e}{E_{dc} - E'}.$$

Writing the loop equation for i in Fig. 4-17,

$$E_{dc} = \left((R' + R'') + Lp + \frac{1}{Cp} \right) i \tag{4.34}$$

$$E_{dc} = \left(R + Lp + \frac{1}{Cp} \right) i.$$

Here, as before

$$i = i_{ss} + i_t = 0 + i_t. \tag{4.35}$$

The transient current has the form

$$i_t = K_1 \epsilon^{p_1 t} + K_2 \epsilon^{p_2 t}, \tag{4.36}$$

where

$$p_1 = -\frac{R}{2L} + \sqrt{\frac{R^2}{4L^2} - \frac{1}{LC}} \tag{4.37}$$

and

$$p_2 = -\frac{R}{2L} - \sqrt{\frac{R^2}{4L^2} - \frac{1}{LC}}. \tag{4.38}$$

First consider p_1. By the binomial theorem expansion,

$$p_1 = -\frac{R}{2L} + \left(\frac{R}{2L} - \frac{1}{2} \cdot \frac{2L}{R} \cdot \frac{1}{LC} - \frac{1}{8} \cdot \frac{8L^3}{R^3} \cdot \frac{1}{L^2 C^2} + \cdots \right). \tag{4.39}$$

This may be rewritten as

$$p_1 = -\frac{1}{RC} - \frac{L}{R^3 C^2} + \cdots \tag{4.40}$$

Additional terms result in higher orders of L, and thus if

$$L \ll R^2 C, \tag{4.41}$$

$$p_1 \cong -\frac{1}{RC}. \tag{4.42}$$

If

$$L \gtreqless 0.01 \, R^2 C, \qquad p_1 \cong 1.01 \left(-\frac{1}{RC} \right).$$

By similar treatment,

$$p_2 = -\frac{R}{L} + \left(\frac{1}{RC} + \frac{L}{R^3 C^2} + \cdots \right). \tag{4.43}$$

It is obvious here that as $L \to 0$,

$$p_2 \to -\infty. \tag{4.44}$$

Reference to Eq. 4.36 shows that

$$\underset{L \to 0}{\text{Lim}} \, i = K_1 \epsilon^{-t/RC} + K_2 \epsilon^{-\infty t}. \tag{4.45}$$

Briefly, if L is small, the second exponential has a time constant approaching zero and the second term may be neglected. Thus,

$$\underset{L \to 0}{\text{Lim}} \, i \cong K_1 \epsilon^{-t/RC}. \tag{4.46}$$

This is identical to the solution of Eq. 4.27, and thus

$$\frac{E_{dc} - E'}{R} = \frac{E_{dc} - E_e}{R} \epsilon^{-T/RC}, \qquad (4.47)$$

where T is expressed by Eq. 4.33.   The output voltage as shown in Fig. 4-17 is proportional to the derivative of the current i and there-

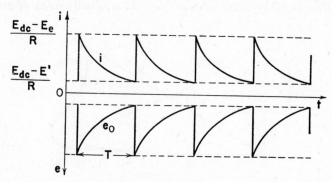

Fig. 4-18.   Plot of current i and output voltage e_0 for oscillator of Fig. 4-17.

fore is also exponential in form.   This is shown graphically in Fig. 4-18.

4.7 Regulators

The reverse volt-ampere characteristic of the crystal rectifier permits its use as a voltage regulator.   The basic regulator circuit is shown in Fig. 4-19.

The purpose of this circuit is to maintain a constant output voltage in spite of changes in input voltage and/or load current within an operating range.   This requires a circuit element that will carry a range of currents at essentially constant terminal voltage. The same circuit is commonly used with cold-cathode gas discharge tubes.

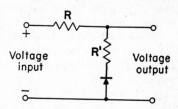

Fig. 4-19. A crystal voltage regulator.

Note that the crystal, because of power limitation, must be operated in a negative current range where its dynamic resistance is negative.   The addition of an approximately equal positive resistance in series results in a composite characteristic suitable for voltage regulation. This superposition is shown in Fig. 4-20. The actual curve varies with different crystals. The current range for such operation is usually between 5 and 25 ma. Two or more such combinations used in series or parallel increase either the voltage or current rating. For parallel operation the characteristics should be as nearly alike as possible. It is usually most desirable

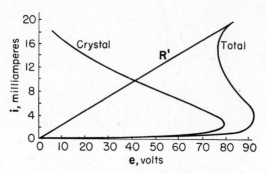

Fig. 4-20.   Combination of crystal and R'.

to design a circuit to the average values and then check the limiting conditions. This procedure is best shown by an example.

Example.   A regulator is used to maintain a constant voltage of 80 v across a load. The load resistance may vary from 4000 to 3200 ohms. The supply voltage is 200 v $\pm$ 10 per cent. It is assumed that the crystal is that of Fig. 4-20 and R' is the value determined from this curve.

Thus
$$R' = \tfrac{75}{18} \times 10^3 \cong 4000 \text{ ohms.}$$

From the figure, the crystal current could vary from 9 to 19 ma, with a voltage change of 10 v. The average is therefore 14 ma.

If the load voltage is assumed constant at 80 v, the load current will vary from 20 to 25 ma, with an average of 22.5 ma. The average current through R is then $14 + 22.5 = 36.5$ ma. The average voltage across R is $200 - 80 = 120$ v.

Thus
$$R = \frac{120}{36.5} \times 10^3 = 3290 \text{ ohms.}$$

It is now necessary to check the maximum and minimum conditions. The crystal is required to carry maximum current when the supply voltage is maximum and the load current is minimum. The maximum current through R is

$$\frac{220 - 80}{3290} = \frac{140}{3290} \cong 42.5 \text{ ma.}$$

At this time, the load current is approximately 20 ma, and thus the crystal current is 22.5 ma. This is slightly high for good regulation of the voltage, but is acceptable. The crystal is required to carry the smallest current when the supply voltage is minimum and the load current maximum. The current through R then is

$$\frac{180 - 80}{3290} = \frac{100}{3290} \cong 30.4 \text{ ma.}$$

The load current is 25 ma, and thus the minimum crystal current is 5.4 ma. This is a little too small. Although this design will operate, the variations are slightly too large for good regulation. A larger supply voltage might be advantageous.

The approximate wattage rating of R can be found with the knowledge of the maximum current and R.

Thus $\qquad w = 3290 \times (0.0425)^2 \cong 5.94 \text{ w.}$

A 10-w resistor would be used.

There are certain advantages and disadvantages in using the crystal to replace a gas tube in a regulator circuit. The chief advantages are size and that a firing voltage considerably larger than the operating voltage is not needed. The chief disadvantage is that the crystal-resistance combination has poorer regulation over the same current range than does the gas tube.

Many other uses can be found for the crystal's characteristics, but it is hoped that the few discussed here will be sufficient to enable the student to make intelligent use of the circuit component.

METALLIC RECTIFIERS

In the consideration of rectifiers there are two other combinations of material that are important because of their almost unilateral conduction properties. One is copper oxide on copper, and the other is selenium on a good conductor. Each of these combinations serves satisfactorily in many rectifier applications, and both have the added advantage of requiring no filament supply. If not overloaded, their lives are almost indefinite, making replacements seldom

Copper oxide rectifier stacks. (Courtesy of General Electric Company.)

necessary. Because of their differences in characteristics and
design, the two types of rectifiers will be considered separately
except for their general theory and application in which they are
similar.

4.8 Theory and Construction of Metallic Rectifier Stacks

Every dry-plate or metallic rectifier must consist of a semiconductor, a barrier layer, and a good conductor, the barrier layer
existing at the boundary between the good conductor and the
semiconductor.

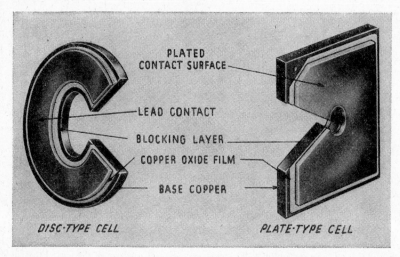

Fig. 4-21.   Cross section of G.E. copper oxide rectifier disc- and plate-type cells.
(Courtesy of General Electric Company.)

The copper oxide rectifier[4] consists of a stack of one or more cells
made from specially selected and processed copper.   A thin film of
cuprous oxide with an outer layer of cupric oxide is produced by
heating the cell to a high temperature and quenching it in water·
The cupric oxide is then removed, leaving the cell with a layer of
cuprous oxide on the base copper.   The semiconductor is the oxide,
the good conductor is the copper, and their junction is the barrier
layer.   Contact with the oxide surface can be made in either of two
ways.   In one a lead disk is held against the oxide surface at a

---

[4] Hamann, C. E. and E. A. Harty, "Applications of the Copper-Oxide
Rectifier," *Gen. Elec. Rev.*, August 1933.

definite pressure.   In the other a metallic conductor such as nickel
is plated onto the oxide surface.   In either case the contact is used
to collect the electrons over the surface.   Cross sections of typical
cells are shown in Fig. 4-21.

The selenium rectifier[5] plate consists of a nickel-plated steel or
aluminum back plate, a thin layer of metallic selenium, a barrier

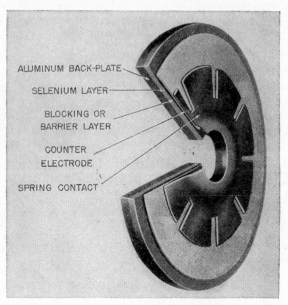

ALUMINUM BACK-PLATE

SELENIUM LAYER

BLOCKING OR
BARRIER LAYER

COUNTER
ELECTRODE

SPRING CONTACT

Fig. 4-22.   Cross section of G.E. selenium cell.   (Courtesy of General Electric
Company.)

layer, and a front electrode.   The front or counter electrode is
formed by spraying a low-melting alloy onto the selenium surface.
The barrier layer is the junction between the semiconductor selenium
and the good conductor which is sprayed onto the selenium.   The
back plate serves only as support.   Connection is made to the cell
by means of light-pressure spring (petal) washers.   A cross section
of this type of cell is shown in Fig. 4-22.

The theory of rectification in a metallic rectifier is most easily
explained by reference to the detailed treatment of crystal rectifiers
in Sec. 4.2.   The principles involved are similar, but a much larger

[5] Harty, E. A., "Selenium-Rectifier Cells," *Trans. AIEE*, October 1943.

contact area is used. Thus the effect of bulk resistance, which depends on the semiconductor's ability to supply electrons *to a small contact area*, is negligible.

In considering the crystal rectifier it was noted that the semiconductor was of the excess type, meaning that an energy level was introduced into the forbidden band near the conduction level, and that it was normally occupied. The semiconductors copper oxide and selenium are not of the "excess" type but rather are of the "deficit" type. Thus they have impurity energy levels which are near the normal band and are normally empty. They are sometimes referred to as "holes." The barrier layer of the metallic rectifier exists as a transition layer between the semiconductor and the metal. It is not a part of either, and is thus different from the crystal. With few electrons normally present at energies appreciably above the normal band in deficit semiconductors, the work functions of these materials are greater than those of the metals. Thus electron conduction takes place more easily from metal to semiconductor than from semiconductor to metal. This is opposite to the crystal rectifier. As an example, the work function of copper oxide is 5.33 electron volts, while the work function of copper varies from 3.84 to 4.82 electron volts. On the other hand the work function of tungsten is 4.52 electron volts, and of germanium is 4.3 electron volts.

The potential gradient appears across the barrier, but it is easier for the abundant, higher-energy electrons of the metal to be accelerated across the barrier into the normally empty "holes" than it is for the relatively scarce lower-energy electrons of the semiconductor to be accelerated into the metal. Greater voltages may be placed across the barrier of a selenium cell than across the barrier of a copper oxide cell, and thus fewer are needed in series for a particular application.

4.9 Characteristics of Copper Oxide Cell

The practical operation of the rectifier is based upon its property of conducting more easily in one direction than the other. These characteristics, being nonlinear, can best be shown graphically, as in Fig. 4-23. It can be seen from the curves of Fig. 4-23 that the ratio of forward voltage to forward current is not constant, but decreases as the current increases. This is true of the dynamic resistance, as well as the total or d-c resistance. In this respect the copper oxide rectifier is similar to the vacuum diode, whose volt-ampere characteristic closely follows the law of the $\frac{3}{2}$ power of the voltage. In the reverse direction the resistance is not infinite as would be desired, but is very high. In Fig. 4-23 the change of scale should be noted. It is customary to limit the back voltage to 5 volts per cell, and thus the back current will be 5 ma or less per square inch. The cell is a

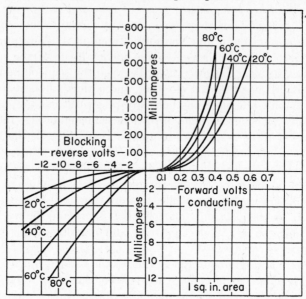

Fig. 4-23. D-c voltage-current characteristics in copper oxide rectifier plate-type cell. (Courtesy of General Electric Company.)

resistance device at low frequencies, and is affected by the capacitance of its surfaces only at high frequencies.

It can also be seen from Fig. 4-23 that the resistance of the cell in either direction decreases with an increase of temperature. The temperature of operation depends upon the ambient temperature surrounding the cell, the heat produced due to its own IR drop, and the means of cooling provided. In the forward direction the rise seems desirable because of the decrease in voltage drop, but the same temperature increase also increases the reverse leakage current for a definite reverse voltage. Temperature rise is the usual limiting factor on the maximum current rating. If it is necessary to operate the cell above rated temperature, the rated voltage must be decreased. An empirical relation is shown in Fig. 4-24. Another important characteristic is the effect of aging. As the cell gets older, its resistance increases. However, in about six months to a year it approaches a stable condition. This is one of the most desirable properties, since there is practically no further change for the life of the cell. The effect of this increase naturally varies with the circuit application. If the load resistance is many times the resistance of the stack, the increase has little effect. On the other hand,

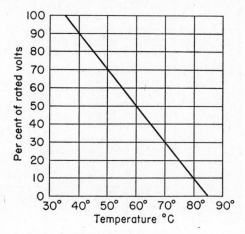

Fig. 4-24.   Output rating above 35°.   (Courtesy of General Electric Company.)

if the load and stack resistances are of similar magnitude, this aging requires a substantial increase in a-c input voltage. This is usually accomplished by providing a tapped transformer supply.

Since one of the chief factors of operation is the temperature, it is common practice, when desirable, to overload the rectifiers by as much as 15 times if the operation is to be for only a few seconds followed by a cooling period. The cell temperature should never be allowed to increase beyond 15°C above ambient.

4.10 Empirical Design Information for Copper Oxide Stacks[6]

Copper oxide cells are connected in series or parallel combinations called "stacks" to increase the voltage or current values, but the

[6] General Electric Company, *Battery Chargers and Rectifiers.*

Table 4.1 Design Data for Copper Oxide Stacks.*

(Rating per cell at 35°C maximum. Single-phase half-wave rectifier with resistance load.)

No. of Cells in Stack														
	Cell Size—In.	3/16	¾	1⅛	1½	1½	1½	1½	1½	1½	3⅝x4½	3⅝x4½	4⅜x5	4⅜x5
	Cell Area—Sq In.		0.28	0.56	1.1	1.1	1.1	1.1	1.1	1.1	13	13	38	38
	Fin Size—In.					2¼	3	3⅝	3⅝	3⅝				
	Spacer Size—In.						1/16		1/16	3/16				
	DC Blocking V.	3.0	2.9	2.9	2.9	3.1	3.5	3.6	4.0	4.5	3.6	4.5	3.6	4.5
	Cooling	N	N	N	N	N	N	N	N	N	N	F	N	F
1 to 8	DC Volts	1.5	1.5	1.5	1.5	1.55	1.75	1.80	2.0	2.25	1.8	2.25	1.8	2.25
	DC Amps	0.002	0.032	0.062	0.1	0.13	0.13	0.16	0.2	0.25	2.0	2.20	3.0	6.30
	AC Volts Normal	4.7	4.2	4.2	4.2	4.40	4.70	4.90	5.4	6.20	4.9	6.20	4.9	6.20
	AC Volts Max.	8.5	5.0	5.0	5.0	5.30	5.90	6.30	7.0	8.20	6.3	8.20	6.3	8.20
9 to 16	DC Volts	1.5	1.5	1.5	1.50	1.55	1.75	1.80	2.0	2.25	1.8	2.25	1.8	2.25
	DC Amps	0.002	0.026	0.05	0.08	0.11	0.13	0.16	0.2	0.25	2.0	2.20	3.0	6.30
	AC Volts Normal	4.7	4.1	4.1	4.10	4.30	4.70	4.90	5.4	6.20	4.9	6.20	4.9	6.20
	AC Volts Max.	8.5	4.8	4.8	4.80	5.20	5.90	6.30	7.0	8.20	6.3	8.20	6.3	8.20
17 to 32	DC Volts	1.5	1.45	1.45	1.45	1.55	1.75	1.80	2.0	2.25	1.8	2.25	1.8	2.25
	DC Amps	0.002	0.022	0.041	0.07	0.09	0.13	0.16	0.2	0.25	2.0	2.20	3.0	6.30
	AC Volts Normal	4.7	4.0	4.0	4.00	4.30	4.70	4.90	5.4	6.20	4.9	6.20	4.9	6.20
	AC Volts Max.	8.5	4.5	4.5	5.00	5.00	5.90	6.30	7.0	8.20	6.3	8.20	6.3	8.20
32 and Over	DC Volts	1.5	1.45	1.45	1.45	1.55	1.75	1.80	2.0	2.25	1.8	2.25	1.8	2.25
	DC Amps	0.002	0.019	0.04	0.06	0.08	0.13	0.16	0.2	0.25	2.0	2.20	3.0	6.30
	AC Volts Normal	4.7	3.9	3.90	3.90	4.20	4.70	4.90	5.4	6.20	4.9	6.20	4.9	6.20
	AC Volts Max.	8.5	4.4	4.40	4.40	4.90	5.90	6.30	7.0	8.20	6.3	8.20	6.3	8.20

* Courtesy of General Electric Company

Table 4.2 Design Data for Copper Oxide Stacks.*

(Single-phase full-wave midtap, resistance load.)

No. of Cells in Stack														
	Cell Size—In.	3/16	¾	1⅛	1½	1½	1½	1½	1½	1½	3⅝x4½	3⅝x4½	4⅜x5	4⅜x5
	Cell Area—Sq In.	....	0.28	0.56	1.1	1.1	1.1	1.1	1.1	1.1	13	13	38	38
	Fin Size—In.	....	......	......	......	2¼	3	3⅝	3⅝	3⅝	....	....	....	....
	Spacer Size—In.	....	......	......	......	......	1/16	......	1/16	3/16	....	....	....	....
	Cooling	N	N	N	N	N	N	N	N	N	N	F	N	F
1 to 8	DC Volts	1.5	1.5	1.5	1.5	1.55	1.75	1.80	2.00	2.25	1.8	2.25	1.8	2.25
	DC Amps	0.005	0.064	0.124	0.2	0.25	0.26	0.32	0.39	0.50	4.0	4.30	6.0	12.50
	AC Volts Normal	4.7	4.2	4.2	4.2	4.40	4.70	4.90	5.40	6.20	4.9	6.20	4.9	6.20
	AC Volts Max.	8.5	5.0	5.0	5.0	5.30	5.90	6.30	7.00	8.20	6.3	8.20	6.3	8.20
9 to 16	DC Volts	1.5	1.5	1.5	1.50	1.55	1.75	1.80	2.00	2.25	1.8	2.25	1.8	2.25
	DC Amps	0.005	0.052	0.1	0.16	0.22	0.26	0.32	0.39	0.50	4.0	4.30	6.0	12.50
	AC Volts Normal	4.7	4.1	4.1	4.10	4.30	4.70	4.90	5.40	6.20	4.9	6.20	4.9	6.20
	AC Volts Max.	8.5	4.8	4.8	4.80	5.20	5.90	6.30	7.00	8.20	6.3	8.20	6.3	8.20
17 to 32	DC Volts	1.5	1.45	1.45	1.45	1.55	1.75	1.80	2.00	2.25	1.8	2.25	1.8	2.25
	DC Amps	0.005	0.043	0.08	0.13	0.18	0.26	0.32	0.39	0.50	4.0	4.30	6.0	12.50
	AC Volts Normal	4.7	4.0	4.0	4.00	4.30	4.70	4.90	5.40	6.20	4.9	6.20	4.9	6.20
	AC Volts Max.	4.5	4.5	4.5	4.50	5.00	5.90	6.30	7.00	8.20	6.3	8.20	6.3	8.20
32 and Over	DC Volts	1.5	1.45	1.45	1.45	1.55	1.75	1.80	2.00	2.25	1.8	2.25	1.8	2.25
	DC Amps	0.005	0.037	0.07	0.11	0.15	0.26	0.32	0.39	0.50	4.0	4.30	6.0	12.50
	AC Volts Normal	4.7	3.9	3.9	3.90	4.20	4.70	4.90	5.40	6.20	4.9	6.20	4.9	6.20
	AC Volts Max	8.5	4.4	4.4	4.40	4.90	5.90	6.30	7.00	8.20	6.3	8.20	6.3	8.20

N = Natural cooling. F'= Fan cooling.

* Courtesy of General Electric Company

Table 4.3 Design Data for Copper Oxide Stacks.*

(Rating per cell at 35°C maximum. Single-phase full-wave bridge, resistance load.)

No. of Cells in Stack		(1)	(2)	(3)	(4)	(5)	(6)	(7)	(8)	(9)	(10)	(11)	(12)	(13)
	Cell Size—In.	1/16	3/4	1 1/16	1 1/2	1 1/2	1 1/2	1 1/2	1 1/2	1 1/2	3 3/8 x 4 1/2	3 3/8 x 4 1/2	4 3/8 x 5	4 3/8 x 5
	Cell Area—Sq In.	.28	.56	1.1	1.1	1.1	1.1	1.1	1.1	1.1	13	13	38	38
	Fin Size—In.				1	1 1/16	1 1/2	1 1/2	1 1/2	1 1/2	3/8	3/8	1/4	1/4
	Spacer Size—In.						2 1/4	3	3 3/8	3 3/8				
	Cooling	N	N	N	N	N	N	N	N	N	N	F	N	F
1 to 8	DC Volts	3.0	3.0	3.0	3.0	3.10	3.50	3.60	4.00	4.50	3.6	4.5	3.6	4.5
	DC Amps	0.005	0.064	0.124	0.2	0.25	0.26	0.32	0.39	0.50	4.0	4.3	6.0	12.5
	AC Volts Normal	4.7	4.2	4.2	4.2	4.40	4.70	4.90	5.40	6.20	4.9	6.2	4.9	6.2
	AC Volts Max.	8.5	5.0	5.0	5.0	5.30	5.90	6.30	7.00	8.20	6.3	8.2	6.3	8.2
9 to 16	DC Volts	3.0	3.0	3.0	3.00	3.10	3.50	3.60	4.00	4.50	3.6	4.5	3.6	4.5
	DC Amps	0.005	0.052	0.1	0.16	0.22	0.26	0.32	0.39	0.50	4.0	4.3	6.0	12.5
	AC Volts Normal	4.7	4.1	4.1	4.10	4.30	4.70	4.90	5.40	6.20	4.9	6.2	4.9	6.2
	AC Volts Max.	8.5	5.0	4.8	4.80	5.20	5.90	6.30	7.00	8.20	6.3	8.2	6.3	8.2
17 to 32	DC Volts	3.0	2.9	2.90	2.90	3.10	3.50	3.60	4.00	4.50	3.6	4.5	3.6	4.5
	DC Amps	0.005	0.043	0.08	0.13	0.18	0.26	0.32	0.39	0.50	4.0	4.3	6.0	12.5
	AC Volts Normal	4.7	4.0	4.0	4.00	4.30	4.70	4.90	5.40	6.20	4.9	6.2	4.9	6.2
	AC Volts Max.	8.5	4.5	4.50	4.50	5.00	5.90	6.30	7.00	8.20	6.3	8.2	6.3	8.2
32 and Over	DC Volts	3.0	2.9	2.90	2.90	3.10	3.50	3.60	4.00	4.50	3.6	4.5	3.6	4.5
	DC Amps	0.005	0.037	0.07	0.11	0.15	0.26	0.32	0.39	0.50	4.0	4.3	6.0	12.5
	AC Volts Normal	4.5	3.9	3.9	3.90	4.20	4.70	4.90	5.40	6.20	4.9	6.2	4.9	6.2
	AC Volts Max.	8.5	4.4	4.40	4.40	4.90	5.90	6.30	7.00	8.20	6.3	8.2	6.3	8.2

* Courtesy of General Electric Company

Table 4.4 Design Data for Copper Oxide Stacks.*

(Three-phase full-wave bridge, resistance load.)

Cell Size—In.		1⅛	1½	1½	1½	1½	1½	1½	3⅝×4½	3⅝×4½	4⅜×5	4⅜×5
Cell Area—Sq In.		0.56	1.1	1.1	1.1	1.1	1.1	1.1	13	13	38	38
Fin Size—In.				2¼	3	3⅜	3⅜	3⅜				
Spacer Size—In.					1/16		1/16	1/8				
No. of Cells in Stack	Cooling	N	N	N	N	N	N	N	N	F	N	F
1 to 8	DC Volts	4.00	4.0	4.10	4.70	4.80	5.30	6.00	4.8	6.0	4.8	6.0
	DC Amps	0.19	0.3	0.38	0.39	0.48	0.59	0.75	6.0	6.5	9.0	19.0
	AC Volts Normal	3.20	3.2	3.20	3.80	4.00	4.50	5.30	4.0	5.2	3.8	5.2
	AC Volts Max.	4.80	4.5	4.80	5.40	5.60	5.60	7.40	5.7	6.7	4.3	6.7
9 to 16	DC Volts	4.00	4.00	4.10	4.70	4.80	5.30	6.00	4.8	6.0	4.8	6.0
	DC Amps	0.15	0.24	0.33	0.39	0.48	0.59	0.75	6.0	6.5	9.0	19.0
	AC Volts Normal	3.40	3.10	3.10	3.80	4.00	4.50	5.30	4.0	5.2	3.8	5.2
	AC Volts Max.	4.60	4.30	4.50	5.40	5.60	5.60	7.40	5.7	6.7	4.3	6.7
17 to 32	DC Volts	3.90	3.9	4.00	4.70	4.80	5.30	6.00	4.8	6.0	4.8	6.0
	DC Amps	0.12	0.2	0.27	0.39	0.48	0.59	0.75	6.0	6.5	9.0	19.0
	AC Volts Normal	3.60	3.0	3.00	3.80	4.00	4.50	5.30	4.0	5.2	3.8	5.2
	AC Volts Max.	4.50	4.1	4.40	5.40	5.60	5.60	7.40	5.7	6.7	4.3	6.7
32 and Over	DC Volts	3.90	3.90	4.00	4.70	4.80	5.30	6.00	4.8	6.0	4.8	6.0
	DC Amps	0.11	0.17	0.23	0.39	0.48	0.59	0.75	6.0	6.5	9.0	9.0
	AC Volts Normal	3.80	3.00	3.00	3.80	4.00	4.50	5.30	4.0	5.2	3.8	5.2
	AC Volts Max.	4.30	4.00	4.30	5.40	5.60	5.60	7.40	5.7	6.7	4.3	6.7

N = Natural cooling.   F = Fan cooling.

* Courtesy of General Electric Company

ratings of each cell depend upon current, temperature, and time. Any exact computation would have to include all three variables. Since the load is usually specified, it is common practice for the engineer to refer to a table in which all these data have been assembled on a per cell basis for the most-used circuits. To reduce the effect of any of the variables on the output it is desirable to make the rectifier resistance much smaller than that of the load. This procedure may be taken as general practice. Four tabulations of design data appear in Tables 4.1, 4.2, 4.3, and 4.4.

The information given in these four tables is based on the assumptions of full utilization of the current capacity and a resistance load with full period conduction.

Example. A certain resistance load requires 4.0 amp at 72.0 v d-c. A single-phase bridge rectifier is to be used. Find the size and number of cells per stack and the a-c voltages required when the cells are new and when they are aged. The data for single-phase bridge rectifiers show that a cell $3\frac{5}{8}$ by $4\frac{1}{2}$ in. is able to carry 4.0 amp d-c. The d-c voltage per cell is 3.6. It is therefore necessary to use 20 cells per stack to provide the required 72.0 v. Normally, the a-c voltage will be $20 \times 4.9 = 98$ v rms. In extreme cases this might increase to a maximum of $20 \times 6.3 = 126$ v rms. The supply transformer should therefore have taps between 98 and 126 v. For a full-wave bridge rectifier the ratio of the rms current to the average current is the form factor, 1.11. The alternating current is thus approximately $4.0 \times 1.11 = 4.44$ a rms. This calculation assumes perfect rectification and thus a source capable of supplying 5 amp probably would be used.

Actually the ratings are a function of the average current per unit and the type of load. Thus a more exact type of design information is given in Fig. 4-25 and Fig. 4-26. The effect of the cell voltage drop and its change in resistance are taken into account, making the curves nonlinear. Values are given for both resistance and battery loads on a per unit area basis. With a battery load which is similar to a capacitor and resistor in parallel, the d-c voltage tends to approach the a-c peak voltage. With a pure resistance load the d-c voltage is more nearly the average of one-half cycle of the alternating voltage. Data are given only for the generally used bridge circuits.

In the last example, the cell area was given in the tables as 13.0 sq in. The current density is therefore $4.0/13 = 0.308$ a d-c

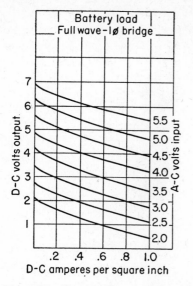
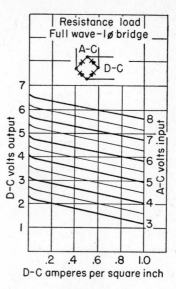

Fig. 4-25.   Output characteristics of single phase copper oxide rectifier circuits.   (Courtesy of General Electric Company.)

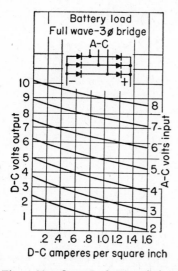
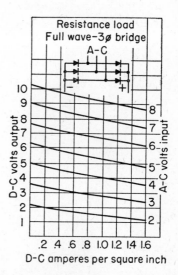

Fig. 4-26.   Output characteristics of three phase copper oxide rectifier circuits.   (Courtesy of General Electric Company.)

183

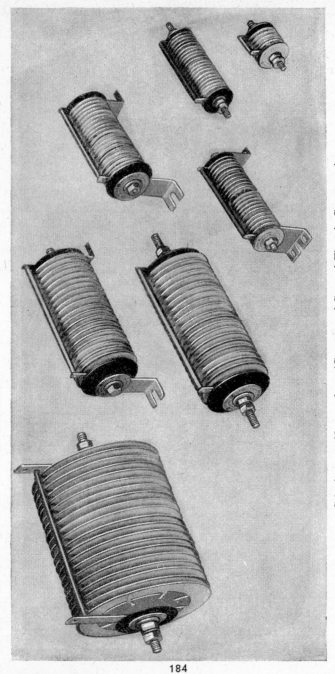

Selenium rectifier stacks. (Courtesy of General Electric Company.)

per sq in. If 20 cells are to be used to produce 72 volts, the d-c voltage per cell is 3.6 v. From the curves of Fig. 4-25, the a-c voltage per cell is 5.0 v, or a total of 100 v rms. This result is nearly the same as the 98 v rms obtained by the first solution. If the current utilization had been over- or underrated, a considerable change in a-c voltage would have been indicated. The correction for aging can be taken roughly as the percentage increase indicated in Tables 4.1, 4.2, 4.3, and 4.4.

4.11   Characteristics of the Selenium Cell

· Basically the selenium cell is a metallic rectifier which possesses the general characteristics of negative temperature coefficient of resistance, almost unilateral conduction, and a

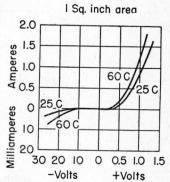

Fig. 4-27. Volt-ampere characteristics of selenium cell. (Courtesy of General Electric Company.)

decreasing resistance with increasing current. The selenium cell has an advantage over the copper oxide cell, because it can withstand considerably higher back voltages and can operate satisfactorily over a greater temperature range. The volt-ampere characteristic is shown by the curves of Fig. 4-27. Unless otherwise stated, all cells are rated on a basis of ambient temperature at 35°C. If this ambient temperature is to be exceeded, the ratings must be decreased for satisfactory operation. Curves of current and voltage deratings are shown in Fig. 4-28. The cell may be overloaded for short periods if a cooling time is available between duty cycles. An approximate curve of allowable overloads versus time of overload is shown in Fig. 4-29.

After an overload corresponding to some point on the curve, the load should be entirely removed until normal room temperature is reached by the stack, rather than returning to normal load and thus retarding temperature recovery. In contrast to the copper oxide cell, the operation of a selenium rectifier seems to change little with age. If the rectifier is idle for long periods, such as several months, the back resistance decreases. However, the original characteristics are restored in a few seconds after a-c power is supplied. The only disadvantage this presents is in circuits requiring occasional but instantaneous rectification.

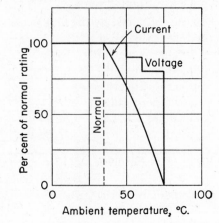

Fig. 4-28. Values for derating selenium cells. (Courtesy of General Electric Company.)

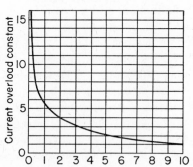

Fig. 4-29. Overload rating of G.E. selenium rectifier. (Courtesy of General Electric Company.)

4.12 Empirical Design Information for Selenium Rectifiers

Design information for the selenium rectifier is given on a per cell basis with the knowledge that cells may be added in series or parallel as needed to increase the voltage or current ratings. Four basic cell sizes are made, from which a wide variety of outputs is obtainable through various circuits and combinations. As was true of the copper oxide cell, it is desirable to make the cell resistance as small as possible compared with the load resistance. In this way the resistance change of the rectifier has little effect on the output.

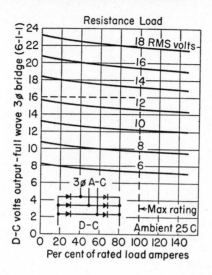

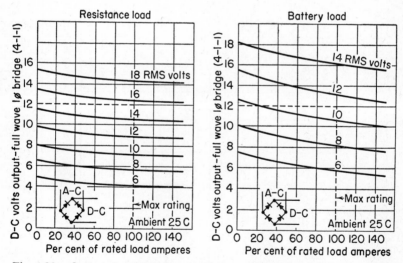

Fig. 4-30.   Output characteristics of selenium rectifiers per cell.   (Courtesy of General Electric Company.)

The tabulated design data for selenium cells are given on a basis of maximum current ratings at 25°C, good up to 35°C, in Table 4.5. The cells may be safely operated at any fraction of full load current. The maximum inverse a-c voltage and d-c blocking voltage are also given for each cell.   For actual rectifier design it is usually necessary

Table 4.5   Maximum Load Currents on Per Cell Basis.*
(G. E. selenium rectifiers rating at 35°C ambient unit rectifier circuit.)

Cell Type	1	K-2	K-3	K-4	G			F			T			A			R
Dimensions	3/32 In. Dia.	3/32 In. Dia.	3/32 In. Dia.	9/32 In. Sq.	1 In. Sq.			1 In. Dia.			1 1/2 In. Sq. 1.67 In. Sq.			1 1/2 In. Dia. 1.15 In. Sq.			1 1/2 In.×2 In.
Active Cell Area (Cross Sectional)	0.005 In. Sq.	0.012 In. Sq.	0.028 In. Sq.	0.028 In. Sq.	0.58 In. Sq.			0.45 In. Sq.			1.67 In. Sq.			1.15 In. Sq.			On Application
No. of Cells in Stack	.....	.....	.....	.....	1–16	17–24	25–40	1–16	17–24	25–40	1–16	17–24	25–40	1–16	17–24	25–40	On Application
(units)	Milli-amp	Milli-amp	Milli-amp	Milli-amp	Amp	Amp	Amp	Amp	Amp	Amp	Amp	Amp	Amp	Amp	Amp	Amp	Amp
SINGLE PHASE Half Wave	0.1	2.5	5	5	0.13	0.11	.1	0.125	0.1	0.08	0.375	0.325	0.275	0.25	0.2	0.18	On Application
Full-wave Center Tap	.2	5	10	10	.26	.225	.2	.25	.2	.15	.75	.65	.55	.5	.4	.35	
Full-wave Bridge	.2	5	10	10	.26	.225	.2	.25	.2	.15	.75	.65	.55	.5	.4	.35	
THREE PHASE Wye	0.34	8.5	17	17	0.42	0.37	0.34	0.42	0.34	0.25	1.28	1.12	0.93	0.85	0.68	0.59	On Application
3-phase, Full-wave Bridge	.3	7.5	15	15	.375	.33	.3	.37	.3	.22	1.12	.975	.825	.75	.6	.52	
6-phase Star No Interphase	On Application	On Application	On Application	On Application	On Application	On Application		.65	.53	.39	On Application	On Application		1.31	1.05	.91	
Double Wye Interphase Coil								.7	.57	.42				1.41	1.13	.98	
D-c Circuit Value	0.157	0.392	0.784	0.784	0.19	0.17	0.16	0.2	0.16	0.13	0.59	0.51	0.43	0.39	0.31	0.28	On Application

Table 4.5 (Continued)

	C — 2 3/16 In. Dia. / 2.7 In. Sq.			D — 3 3/8 In. Dia. / 7.5 In. Sq.			H — 4 3/8 In. (Narrow Spacing) Dia. / 13 In. Sq.		J — 4 3/8 In. Dia. / 13 In. Sq.			M — 4 1/4 In. × 6 In. / 22 In. Sq.			Applied Volts → Rms		
Symbol for RMS Voltage Rating →	1-8	9-20	21-36	1-8	9-18	19-36	1-16	17-36	1-8	9-16	17-24	1-8	9-14	15-24	18	26 (H)	45 (3H)
	Amp	Amp	Amp	Amp	Amp	Amp	Amp	Amp	Amp	Amp	Amp	Amp	Amp	Amp	D-c Volts	D-c Volts	D-c Volts
SINGLE PHASE Half Wave	0.6	0.5	0.4	1.35	1.25	1	2	1.88	2.5	2.25	2	4	3.65	3.3	6	9	18
Full-wave Center Tap	1.2	1	.8	2.7	2.5	2	4	3.75	5	4.5	4	8	7.3	6.6	6	9	18
Full-wave Bridge	1.2	1	.8	2.7	2.5	2	4	3.75	5	4.5	4	8	7.3	6.6	12	18	36
THREE PHASE Wye	2.02	1.69	1.35	4.56	4.22	3.38	6.75	6.33	8.44	7.6	6.75	13.5	12.4	11.2	7.3	10.9	21
3-phase, Full-wave Bridge	1.8	1.5	1.2	4.05	3.75	3	6	5.63	7.7	6.75	6	12	11	9.9	16	24	54
6-phase Star No Interphase	3.15	2.62	2.1	7.1	6.56	5.25	10.5	9.85	13.1	11.8	10.5	21	19.2	17.3	7.5	11.3	22.5
Double Wye Interphase Coil	3.39	2.82	2.26	7.62	7.05	5.65	11.3	10.6	14.1	12.7	11.3	22.6	20.7	18.6	7	10.5	21
D-c Circuit Value	0.94	0.78	0.63	2.12	1.96	1.57	3.14	2.96	3.92	3.53	3.14	6.28	5.75	5.19	15	21	36
Peak Volts															25	40	63

* Courtesy of General Electric Company

to go to the curves of Fig. 4-30 in which the input a-c and output d-c voltages are given as a function of current loading.

Example. Consider a 5.0 amp resistance load at 100 v d-c using a single-phase bridge rectifier. From the table it is seen that a type J, $4\frac{3}{8}$-in. cell can carry 5.0 amp if not more than 8 cells are required in series. The d-c voltage per cell is given as 12.0 v. Therefore 8 cells would give $8 \times 12 = 96$ v d-c, which is not quite enough. However, they would probably be used in practice since the rating is so close.

The a-c voltage can be found by referring to Fig. 4-30. The cells are being operated at 100 per cent current rating and the d-c output voltage per cell should be $100/8 = 12.5$ v d-c. This point on the curve of Fig. 4-30 gives 16.0 v rms per cell, or a total of $8 \times 16 = 128.0$ v. This a-c voltage per cell is within the limits of the maximum inverse voltage given in the table, since the maximum inverse voltage in a perfect bridge is equal to the peak value of the supply voltage.

4.13 Circuits for Metallic Rectifiers

The basic single-phase circuits for metallic rectifiers are of three types. The half-wave circuit, which makes use of a single stack

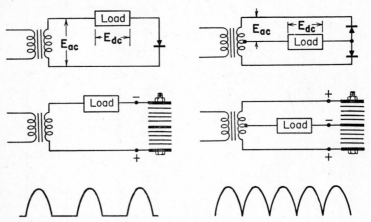

Fig. 4-31. Half- and full-wave rectifiers. (Courtesy of General Electric Company.)

with two taps is shown in Fig. 4-31. The full-wave circuit, also shown in Fig. 4-31, is essentially two half-wave circuits, but makes use of a center-tapped rectifier stack and transformer. For the full-wave rectifier, half the stack is piled one way, while the other half is piled opposite. In the half-wave rectifier stack all cells must be piled the same way.   Because it does not require a center-tapped transformer, the most used circuit is the single-phase bridge circuit, which is shown in Fig. 4-32.   All three circuits lend themselves easily to perfect rectifier theory as discussed in the chapter on rectifiers and inverters.   For design information it will be remembered that in either of the full-wave circuits, with resistive load and

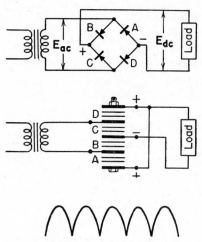

Fig. 4-32.   Full-wave bridge rectifier.   (Courtesy of General Electric Company.)

assuming perfect rectification, the d-c voltage is equal to the average value of the half sine wave supply.

$$E_{dc} = \frac{2}{\pi} E_m = \frac{2}{\pi} \sqrt{2}\, E_{rms} = 0.9 E_{rms}. \qquad (4.48)$$

The ripple factor E_{ac}/E_{dc} at the load is also independent of the load current as long as it has the wave form shown in Fig. 4-32.   It is equal to 48 per cent.   These relations also hold true at the input terminals of a choke input filter.

If the load is a battery or a capacitor input type filter, the d-c voltage approaches the maximum value of the applied sine wave. In the case of a parallel R-C load and full-wave rectification,

$$E_{dc} \cong E_m - \frac{\Delta E}{2}, \qquad (4.49)$$

where
$$\Delta E = \frac{I_{dc}}{2fC} = \frac{E_{dc}}{2fR_L C}. \qquad (4.50)$$

The ripple factor at the rectifier output is then equal to

$$\frac{0.29\Delta E}{E_{dc}} = \gamma. \tag{4.51}$$

$$\gamma = \frac{0.29}{2fR_LC} = \frac{29}{2fR_LC} \ \%. \tag{4.52}$$

In half-wave rectifiers, ΔE is twice as large as the value of Eq. 4.50. The battery type load approaches this analysis, but is not identical.

It is customary to use a three-phase power supply where higher power outputs are required and efficiency of operation is important. The two most common circuits are the full-wave double Y, with or without interphase transformer, and the full-wave bridge. These circuits are shown in Fig. 4-33. In all these connections it will be noticed that the rectifier stacks are of the same type as those used in single-phase half-wave circuits. The cells in each stack are all piled in one direction. It will be remembered that with the interphase transformer, conduction in each stack is for one-third cycle, while without the interphase transformer only one stack conducts at a time, and thus there is conduction in each stack for only one-sixth cycle.

In the bridge circuit each tube conducts for one-third cycle, but only three secondaries are required compared to the six secondaries and interphase transformer of the double Y. With the interphase transformer, the theoretical d-c voltage for perfect rectifiers with resistance load is $1.17E_{rms}$ per phase, and without the interphase transformer it is $1.35E_{rms}$ per phase. The ripple factor is again independent of load size and is about 4 per cent. For the bridge circuit the output voltage per phase is

$$E_{dc} = 2.34E_{rms}. \tag{4.53}$$

The ripple is the same as before, 4 per cent.

Because of the a-c component in the output of all rectifiers, it is essential to consider the efficiency from two different standpoints. Basically, efficiency is the ratio of the output power to the input power, usually expressed in per cent. The power input for rectifiers is always the a-c power and is easily measured with a-c instruments. The output power may be the total effective value if the a-c component is utilized, or it may be only the d-c value if the a-c com-

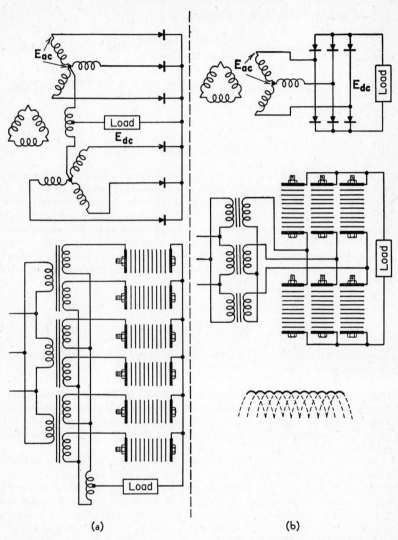

(a)   (b)

Fig. 4-33. Three-phase full-wave rectifier. (a) Three-phase full-wave (double-Y). (b) Three-phase full-wave bridge. (Courtesy of General Electric Company.)

ponent is lost. The two expressions are

$$\% \text{ rms efficiency} = \frac{\text{a-c watts output}}{\text{a-c watts input}} \times 100 \tag{4.54}$$

and $\quad \% \text{ d-c or average efficiency} = \dfrac{\text{d-c volts} \times \text{d-c current}}{\text{a-c watts input}} \times 100.$

$$\tag{4.55}$$

PROBLEMS

4.1. A 5-mil, 50-ohm d'Arsonval movement is to be used in conjunction with a bridge crystal rectifier to measure a-c sinusoidal voltages up to 500 v rms. (a) Specify the value and wattage of the series dropping resistor. (b) What is the maximum inverse voltage that appears across each rectifier? (c) Repeat parts (a) and (b) if the voltage to be measured was 5.0 v rms and the rectifiers were of the type whose characteristics are shown in Fig. 4-10.

4.2. Referring to the circuit of Fig. 4-17, calculate and plot the relation between the frequency of oscillation and the d-c voltage required for the following circuit values:

$$C = 0.001 \ \mu\text{f} \quad R'_p = 200 \text{ ohms} \quad R'_s = 28 \text{ ohms} \quad M = 20 \text{ mh}$$

$$R_L = 72 \text{ ohms} \quad L'_p = 200 \text{ mh} \quad L'_s = 10 \text{ mh} \quad R' = 10^5 \text{ ohms}$$

The crystal is the one whose characteristic is shown in Fig. 4-10, with the current scale multiplied by $\frac{1}{4}$.

4.3. A single-phase full-wave bridge rectifier is to be built with copper oxide rectifiers to supply a capacitor input load of 100 ma at 300 v d-c. Design the transformer, voltage, and taps, the size and number of cells in series or parallel, and calculate the ripple at the input to the capacitor, which has a value of 10 μf. For rectifier selection purposes consider the capacitor input to be the same as a battery input.

4.4. It is necessary to design a copper oxide rectifier to charge a storage battery. The curve of battery terminal voltage versus charging current is given by $E_t = E' + 0.2I$. It is assumed that the battery will be charged every night for 10 hours and that when it is put on the charger $E' = 5.8$ v. It is further assumed that E' varies according to the relation $E' = 5.8 + 0.1It$ where t is in hours and I is in amperes d-c. Design the circuit so that at the end of the 10 hours $E' = 7.2$ v.

4.5. A resistance load requires 3.0 amp at 40 v d-c. (a) Design a single-phase bridge copper oxide rectifier to do the job. (b) Repeat (a) using selenium cells. (c) Calculate the theoretical d-c efficiency for both cases, assuming a transformer efficiency of 95 per cent. Assume the transformer is perfect as far as coupling and leakage inductance are concerned. (d) Calculate the a-c efficiency for parts (a) and (b).

4.6. Referring to the volt-ampere characteristic of the copper oxide cell, find a mathematical expression that approximates the variation of resistance per sq in. of surface with direct current at 20°C.

4.7. Work out the theoretical value of d-c voltage across a load R_L in a single-phase bridge rectifier in terms of $E_{ac\ rms}$, assuming the rectifier's resistance remains constant in the forward and reverse direction at R_1 and R_2, respectively.

4.8. Design a selenium 3ϕ full-wave bridge rectifier to supply a 75-ohm load with 2.0 amp d-c.

4.9. Explain the cell combinations: 4-2-1, 4-48-1, 4-4-4, 4-7-2.

4.10. Derive the expressions for the average voltage, the average current, and the ripple factor for a full-wave rectifier with battery load. Assume the battery to have a constant voltage drop plus the drop across a series resistance R. Also assume the rectifiers to be perfect.

4.11. Using the solution of problem 4.10, calculate the additional supply voltage as a function of current if the rectifiers are considered to be linear resistors in the forward direction. Also calculate the power dissipated in each rectifier.

CHAPTER 5

PHOTOTUBES AND ASSOCIATED CIRCUITS

The importance of phototubes is becoming greater to the electrical engineer as the field of automatic control broadens and their applications increase. It is not practical to study all, or even an appreciable percentage, of these applications. Therefore in this chapter the fundamental principles which operate in all phototube circuits will be discussed, and their application will be illustrated by a few typical circuits.   With this background the engineer should be able to attack a variety of problems.

5.1 Photoelectric Phenomena[1]

The electrical effects of light on matter can be conveniently divided into three groups.
(a) Photoconductive effect.
(b) Photovoltaic effect.
(c) Photoemissive effect.
Although our main interest is with the last group, a brief study of the others is of value.   They will be treated first.

5.2 Photoconductive Cells

As might be suggested by the name, the principle of the photoconductive cell is the changing of the electric resistance of a conductor by light.   The word "conductor" here might be misleading, since the materials that exhibit this effect to any marked degree are semiconductors.   The most common of the materials is selenium, and for this reason photoconductive cells are often called selenium cells.

---

[1] Electronics Engineers of Westinghouse Electric Corp., *Industrial Electronics Reference Book*, John Wiley & Sons, Inc., New York, 1948.

Phototubes. (Courtesy of Radio Corporation of America.)

The effect of light on selenium is to change its resistance. Although the resistance is numerically high, the percentage change is quite large. As an example, a commercially manufactured cell (G.E.-FJ-31) has a dark resistance of 6 megohms as compared to 0.75 megohm when subjected to normal light. This percentage change is typical of all such cells, although their absolute values obviously depend on their construction. The current rating of these cells is necessarily small because of the low power dissipating ability.

In order to increase the current-carrying capacity and reduce the absolute resistance to as low a value as possible, the cell is built with a short conduction path of large cross-sectional area. An added difficulty in this construction is that to secure the desired resistance change the surface exposed to light must be large and of shallow depth. A typical method of construction is shown in Fig. 5-1. The cell consists of two conducting grids separated by a layer of selenium. If the depth of the grids is small, the device offers the short, large cross-sectional path open to light that is required. By paralleling a number of these individual cells, units capable of carrying up to 0.5 ampere have been built.

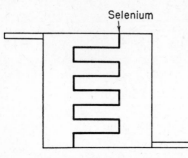

Selenium

Fig. 5-1.   Selenium cell.

5.3   Photovoltaic Cells

The photovoltaic cell by its name indicates that a voltage is produced by the application of light. There are basically two types of these cells, the wet cell and the dry or barrier layer cell.

Although the wet cell was discovered first, it has now been completely replaced by the more efficient barrier layer cell. These barrier layer cells have found widespread use in meters for the measurement of illumination and in exposure meters for photographic purposes.

The cell consists of a compound on a metal. Electrons are emitted from the compound to the metal at their common boundary when the surface is illuminated. An example is the combination of cuprous oxide on copper used in copper oxide rectifiers. The oxide-coated surface is illuminated. It is of interest to note that the current flow is opposite to that existing when the disk is used as a rectifier element. Another type in production is the iron selenide cell.

The problem of making contact with the two elements of the cell without interfering with light reaching the active border between the compound and the metal has been solved in two ways. These solutions have led to the two common types of cell. These are known as the back-effect and the front-effect cells.

In the back-effect cell, contact to the compound is made either by a ring pressed against it near the outside edge or by a thin film of metal deposited on the edge. The light passes through the compound itself and reaches the active border where the voltage is produced. Since the light must pass through the compound, the shorter wavelengths are absorbed, and the greatest sensitivity of the cell is usually near the red end of the spectrum.

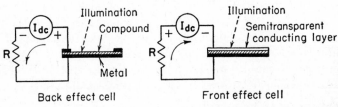

Fig. 5-2. Circuits of photovoltaic cells.

In the front-effect cell a semitransparent conducting layer is placed over the compound and makes possible the electric connection. Two voltages are now generated, one between the compound and the base metal, and one between the semitransparent layer and the compound. The net voltage is their difference. Since the light intensity is greatest at the front, this voltage determines the direction of current flow. Any useful voltage response to light is not linear, as can be seen from Fig. 5-3. However, if a small resistor is used as a load, the response of current to light is approximately linear. (Fig. 5-4.) This property aids in its use as a light meter using a sensitive microammeter as an indicator. It can also be used to operate very sensitive relays. The short-circuit current is directly proportional to the total flux incident upon the surface, and is independent of the area illuminated.

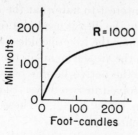

Fig. 5-3. Static characteristic of   Fig. 5-4. Dynamic characteristic of
photovoltaic cell.*   photovoltaic cell.*

5.4 Photoemissive Phenomena

Photoemission[2] is probably the most important of the three types of photoelectric phenomena. The electrons are thrown off or emitted from the material due to absorbed radiant energy. After emission the electrons may be accelerated by an electric field. Unless otherwise directed the acceleration takes place along the electrostatic lines of force. The number and energies of the electrons emitted depend upon the intensity and frequency of the radiation or light as well as upon the material.

In order to understand more fully the process of emission it is necessary to consider a brief treatment of light and radiation.

5.5 Physics of Light and Radiation

Although both light and radiant energy refer to the same phenomenon in certain ranges, it is important to understand that the term *radiant energy* is much broader than the term *light*. Radiant energy refers to the entire spectrum of energy propagation by means of the electromagnetic field from 60-cycle power elements up through the gamma and cosmic rays. The detection of this radiant energy is possible with many devices, including the common radio receiver. Detection of a small band of frequencies is possible by the human eye. As in any other device for detection, the eye does not respond equally well to all the frequencies within its range. The eye sees only a limited range of frequencies defined as light. With this conception of light it is not difficult to understand that a device sensi-

[2] M.I.T. Electrical Engineering Staff, *Applied Electronics*, John Wiley & Sons, Inc., New York, 1943.

*Figs. 5-3 and 5-4 are after an article by Colin G. Fink and Dwight K. Alpern, *Trans. Am. Electrochem. Soc.*, **58**, 281 (1930).

tive to radiant energy may operate in a range of frequencies wholly
or partly invisible to the human eye.

5.6 Radiation of Energy

Radiation of energy is produced by the propagation of inter-
linking electric and magnetic fields.   The velocity of propagation is
known to be the constant $c = 299.79 \times 10^6$ meters per second.

If the strength and direction of the fields are varying according
to some periodic or oscillatory function of time such as a sine wave,
the distance in space that the wave will have moved during one cycle
depends upon the frequency, and is called a wavelength.   Since

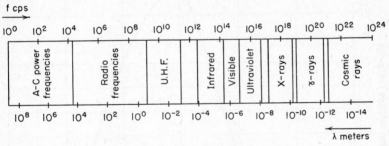

Fig. 5-5.   Energy spectrum.

c is constant, the wavelength is inversely proportional to the frequency.   This relation may be stated by the familiar relation

$$c = \lambda f, \tag{5.1}$$

where $c = 299.79 \times 10^6 \cong 300 \times 10^6$ meters per second,
    $\lambda = $ wavelength in meters,
    $f = $ frequency in cycles per second.

If f is given in megacycles, the equation takes the following form

$$300 = \lambda f. \tag{5.2}$$

An interesting chart relating frequencies and wavelengths is shown
in Fig. 5-5.

5.7 Characteristics of the Eye

The chart of Fig. 5-5 emphasizes the very small range of radiation frequencies to which the eye has any response.   The fact that

the eye does not respond uniformly even over this range has already been mentioned.

However, it is the radiation seen by the eye that is called light. The average eye has at least some response between 4000 and 7000 angstrom units, usually written 4000Å to 7000Å. The angstrom unit is a measure of wavelength and is useful because of the very

Violet	Blue	Green	Yellow	Red
400	500	600		700 mμ

Fig. 5-6.   Color-wavelength chart.

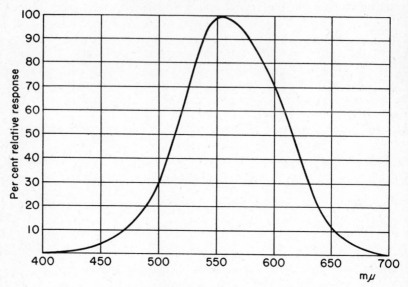

Fig. 5-7.   Response of the human eye.

small numbers involved if wavelength is expressed in meters or some other common length.

$$1\text{Å} = 10^{-10} \text{ meter.} \tag{5.3}$$

The wavelength in the visual range is sometimes expressed in another unit called the millimicron. The millimicron (mμ) is 1×10^{-9} meter.

$$1 \text{ m}\mu = 10^{-9} \text{ meter.} \tag{5.4}$$

What we think of as color is merely the eye's response to the different frequencies within its range. The general color distribution is shown in Fig. 5-6.

The relation between wavelength and frequency reveals immediately that red is at the low-frequency end of the scale while violet is at the high end. Infrared then becomes a radiation with a frequency too low for the eye to see, while ultraviolet is a frequency above visibility. The frequency response of the average eye to radiation of constant intensity is given in Fig. 5-7.

It is clear then that all units of light refer to the eye's sensitivity, while radiant energy is measured in terms of total energy irrespective of the detector. The response of a device such as a photoelectric tube to radiant energy may then be considerably different from that of the human eye. The usual assumption that phototubes respond to light is therefore not correct. It is convenient that they do respond to frequencies of radiant energy that are visible, but the fundamental principles must always be kept in mind. The actual laws governing the phototube's response will be discussed in a following section.

5.8   Units of Light and Radiation

Because photoelectric devices are often rated and calibrated using units of light, it is necessary that these units be understood by the electronic engineer.

Total radiation is energy, and thus may be expressed either in terms of energy per unit area, such as watthours per square meter, or in terms of energy per unit area per unit time, such as watts per square meter.

The units of measurement of light are not as simply fundamental, since they are measures of the eye's response to radiant energy. Thus measurements of light become comparisons of one sensation to another which is used as a standard. The following definitions are in common use:

Light is the visual sensation produced by that portion of radiant energy that is known as *luminous flux*.

The *lumen* is the unit of luminous flux.

The *candle* is the unit of intensity (flux emitted per unit solid angle) produced by a standard candle burning under standard conditions. A 1-candle source emits a total flux of 4π lumens.

The *foot-candle* is the illuminance produced, upon the spherical surface, by a 1-candle source situated at the center of a sphere of 1 foot radius. It is equivalent to 1 lumen per square foot, which is the preferred expression.

It can be seen that although the number of lumens per unit solid angle remains the same regardless of distance from the source, assuming perfect transmission, the light intensity from a point source decreases inversely with the square of the distance from the source.   It remains constant if the lines of luminous flux are made parallel by a lens or some similar arrangement.   Point sources are very convenient for calculation and may be converted to parallel

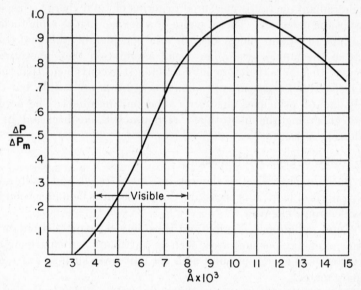

Fig. 5-8.   Energy distribution of tungsten filament at 2870°K.   [Graph and data from Fig. 1, p. 78, Art. 2, Vol. 32 (1937), *Journal of the Scientific Laboratories* (Denison University).   This is a part of the article by W. E. Forsythe and E. Q. Adams, "The Tungsten Filament Incandescent Lamp."]

radiation sources by use of lenses.   Since any general physics book treats of the use of the lens, it will be assumed that the student is already familiar with their use.

The incandescent lamp is often used as a light source, and until recently was the means of standardizing or rating phototubes.   For this reason it is desirable to study its characteristics.

The relative radiation distribution of a lamp with a tungsten filament operating at 2870°K is shown in Fig. 5-8.   This curve shows that the greater part of the radiant energy appears in the frequency band below the lower visible limit, or in the infrared.   Although the incandescent lamp is rather inefficient from a light standpoint it is high in total efficiency.   For example, the average lamp is approximately 95 per cent efficient with respect to total radiation, but 85 per cent of the energy is in the infrared region and 10 per cent in the visible region.   Therefore when phototubes are rated with respect to such sources, the exact source must be given.   A typical rating might be 5 μa per lumen from a tungsten lamp at 2870°K.   Recently, ratings such as 5 μa per watt of radiant energy have appeared. Both ratings are often given.   The latter refers to total energy reaching the cathode.

The concepts of light and radiation have been outlined briefly, and now the fundamentals of photoemission will be considered.

5.9   Physics of Photoemission

It should first be realized that emission of electrons from any material occurs because some of the electrons of the material absorb sufficient energy from a source to allow them to overcome the work function of the material's surface.   This amount of energy is often stated in volts since an electron accelerated through a potential takes on a definite amount of kinetic energy.   The work function may then be expressed in electron volts.   A complete treatment of this work function and how it is determined will be left to the many books devoted to the subject.   It is sufficient here to state that a certain amount of energy must be absorbed by an electron before it can be emitted.   Various methods of obtaining this energy are possible.   These include:

(a) Thermal agitation.
(b) Particle bombardment.
(c) Radiation by electromagnetic fields.

We are particularly interested in the method in which the electrons absorb radiant energy of frequencies that are visible to the human eye.

5.10   Quantum Theory of Emission

As expressed in the last section, it is necessary that an electron in a material receive energy from some source in order that it may be emitted.   However, it is possible for an electron to absorb energy only in certain amounts called quanta.   The size of a quantum or photon, as it is sometimes called, varies, depending upon the frequency of the radiant energy.

A quantum of energy is equal to the product of the frequency and a constant known as Planck's constant.

$$1 \text{ quantum} = hf \qquad (5.5)$$

where h = Planck's constant = 6.57×10^{-34} joule-second.

f = frequency of radiation, cycles per second.

Since the amount of energy needed by an electron to emerge from a material's surface has a definite value, there is a certain frequency of radiation for each material below which a quantum is too small to cause emission.   This is known as the threshold frequency f_0, or may be referred to in terms of threshold wavelength λ_0.   These are related by $c = f_0\lambda_0$.

On the other hand, if the frequency of radiation is greater than the threshold value, and since the energy can be absorbed only in certain amounts, the electrons emitted have a balance of energy in kinetic form.   It is from these facts that the Einstein equation may be written:

$$hf = w + \tfrac{1}{2}mv^2 \qquad (5.6)$$

where w = the energy of the work function,

m = the mass of an electron = 9.038×10^{-31} kg,

v = the velocity of the electron after emission, meters per second.

This equation states in concise form the relations discussed previously.

With this equation it is immediately possible to solve for the threshold frequency or wavelength since this corresponds to the solution when the emitted electrons have zero energy.   Thus

$$hf_0 = w + 0$$

or
$$f_0 = \frac{w}{h}. \qquad (5.7)$$

It is also possible to formulate the two general laws of photo emission.

(a) The number of electrons emitted for any particular spectral distribution is directly proportional to the light intensity or the number of lumens falling on any particular area.

(b) The maximum energy of emitted electrons is entirely independent of the amount of light flux or lumens on the surface, but is directly proportional to the frequency of the radiation.

The first law is obvious from the fact that energy may be absorbed only in certain amounts.   Thus the greater the number of incident quanta, the more electrons are emitted.

The second law is of course a statement of the fact that all energy not required by the work function appears as kinetic energy, and therefore the velocity at emission depends directly upon frequency.

5.11   Emission from Photoemissive Materials

It is now obvious that in order to have photoemission due to visible light from a material it is necessary to have a material

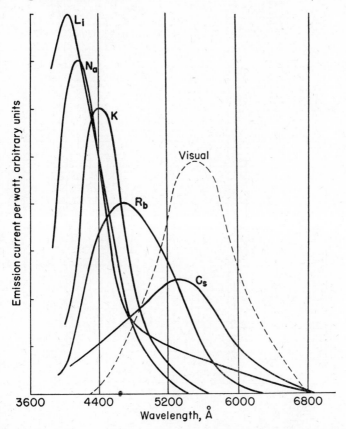

Fig. 5-9.   Relative response of the alkali metals.   (By permission from *Theory and Applications of Electron Tubes,* by Herbert J. Reich.   Copyright, 1944, McGraw-Hill Book Company, Inc.)

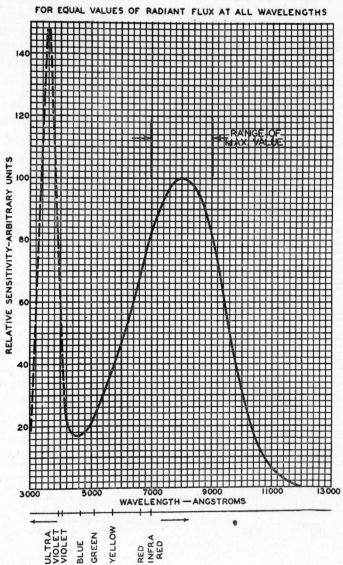

FOR EQUAL VALUES OF RADIANT FLUX AT ALL WAVELENGTHS

Fig. 5-10. Spectral sensitivity characteristics of phototube having S-1 response. (Courtesy of Radio Corporation of America.)

whose work function is equal to or less than a photon of radiant energy in the visible spectrum. It is found that only a few metals exhibit this property to any degree. They are the alkali metals lithium, sodium, potassium, rubidium, and cesium. The responses of these metals to a monochromatic source of constant intensity are given in Fig. 5-9. From this it can be seen that cesium has a response most like that of the average human eye. Combinations of the elements may be used to extend the range.

As in the case of thermionic cathodes, greater emission may be obtained from thin coatings of the metals or combinations than can be obtained from the pure metal. A complete treatment of the films and coatings used is beyond the scope of this text, but in general it may be said that the best emission is obtained from films about one atom thick. The most common phototube responding to visible incandescent light has a cathode consisting of films of cesium on cesium oxide on silver. The relative response curve of this tube is given in Fig. 5-10.

It can be seen that this response extends well into the infrared range, as does the output of the incandescent lamp.

It might well be asked why there is a drop in emission at higher frequencies or shorter wavelengths. This does not seem to fit the general equation or the laws of emission. It should be noted that all the materials seem to cut off at approximately the same point on the high frequency range. If the frequencies associated with these wavelengths are calculated, it is apparent that they are in the ultraviolet range. The materials were obviously studied in some type of evacuated shell through which light or radiant energy could pass, presumably glass. In the ultraviolet range glass no longer is a transmitter, but absorbs a great majority of the energy. If a quartz window were used the range could be extended. The upper limit, however, depends on the highest frequency it is possible to get to the cathode.

5.12 The Vacuum Phototube

The vacuum phototube consists of a cathode and an anode enclosed in an evacuated shell. No heater is required since the cathode is coated to have emission from radiant energy in the visible range. The cathode shape is not important as long as it receives light. The greater the surface area the greater the emission for any particular light intensity. A very common construction is a half cylinder of silver or silver-plated copper, with various films being used, depending upon the desired characteristics.

The anode must be in a position to collect the emitted electrons and yet not interfere with light reaching the cathode. It usually consists of a single wire at the center of the half cylinder. A typical tube construction is shown in Fig. 5-11.

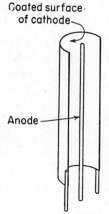

Coated surface of cathode

Anode

Fig. 5-11. Electrode structure of phototube.

5.13 Vacuum Phototube Characteristics

The operation of the vacuum phototube is not fundamentally different from that of the vacuum thermionic tube except that the source of electrons is different in the two tubes. In the phototube electrons are emitted from the cathode surface by radiant energy, and are then in a position to be accelerated to an anode if an electric field is established. This situation is similar to that in the thermionic vacuum tube in which the electrons are emitted as the result of heating. As might be suspected, however, the amount of emission is considerably different. In the thermionic tube the emission is sufficient to require considerable plate voltage to attract all electrons, and as a result the tube current is usually space-charge-limited. However, it is known that a sufficiently large plate voltage will attract all emitted electrons, and a condition of temperature saturation can be reached. In the phototube the emission is so small that only a small plate voltage is required to obtain a similar condition, which might be called light saturation. Unlike the thermionic tube, the phototube is operated under this saturation condition.

The absolute current values are of course a function of the cathode material used and the light source, but a typical characteristic curve is shown in Fig. 5-12. In accordance with the fundamental law that the amount of emission is directly proportional to the total radiant energy, the curves of Fig. 5-12 are parallel and equally spaced for a constant light source as the total lumens on the cathode increase.

If the current output is plotted against lumens it is seen that the

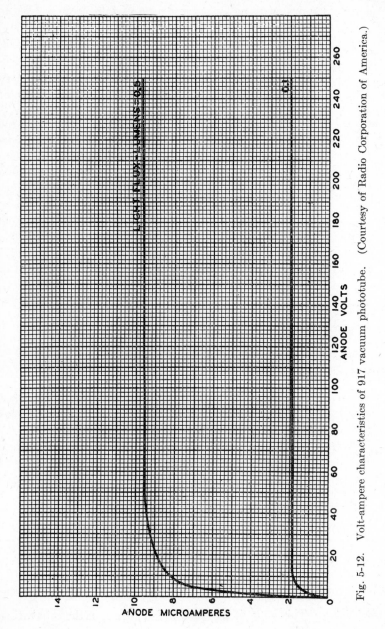

Fig. 5-12.   Volt-ampere characteristics of 917 vacuum phototube.   (Courtesy of Radio Corporation of America.)

relation is approximately linear for all plate voltages over about 40

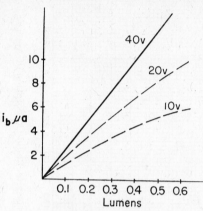

volts for this tube. This fact is shown in Fig. 5-13. This is a very important relation when a linear relation is desired between light input and electric output. It should be obvious that the phototube is a typical current generator. At plate voltages below 40, the tube current is space-charge-limited or in the transition condition between space-charge limitation and light saturation.

Fig. 5-13. Current response curves of vacuum phototube.

5.14 Mathematical Analysis of Phototube

In general terms it can be said that the current through a phototube is a function of two parameters, the light flux F and the plate voltage e. Here e is the voltage *rise* from cathode to anode.

$$i = f(F, e).\qquad (5.8)$$

The total current change could be expressed by the superposition theorem as

$$di = \frac{\partial i}{\partial e}\,de + \frac{\partial i}{\partial F}\,dF\qquad (5.9)$$

where $\frac{\partial i}{\partial e}$ is the coefficient relating current to voltage, and $\frac{\partial i}{\partial F}$ is the coefficient relating current to light flux.

$$\frac{\partial i}{\partial e} = \text{amperes per volt} = \frac{1}{r_p}.$$

$$\frac{\partial i}{\partial F} = \text{amperes per lumen} = \sigma.$$

The term $\frac{\partial i}{\partial F}$ from this definition becomes the sensitivity σ of the phototube. This value is normally given as part of the tube rating or can be taken directly from the characteristic curves. The term $\frac{\partial i}{\partial e}$ has the form of conductance, or the reciprocal of resistance, analogous to the plate resistance of the triode. If these terms are evaluated for the point of operation under consideration, the change of current becomes

$$di = \frac{1}{r_p} de + \sigma\, dF. \tag{5.10}$$

Integrating Eq. 5.10 gives

$$i = \frac{e}{r_p} + \sigma F + K. \tag{5.11}$$

For the case where i is interpreted to be only the *change* in current from some operating point, or for some special case where the char-

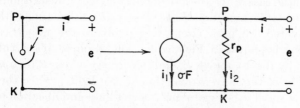

Fig. 5-14.   Equivalent circuit of phototube.

acteristics of the vacuum phototube are nearly linear over the entire first quadrant, K may be considered equal to zero.

Then
$$i = \sigma F + \frac{e}{r_p} = i_1 + i_2. \tag{5.12}$$

Thus the equivalent a-c circuit of any tube or the complete equivalent circuit of a vacuum tube would be that of Fig. 5-14.   In this circuit, the current i_1 flows from plus to minus since in the tube conventional current flow is from plate to cathode.

From the characteristic curves of the vacuum phototube, r_p is seen to be very large in the operating range, approaching infinity for practical purposes.   The value of σ is seen to be substantially a constant in the operating range, and thus

$$i \cong \sigma F. \tag{5.13}$$

This is merely a mathematical statement that the current is directly proportional to the light flux.   The equivalent circuit of such a source is shown in Fig. 5-15.

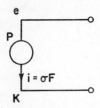

Fig. 5-15. Practical equivalent circuit of vacuum phototube.

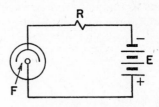

Fig. 5-16. Basic phototube circuit.

5.15   Fundamental Phototube Circuit

As in the case of the thermionic tube, a phototube without a load is useless.   It is important that the operation of the tube with a load be considered.   A basic circuit making use of the properties of the phototube is shown in Fig. 5-16.   The required plate voltage is supplied by the d-c source E, and the voltage across R then becomes a function of the current and thus of the light.   Since the actual current is small it is usually necessary to use amplification even for relay operation, and thus a voltage across R which can be applied to a grid is satisfactory.

To determine the size of the components and the voltages involved, reference is made to the volt-ampere characteristic of Fig. 5-12.   It is important to note that in the operating range above about 40 volts the current is no longer an appreciable function of plate voltage.   This shows that if E is sufficiently large, the current through, and hence the voltage across R is almost a linear function of the light.   Since the magnitude of the current is small, R is necessarily large, if an appreciable voltage is to be obtained.

Such problems as those involving a resistance load were easily solved for the thermionic tube by use of the load line.   It is also of use here.   In Fig. 5-17(a), a possible load line might be represented by line A, assuming $E = 100$ v.   The division of voltage across R and the tube may be read directly from the curve.   The change in voltage across R would be linear only to slightly less than 0.2 lumen. Two things may be varied: the supply voltage E may be increased or the slope of the load line changed. If the slope of the load line is increased by decreasing R, the response is linear for a greater range of light, but the sensitivity (volts output per unit change of light input) is decreased. This fact is shown by curve B. However, if E had been increased and R left the same as in A, the range would have been increased with the same sensitivity. See curve C. This condition is certainly more desirable. If the range of light change is low, it might be advantageous to increase R still further, as in curve D.

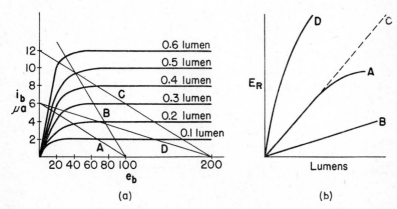

Fig. 5-17.   (a) Typical vacuum phototube characteristics.   (b) Output voltage versus lumens for vacuum phototube.

The upper limit of plate voltage regardless of current is approximately 300 volts. The size of R is then determined by the range of light involved and the output voltage sensitivity desired.

Plots of output voltage versus lumens are shown in Fig. 5-17(b). The letters on the curves refer to the similar notation of Fig. 5-17(a). In general, both R and E should be as large as possible, thus producing high sensitivity and linearity. As will be seen in Sec. 5.27, certain conditions such as high-frequency change of light will make the large resistance impractical. It is sometimes desirable to replace the d-c power supply with an a-c source. This will be discussed in Sec. 5.24.

5.16 Fundamental Circuit Analysis

If a load resistor R_L is inserted in series with a vacuum phototube, the circuit of Fig. 5-18 results. Writing the node equation for point P gives

$$\sigma F + \frac{E_b}{r_p} = \frac{E - E_b}{R_L}, \qquad (5.14)$$

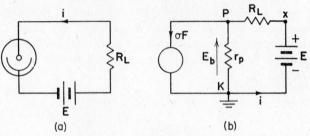

Fig. 5-18.   Basic phototube circuit.

where E_b is the voltage rise from cathode to anode.   Thus

$$E_b = \frac{E - \sigma F R_L}{1 + R_L/r_p}. \qquad (5.15)$$

If the operating point is such that $r_p \cong \infty$, the current i does not depend upon R_L, and the tube voltage drop E_b is

$$E_b = E - \sigma F R_L. \qquad (5.16)$$

Then $E_{R_L} = E_{px} = E - E_b = \sigma F R_L - E + E = \sigma F R_L.$ (5.17)

If this assumption is not valid and the effect of r_p must be considered, Eq. 5.15 substituted into Eq. 5.17 gives

$$E_{R_L} = E - E_b = \frac{E R_L/r_p + \sigma F R_L}{1 + R_L/r_p} \qquad (5.18)$$

which reduces to Eq. 5.17 if $r_p \gg R_L$.   If only the response to the modulated portion of a light signal is desired, the equivalent a-c circuit of Fig. 5-19 may be analyzed.

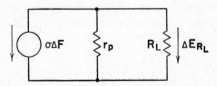

Fig. 5-19.   A-c equivalent circuit.

Writing the loop equation gives

$$\sigma \, \Delta F = \Delta E_{R_L} \left(\frac{1}{r_p} + \frac{1}{R_L} \right), \tag{5.19}$$

whence

$$\Delta E_{R_L} = \frac{\sigma \, \Delta F R_L}{1 + R_L/r_p}. \tag{5.20}$$

If $r_p \gg R_L$, this reduces to

$$\Delta E_{R_L} = \sigma \, \Delta F R_L. \tag{5.21}$$

If ΔF is sinusoidal and the effective value of the variation of F is given by F', the effective voltage across R_L is given by

$$E_{R_L} = \sigma F' R_L. \tag{5.22}$$

Example. Consider a vacuum phototube in series with a load resistance of 16.7 megohms and a d-c source of 200 v. The sensitivity σ is assumed to be 20 μa per lumen, and $F = 0.4$ lumen. The practical equivalent circuit is shown.

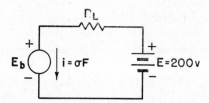

The iR_L drop $= iR_L = \sigma F R_L = 20 \times 10^{-6} \times 0.4 \times 16.7 \times 10^6 = 133.7$. Thus the tube voltage E_b, is $200 - 133.7 = 66.3$ volts. These answers check closely with the graphical solution using curve C in Fig. 5-17, which is for the same problem.

5.17   The Gas Phototube

The general physical construction of the gas phototube is similar to that of the vacuum tube with the exception of the gas which is introduced into the envelope.

In considering the use of the gas it might be well to review the function of gas in a thermionic tube. A thermionic vacuum tube is operated under space-charge limitation. This means that an excess of electrons is being emitted from the cathode, and the number reaching the anode is determined by the amount required to cancel the electric field near the cathode. The electrons in transit which cancel the field are called the space charge, and thus the tube is said to operate under space-charge saturation. The introduction of gas and its ultimate ionization, although it produces additional electrons and positive ions, is not of use because of these free charges. Rather, due to the great difference in mass of the electron and the positive ion, the electrons are removed from the field more rapidly, and a net positive charge is left. These positive charges cancel the negative space charge of the electrons in transit and give the field near the cathode a large positive value. Under these conditions the tube current must be limited externally.

In the vacuum phototube all electrons emitted are drawn to the anode, or the tube is considered to be operated under light saturation. Thus the mere canceling of the space charge set up by these electrons could not lead to an increased current. Rather, the additional electrons and positive ions available from collisions make the gas phototube current greater than that of a vacuum phototube. From this consideration it is desirable that the electrons freed by collisions be able to attain sufficient energy to ionize other atoms, and in turn the electrons of these collisions should ionize still more atoms. This process would be most effective if the ionization potential of the gas were low. If the positive ions are also to produce ionizing collisions they should have low molecular weight. Unfortunately, low ionization potential and low molecular weight do not go together. A compromise is usually made by using argon. Another action of the light must also be considered. In phototubes the light flux takes the place of the grid action of the vacuum triode. In a gas thermionic tube the grid has control only until the tube fires. This trigger action is not desirable in the phototube. It is required that the current at all times be some continuous function of the light. This condition corresponds to the operation of cold-cathode tubes in the nonself-maintaining discharge region. If this is to be true in the gas phototube, the positive ions must never attain sufficient energy to remove on the average one electron from the cathode by bombardment for every electron avalanche. Such operation places a limit on the maximum plate voltage that may be applied to the tube. It is usually of the order of 90 volts as compared to the 300 to 400 volts of the vacuum phototube. If this voltage is exceeded, the glow characteristic of the self-maintained discharge appears. This is known as the glow region.

5.18 Gas Phototube Characteristics

Consideration will now be given to the volt-ampere and associated characteristics of the gas phototube. Consider that a certain constant light is illuminating the cathode. As the plate voltage is increased from zero the emitted electrons are attracted to the anode. At very low values of voltage the current is determined by negative space charge. A region of voltage then follows in which all the emitted electrons are reaching the plate, and the additional voltage serves only to increase their velocity and hence their kinetic energy. Although up to this time each electron possesses some kinetic energy, none has sufficient energy to ionize a gas molecule if a collision occurs. A further increase in plate voltage results in a few electrons ionizing gas molecules before they reach the plate. Since the total current up to this time has been limited by the light emission, these added ions show up as an increase in the current. As the voltage is increased, the process multiplies rapidly and the slope of the current curve increases. If additional voltage were applied, a point would soon be reached where the positive ions would cause sufficient secondary emission for the discharge to become self-maintaining, and a glow would appear. Since this condition is not desirable, the voltage is kept below this glow point.

A typical set of curves for a series of light values is shown in Fig. 5-20. It can be seen from Fig. 5-20 that the current in the operating range is not independent of plate voltage as was true in the vacuum tube. However, the magnitude of the current is approximately 8 to 10 times greater. The ratio of the current for a stated light in a gas tube to that in the same tube without gas is called the gas amplification factor. A plot of current versus lumens for various plate voltages is shown in Fig. 5-21.

There is also a time lag in response that is not seen in the vacuum tube. The time necessary for emission to take place is so short that it may be neglected. However, in the gas tube considerable time is required for the ionization products to build up. For a square wave of incident light Fig. 5-22 shows the relative response of the vacuum and gas types.

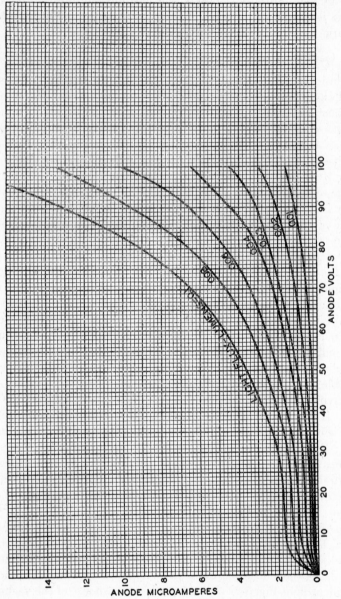

Fig. 5-20. Characteristics of 1P41 gas phototube. (Courtesy of Radio Corporation of America.)

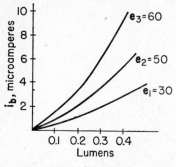

Fig. 5-21. Curves of output current versus luminous flux for gas phototube.

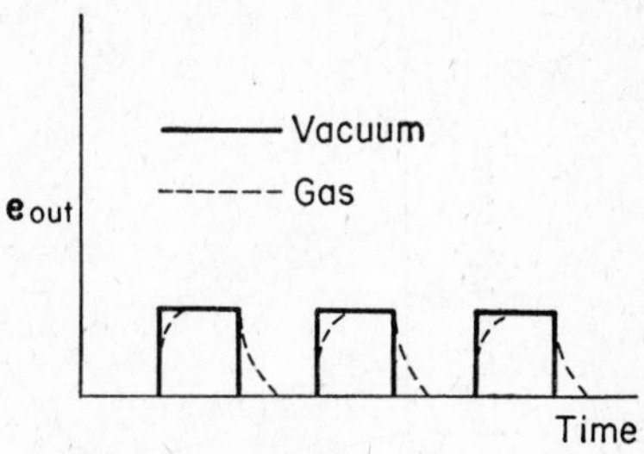

Fig. 5-22. Time response of vacuum and gas phototubes to square light waves.

5.19 Fundamental Circuit of Gas Phototube

The basic circuit of the gas phototube, as for the vacuum phototube, consists of the tube, a d-c supply, and a load resistor. The solution of the current and the voltage division can be most easily obtained by use of the load line. Figure 5-23(a) shows a typical plot of the volt-ampere characteristic of a gas tube with several load lines. Figure 5-23(b) shows the plot of the output voltage across the load as a function of light.

Figure 5-23(b) shows that the output is not a linear function of the light flux. Therefore, this tube is limited to applications such as "on-off" relays where linearity is not an important feature. The gas phototube is an application in which r_p cannot be considered infinite but must have a finite value which can be evaluated for the particular point of operation from the characteristic curves.

Example. If a load resistance of 10 megohms is placed in series with a gas phototube and a supply voltage of 100 v, what is the voltage change across the resistance if the light changes from 0.04 to 0.06 lumen? The characteristics of the gas tube are assumed to be those of Fig. 5-23.

The graphical solution using the load line gives the answer directly to be 11v. This is undoubtedly easier and more correct where possible than the analytical solution. However, the analytical solution follows as an example of its use. From Eq. 5.20,

$$\Delta E_{R_L} = \frac{\sigma R_L\, \Delta F}{1 + R_L/r_p}.$$

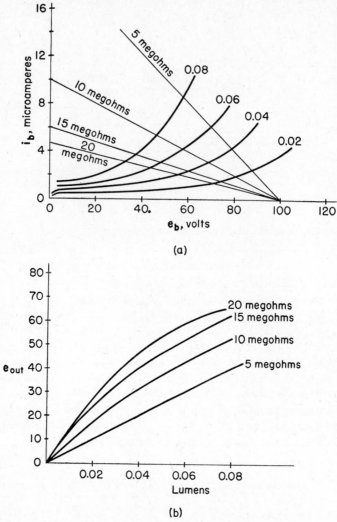

Fig. 5-23. Characteristics of gas phototube.

σ is approximately 150 μa per lumen; ΔF is 0.02 lumen; $R_L = 10 \times 10^6$ ohms; $r_p = 7.5 \times 10^6$ ohms at the estimated operating point. Therefore

$$\Delta E_{R_L} = \frac{150 \times 10^{-6} \times 0.02 \times 10 \times 10^7}{1 + 10^7/(7.5 \times 10^6)} = 12.9 \text{ v.}$$

The two solutions are in close enough agreement to be useful.

5.20   Multiplier Tubes

An important class of phototube is known as the multiplier tube, which takes its name from its method of operation. Although the initial emission, and hence the control, is due to photoemissive effects, the multiplying effect in the tube is an application of secondary emission rather than of photoemission.

A light-sensitive cathode is used from which emission is obtained by the same photoemissive effect that has already been discussed. These electrons are then accelerated by an electric field to a plate called a dynode. This plate is coated with material well suited to secondary emission, so that each bombarding electron causes the emission of several more electrons. All these electrons are then accelerated to a second dynode and the process is repeated. The common tube in present use has nine dynodes. From the last dynode the electrons are accelerated to a plate which serves the same purpose as the plate of any tube.

As might be expected, large gains or current amplifications are possible. Since the process of secondary emission is very rapid and linear as a function of the number of bombarding electrons, this process carried on in a vacuum tube leads to a linear response at the output plate. The gain is, however, a function of the voltage between dynodes. The tube has great use in modulated-light applications where the large load resistor of the conventional phototube is made impossible because of leakage currents through the stray capacitances. In the multiplier tube a large linear gain is obtained without the use of high-gain amplifiers.

In use the last dynode serves as the conventional cathode and the plate as the anode. Using these two electrodes, the circuit is quite similar to that for the vacuum phototube. A separate source is usually provided to supply the voltage to the preceding dynodes. Figure 5-24(a) shows the output volt-ampere characteristics of a typical tube. From the values given it can be seen that gains of the order of 0.2×10^6 to 10^6 can be obtained over the conventional vacuum phototube. A plot of this gain as a function of voltage per stage is shown in Fig. 5-24(b).

5.21   Methods of Controlling Electron Paths in Multiplier Tubes

Two methods used to control the electron path in a multiplier tube will be discussed here. One is the use of shields, baffles, and

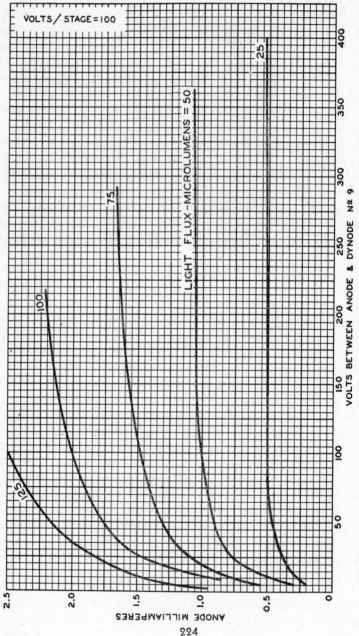

Fig. 5-24. (a) Characteristics of a 931-A multiplier tube. (Courtesy of Radio Corporation of America.)

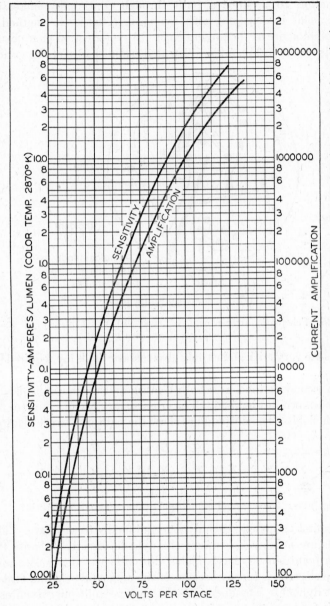

Fig. 5-24. (b) Characteristics of a 931-A multiplier tube. (Courtesy of Radio Corporation of America.)

225

construction to produce a path through continually increasing electric fields interspersed with dynodes. This is the method in most common use at the present time. A cross section view of such a tube is shown in Fig. 5-25. The angles and shapes of the various

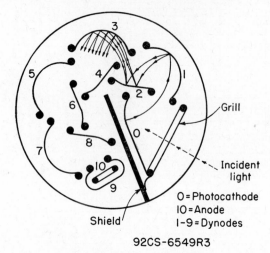

92CS-6549R3

Fig. 5-25. Schematic arrangement of type 931-A. (Courtesy of Radio Corporation of America.)

dynodes are very critical, but only electrostatic fields are required for operation.

The second method uses both electric and magnetic fields. A sketch is shown in Fig. 5-26. The crosses show the direction of the magnetic field. The dotted lines show the path of a single electron

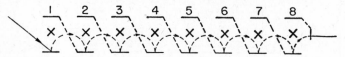

Fig. 5-26. Cross section of multiplier tube using magnetic field.

from the first cathode to each dynode and finally to the plate. The electrons are accelerated toward the dynode directly opposite the emission point since it has a higher d-c voltage. In transit, however, the electron is turned because of the magnetic field and strikes the next dynode. The operation of this type multiplier requires a magnetic field and therefore is not as convenient as the first type.

5.22 Phototube Circuits

Having completed a rather brief coverage of the theory of photo-electric emission and phototube characteristics, it is possible to consider some of the practical circuits in which this phenomenon has found application. Any circuit that makes use of the fundamental properties of phototubes is of course a phototube circuit. No attempt will be made to discuss all possible applications, but a few of the more common ones will be studied to form the basis for a large number of applications.[3]

5.23 The D-C Relay

One of the simplest and most useful applications of the phototube is the use of the fundamental circuit discussed in Sec. 5.14 to change

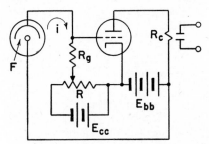

Fig. 5-27.   Forward control circuit.

the bias of a vacuum thermionic triode. This produces an accompanying change in plate current that may be used to open or close a relay. The thermionic tube is necessary since the magnitude of current in the phototube itself is not sufficient to operate even the most sensitive relay. The polarity of the grid voltage change when light hits the phototube determines whether the relay current goes up or down. If an increase in light results in a more positive grid and hence a larger plate current, the circuit is classified as a forward control circuit. If light increase results in the opposite effect it is known as a reverse circuit. Examples of these circuits are shown in Fig. 5-27 and Fig. 5-28.

In the circuit of Fig. 5-27 an increase in the light flux F results in a current i which produces a voltage drop across R_g. The bias for

[3] Richter, Walther, *Fundamentals of Industrial Electronic Circuits*, McGraw-Hill Book Company, Inc., New York, 1947.

the triode is determined by the setting of the potentiometer R. Other things remaining constant, the sensitivity of the circuit is determined by the setting of R and the value of R_g. The larger the negative bias is made, the more light is required to make the grid sufficiently positive to operate the relay.

Frequently the triode is operated in its linear range. In calculating the circuit constants several things must be kept in mind. The voltage E_{bb} must be sufficient to ensure operation of the amplifier tube in the desired region and also to operate the phototube in its proper range. If these two requirements cannot be met, some type of voltage divider is necessary so that the two supplies are not identical. The constant bias required depends upon the triode, on

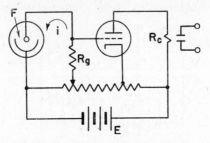

Fig. 5-28.   Reverse control circuit.

whether the light is normally off or only dimmed, and on the amount of light change obtainable.

In most circuits the tubes are chosen first, so that the supply voltages may then be determined. The light source and the amount of its variation are either known or may be chosen. The voltage change due to the light variation may be solved for from the characteristic curves of the phototube and a load line or from the sensitivity of the phototube.

Example.   Consider a phototube with a sensitivity of 20 μa per lumen. The light source may change from 0.1 to 0.15 lumen. The triode should be biased at -10 volts to have a plate current just under the drop-out current of the relay, and may be assumed to require a grid change of 3 volts to close the relay. It is obvious that a change of light of 0.05 lumen must change the grid voltage 3 volts.

The change of 0.05 lumen causes a current change in the phototube of $0.05 \times 20 = 1$ μa.

The required voltage change Δe_g is

$$\Delta e_g = i_p R_g = 3 = 1 \times 10^{-6} R_g.$$

$$R_g = 3 \times 10^6 \text{ ohms.}$$

The voltage across R must be the sum of the 10 volts bias and the voltage across R_g for minimum light.

$$e_{R_g} = 3 \times 10^6 \times 0.1 \times 20 \times 10^{-6} = 6 \text{ volts.}$$

Therefore the bias across R must be 16 volts.

Reference to the reverse circuit of Fig. 5-28 shows that a similar set of calculations would be required with proper regard to signs, since the effect of the phototube is opposite to that of the preceding example. Although in these two circuits the relay armature is either closed or opened by the increase of light flux, the contacts of the relay may be normally open or closed; thus either circuit could be used in a relay problem. The circuit of Fig. 5-27 does not require the large potentiometer of Fig. 5-28, and a smaller voltage supply may be used. However, a bias voltage is required, and the same voltage must be used on both the triode and the phototube.

Many other circuits may be built using the fundamental circuit of phototube, d-c supply, and resistor, but the same type of calculation would be required. These examples are therefore considered sufficient for this type of circuit.

5.24   The A-C Relay

The use of a phototube in an a-c operated relay amounts to controlling the grid of a triode so that it may or may not act as a half-wave rectifier. Either a gas or vacuum triode may be used for this purpose provided its rating is sufficient to handle the peak and average currents. In this treatment only the gas tube application will be considered. This seems warranted because of the comparative ease of analysis and the fact that most practical circuits use gas tubes.

The basic a-c operated circuit appears in Fig. 5-29. In this circuit grid rectification is used to bias the tube off when no light is present on the phototube. With light present, the phototube not only discharges the capacitor C, but recharges it so that the net grid voltage is sufficiently positive to fire the triode. A more complete analysis will be considered in the following paragraphs.

The magnitude of the current that the average phototube can carry is small, so that the size of the capacitor C and the magnitude of the voltage e_g should both be small.   In the analysis of this circuit the following approximations will be assumed.

1. The phototube P conducts as long as its plate is positive and light strikes its cathode.

2. The capacitor is assumed to be perfect.

3. The gas triode T is assumed to be a perfect rectifier between plate and cathode and grid and cathode.

4. The self-impedance of the transformer winding provides adequate grid current limitation.

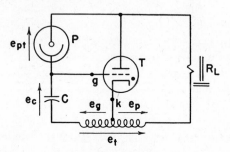

Fig. 5-29.   A-c operated phototube relay circuit.

Figure 5-30 shows the various instantaneous voltages that are of importance in the analysis of the circuit.   Consider first a period of time during which the phototube is dark.   Assume the circuit to be energized just as the voltage e_g is passing through zero and is becoming positive.   The tube T cannot conduct between plate and cathode, since the voltage e_p is becoming more negative.   However, since the grid and cathode may act as a rectifier, conduction takes place and the capacitor C is charged negatively to the peak value of e_g during the first quarter cycle.   The total grid voltage $e_{kg} = e_g +$ e_c remains at zero.   During the next quarter cycle the capacitor cannot discharge, because of the rectifying properties of the tube, and the value of e_{kg} becomes negative.   The next half cycle is the period during which e_p is positive, and the tube could fire.   However, the curves of Fig. 5-27 show that the grid is negative not only by the amount of the voltage e_c but also the value of e_g, which is negative. Thus no conduction takes place.   This cycle, with the exception of the charging of C, is repeated as long as light does not make the phototube conductive.

Assume now that light is directed onto the phototube at time t_1. The voltage $e_{pt} = e_t - e_c$ is negative, and hence the phototube cannot conduct. Therefore the same cycle as before continues to repeat until e_t is just equal to e_c. Beyond this point e_{pt} has a positive value, and the phototube conducts. Since the value of e_{kg} is negative, all current conducted by the phototube comes from C, and C is discharged at a constant rate depending upon the amount of light on the phototube. Subsequently the capacitor is completely

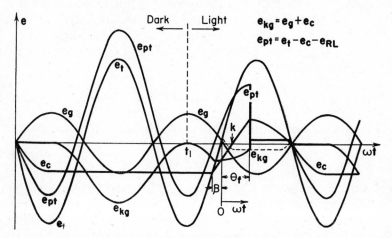

Fig. 5-30.   Instantaneous voltages in Fig. 5-26.

discharged and starts to charge with the opposite polarity as shown at point k. The plot of e_{kg} then crosses the critical firing curve and the tube T fires. As long as the tube is firing, grid and cathode are at the same potential, so that $e_{kg} = 0$. At the end of the quarter cycle under consideration $e_c = 0$, $e_t = 0$, $e_{pt} = 0$, the thyratron current becomes zero, and the phototube stops conduction. Conditions are now identical with those when the circuit was first considered, and tube T may or may not fire during the next cycle depending upon whether or not the phototube is illuminated.

The period of conduction of tube T, when p is illuminated, obviously depends upon R_L, e_p, e_g, C, and the light. All other things remaining constant, the greater the light flux falling on the phototube the more quickly C discharges and the longer is the period of conduction.

A variation in the circuit is the addition of a resistor in parallel with the grid capacitor C. For purposes of analysis this resistor gives the effect of a leaky capacitor. It is suggested in problem 5.9 that the student study the effect of this added resistor by sketching curves similar to those of Fig. 5-30.

The a-c circuit is sometimes referred to as a phase shift circuit because of its effect on the grid voltage, but it is more fundamentally analyzed from the instantaneous point of view used here.

Referring to Fig. 5-30 it is of interest to calculate the firing angle θ_f in terms of the circuit constants, or to calculate the value of C required to give a certain average plate current or firing angle θ_f.

For a resistive load the average plate current I_{dc} may be found as follows, neglecting tube drop.

$$I_{dc} \cong \frac{E_{pm}}{2\pi R} \int_{\theta_f}^{\pi} \sin \omega t \, d\omega t = \frac{E_{pm}}{2\pi R} [1 + \cos \theta_f]. \qquad (5.23)$$

If the average current required is known, solution for $\cos \theta_f$ yields

$$\cos \theta_f = \frac{2\pi R I_{dc}}{E_{pm}} - 1. \qquad (5.24)$$

For aid in designing the circuit constants, the firing angle θ_f must be evaluated in terms of the circuit values.

Referring again to Fig. 5-30, let $-\beta$ equal the angle at which the phototube starts conduction measured from the new reference, $\omega t = 0$. From the curves,

$$-E_{gm} = +E_{tm} \sin (-\beta) \qquad (5.25)$$

or $$\sin \beta = \frac{E_{gm}}{E_{tm}} = \frac{e_g}{e_t}. \qquad (5.26)$$

In words, $\sin \beta$ is the fraction of the total supply voltage that is used to supply the grid.

The slope of the discharge curve e_c is

$$\frac{de_c}{dt} = \frac{\sigma F}{C} \qquad (5.27)$$

during discharge. For the period during which the phototube is conducting with ωt measured from the point at which e_p starts positive

$$e_{kg} = -E_{gm} \sin \omega t + \frac{\sigma F}{C}\left(\frac{\omega t}{\omega} + \frac{\beta}{\omega}\right) - E_{gm}, \qquad (5.28)$$

or $\qquad e_{kg} = \frac{\sigma F}{\omega C}(\omega t + \beta) - E_{gm}(1 + \sin \omega t). \qquad (5.29)$

If the tube is assumed to fire when $e_{kg} = 0$ and the firing angle is represented by θ_f,

$$E_{gm}(1 + \sin \theta_f) = \frac{\sigma F}{\omega C}(\beta + \theta_f), \qquad (5.30)$$

or $\qquad \dfrac{\sigma F}{\omega C E_{gm}} = \dfrac{1 + \sin \theta_f}{\beta + \theta_f}. \qquad (5.31)$

The solution of Eq. 5.31 is most easily accomplished by plotting, and this has been done in Fig. 5-31.

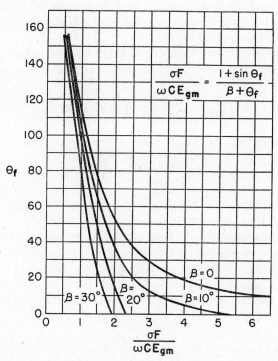

Fig. 5-31.   Plot of Eq. 5-31.

With the angles β and θ_f known from the circuit and the required current, the value of $\sigma F/\omega CE_{gm}$ can be read from the curves. From this result the required value of C can be found for a given photo-tube and light source, or the light source found for a given phototube and capacitor.

The ratio of $e_g/e_t = \sin \beta$ is arbitrary in the circuit design, as long as $2E_{gm}$ is sufficiently large to keep the thyratron from firing during the dark period.

The circuit as shown in Fig. 5-29 gives at best a pulsating current through the relay coil. Although the average plate current may be sufficiently high to keep the relay closed, the instantaneous current is much greater than this for part of one half cycle, and zero for the remaining part of the cycle. This results in considerable chatter of the relay even if the contacts do not actually open.

This condition may be rectified by adding a filter capacitor C_L in parallel with the relay coil. It is of interest to calculate the size of the capacitor necessary to keep the relay coil current greater than the opening value at all times.

Neglecting all circuit inductance, if θ_f is 90° or less, the maximum current in the relay coil R_L occurs when e_p is maximum, and is equal to

$$I_{L\,max} = \frac{E_{pm}}{R_L}. \qquad 0 \leqq \theta_f \leqq 90°. \qquad (5.32)$$

If θ_f is greater than 90°, $I_{L\,max}$ occurs at the time the tube fires and is

$$I_{L\,max} = \frac{E_{pm} \sin \theta_f}{R_L}. \qquad 90° < \theta_f \leqq 180°. \qquad (5.33)$$

Assume that $I_{L\,min}$ is the drop-out current of the relay and that it is desirable that the current never go below this value. The current decreases exponentially from its peak value for slightly less than one full cycle, depending on θ_f. Since a factor of safety is desirable, the slightly larger value of C_L resulting from the assumption that the exponential period is $2\pi/\omega$ is satisfactory. The expression for the current in the relay coil during the exponential decrease is

$$i_L = I_{L\,max}\epsilon^{-t/R_LC_L}. \qquad (5.34)$$

Substituting the period $2\pi/\omega$ and the minimum current $I_{L\,min}$ gives

$$I_{L\,min} = I_{L\,max}\epsilon^{-2\pi/\omega R_LC_L}, \qquad (5.35)$$

or
$$\frac{I_{L\,max}}{I_{L\,min}} = \exp\left(\frac{2\pi}{\omega R_L C_L}\right). \tag{5.36}$$

Taking the natural logarithm of both sides,

$$\frac{2\pi}{\omega R_L C_L} = \ln \frac{I_{L\,max}}{I_{L\,min}}. \tag{5.37}$$

Solution of Eq. 5.37 for C_L gives the minimum value of capacitance to maintain sufficient current,

$$C_{L\,min} = \frac{2\pi}{\omega R_L \ln\left(I_{L\,max}/I_{L\,min}\right)}. \tag{5.38}$$

It should be obvious that the same peak current and thus approximately the same average current result for any firing angle between $0°$ and $90°$. Therefore the circuit is designed to make θ_f some value between $0°$ and $90°$, and C_L is found from Eq. 5.38 with $I_{L\,max}$ given by Eq. 5.32.

$$I_{L\,max} = \frac{E_{p\,max}}{R_L}.$$

If a filter capacitor is added across R_L, the voltage across R_L no longer necessarily goes to zero during the period just preceding phototube conduction, and thus this load voltage must be considered in determining e_{pt}. Therefore

$$e_{pt} = e_t - e_c - e_{R_L}.$$

If it is assumed as an approximation that $e_{R_L} = I_{L\,min}R_L$ during the period determining the firing point of the phototube and until the thyratron fires,

$$e_{pt} = e_t - e_c - I_{L\,min}R_L.$$

At the start of phototube conduction

$$e_{pt} = 0,$$

$$e_t = E_{tm} \sin\left(-\beta\right),$$

and

$$e_c = -E_{gm}.$$

Therefore $E_{tm} \sin\left(-\beta\right) + E_{gm} - I_{L\,min}R_L = 0.$

Thus $$\sin (\beta) = \frac{-I_{L\,min}R_L + E_{gm}}{E_{tm}},$$

or $$\beta = \sin^{-1} \frac{E_{gm} - I_{L\,min}R_L}{E_{tm}}.$$

This value of β may now be used with the curves of Fig. 5-31.

5.25 Circuits for Measurements of Illumination

The measurement of light might be conveniently divided into two classes.   First is the measurement of total light, which is similar to the values obtained by the standard light meter for photographic purposes.   The second is a comparison reading where it is desired to compare one light with another.   The first kind of measurement will be discussed in this section and the second in Sec. 5.26.

For the measurement of total light the simplest procedure is to measure the phototube current directly with a very sensitive microammeter.   The sensitivity can be adjusted by varying a resistance in parallel with the movement.

If a circuit is desired in which a less sensitive meter may be used, amplification is required.   The simplest circuit is that used for d-c relay operation with a milliammeter substituted for the relay coil. This circuit, however, has two basic disadvantages which it is important to overcome.   First, the scale is nonlinear because of the transfer characteristic of the triode, or else there is a finite plate current with zero illumination.   Second, the calibration of the scale depends upon the tube and upon any plate supply changes such as aging of the battery or changes in line voltage.   This means that a calibration must be made for each tube, and the supply voltage must be carefully checked.   Although this is possible and will work, it is certainly undesirable.

The circuit of Fig. 5-32 shows a way of balancing out the operating point current so as to permit operation of the triode in its linear range.   In order that the total change in plate current shall appear mostly through the meter, the resistance R must be many times the resistance of the meter.   Although this circuit eliminates the nonlinearity of the simple circuit, it is still dependent upon the constancy of E_k and therefore must be balanced before each use.

A third circuit which tends to minimize both the nonlinearity and the aging is shown in Fig. 5-33.   The principle of balancing out the operating point current is used again as in Fig. 5-32, but it is accomplished by the use of two tubes operating from a common d-c supply. If the two tubes are identical, any change in supply voltage, and hence in plate current, affects equally the voltage drops in

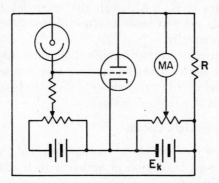

Fig. 5-32.   Circuit for measurement of illumination balancing out zero current.

the load resistances of both tubes.   Double triodes with a common cathode are often used in this application, since any change in cathode emission then affects both by the same amount.   The potentiometer P makes it possible to balance out small differences in the two tubes and thus produce zero current in the meter for any

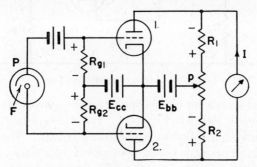

Fig. 5-33.   Balanced illumination measuring circuit.

light value that may be considered as reference.   An increase in light flux F on the phototube results in an increase in current through R_{g1} and R_{g2}.   The resulting grid voltage changes are indicated by $+$ and $-$ signs.   Thus the plate current of tube 1 increases, and that of tube 2 decreases.   It is assumed that both tubes operate in their linear range. The polarities of the resulting voltage changes across the load resistors are shown. The circuit is no longer balanced, and a current I results. The sensitivity and range of the circuit depend upon the sensitivity of the meter, upon the tubes, and upon the values of R_g. Although the values of R_g may be left variable, this is not advisable because of the difficulty in always adjusting them equally.

A great many circuits may be built that utilize the response of the phototube and the gain of the vacuum tube for measuring light. These circuits serve only as examples to show the basic problems and certain methods of overcoming them.

5.26 Comparison Light Circuits

It may often be desirable to compare two light values continuously and have an indication or action if their *difference* or *ratio* exceeds a certain limit.

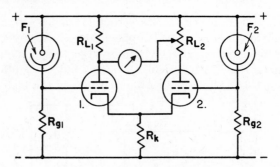

Fig. 5-34.   Light comparison circuit.

A typical circuit for comparing two light sources and indicating their *difference* is shown in Fig. 5-34. It consists of two triodes each having its grid controlled by a phototube circuit. The changes in grid potentials appear as voltage changes of their plates, and may be indicated by the meter. The tap on R_{L2} makes it possible to balance out any differences in the two tubes. *This circuit measures the absolute difference of light fluxes F_1 and F_2 regardless of what percentage this difference represents in terms of either F_1 or F_2.* Thus if both light sources were 1 lumen and one changed by 0.01 lumen, the meter would read the same as if each source had been 10 lumens and the change 0.01 lumen.

A resistance may be substituted for one phototube, and the resulting grid potential may serve as a reference even though there is no second light source. This device is often more convenient than maintaining a constant reference light. This circuit has the disadvantage of being linear only over small light variations or at a small sensitivity.

Another circuit which measures absolute light difference but which is more linear over large ranges takes advantage of the small but definite rise in the volt-ampere characteristic of the vacuum phototube. Although the characteristic curve of a vacuum phototube is usually considered to be flat after light saturation is reached, it actually has a slight rise due to the effect on the cathode of the

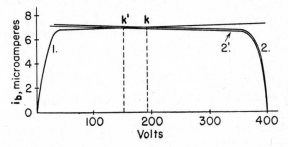

Fig. 5-35.   Enlarged characteristics of two vacuum phototubes.

increased potential. This effect is shown highly exaggerated in Fig. 5-35. For further discussion the curve of a second tube has also been shown on a negative voltage scale.

The two phototubes are used in series to form a voltage divider. If the tubes are identical and have equal illumination they divide the voltage equally as shown by the point k on Fig. 5-35. A slight change in the illumination of either tube results in a large change in the voltage of the point k by shifting the characteristic of the tube up or down. This shift is shown in Fig. 5-35, where the characteristic of tube 2 shifts downward so that k moves to k'. On the scale this is a change of approximately 45 volts. The sensitivity of such a combination is so high that it is usually difficult to keep the two values of light flux being compared within the linear range of the system.

A circuit making use of such a combination is shown in Fig. 5-36. The point k serves to determine the potential of the grid, and thus determines the current in the plate.   The distinct advantage of this circuit is that the phototubes divide the voltage equally well with any value of light within their emission range, and give the same

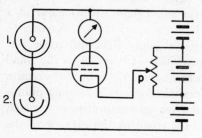

indication for a magnitude change.   The bias on the triode may be adjusted by the potentiometer P so that the tube operates in its linear range.

Because of the great sensitivity of this circuit it is often impossible to use it in a practical application.   It is therefore necessary to provide some means of reducing this sensitivity.   For this purpose it is

Fig. 5-36.   Comparison circuit making use of the voltage division principle.

of interest to study the volt-ampere characteristics of a phototube and resistance in parallel.   The total current of such a combination is the sum of the two currents.   These currents are shown separately and added in Fig. 5-37.   If two such combinations are placed in series as a voltage divider, it can be seen from Fig. 5-38 that the sensitivity has been greatly reduced and is now essentially

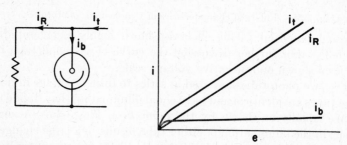

Fig. 5-37.   Characteristic curves of phototube resistor combination.

a function of the resistors.   The values of resistance in this combination are naturally high and offer the difficulty of keeping them balanced if the sensitivity is to be changed by varying the resistors.

Still another circuit making use of the voltage division principle but requiring only one variable to change sensitivity is shown in Fig. 5-39.   Here the two phototubes conduct in opposite directions through the variable resistance R.   The voltage across R is then a

function of the difference in the two phototube currents.   This voltage becomes the variable grid voltage of the triode.   Only R need be
varied to adjust sensitivity.

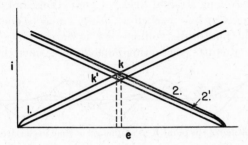

Fig. 5-38.   Curves of two phototube resistors acting as voltage dividers.

As was mentioned at the beginning of the section on light-comparison circuits, it is sometimes required to compare the ratio of
two lights rather than their absolute difference as the previous
circuits have done.   The fundamental principle used in the circuit
of Fig. 5-40 is well adapted to this type of measurement.   The
voltage across the phototubes and capacitor is alternating.   Suppose

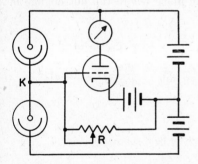

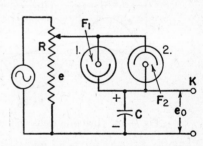

Fig. 5-39. Light-comparing cir-   Fig. 5-40. Circuit giving voltage
cuit having one variable to adjust   output proportional to the ratio of
sensitivity.   two light sources.

first that the two tubes and two light sources are identical.   During
the half cycle in which the anode of tube 1 is positive, conduction
proportional to F_1 charges C to the polarity shown.   During the
next half cycle tube 2 discharges C.   If the two sources of light are
equal the circuit settles down in a few cycles to a point where one
tube removes as much charge as the other puts in and the average

voltage across C is zero. A curve of this charging and discharging cycle is shown in Fig. 5-41 by the solid lines. Since the phototube current is constant and independent of plate voltage, the capacitor voltage varies along straight lines. Conduction can take place only until the capacitor has reached a voltage equal to the supply voltage, since the phototube voltage then is zero. The second phototube, however, starts conducting immediately, since the net voltage

Fig. 5-41.   Voltage of the point K as a function of time in the circuit of Fig. 5-40.

of the supply and capacitor is such as to make its plate positive. The dotted lines of Fig. 5-41 indicate the case in which the light on tube 1 is less than that on tube 2. Under this condition tube 2 charges C more rapidly than tube 1 can discharge it, and a net voltage is left on C. The polarity of this voltage is such as to reduce the conduction time of tube 2 and increase that of tube 1. The average voltage continues to increase until the conduction period of the tubes has been adjusted to the place where the net change of

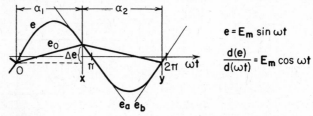

Fig. 5-42.   Instantaneous voltages for light-comparison circuit.

charge per cycle is zero. Thus the average voltage on C is a function of the ratio of the two sources. This voltage may of course be read directly or used to bias the grid of a tube.

In the circuit of Fig. 5-40 it is of interest to know how the average value of e_o varies with F_1 and F_2 and how much it differs from a pure d-c voltage. One cycle of steady-state operation is shown in Fig. 5-42.

In the vicinity of the zero voltage intercepts it is permissible to represent the sine wave of voltage by the two straight lines e_a and

e_b. The equations of these lines are

$$e_a = -E_m\alpha + E_m\pi \tag{5.39}$$

and $$e_b = E_m\alpha - 2E_m\pi. \tag{5.40}$$

Assuming that the charging and discharging curves representing e_o are straight lines, the average value of the voltage e_o is

$$e_{o\ avg} = E_{dc} = \frac{e_a]_x + E_b]_y}{2}. \tag{5.41}$$

Substitution of the expressions for e_a and e_b gives

$$E_{dc} = \frac{-E_m x + E_m\pi + E_m y - 2E_m\pi}{2}$$

or $$E_{dc} = \frac{E_m}{2}(-\pi + y - x). \tag{5.42}$$

From Fig. 5-42 it can be seen that $y - x = \alpha_2$. Therefore,

$$E_{dc} = \frac{E_m}{2}(\alpha_2 - \pi). \tag{5.43}$$

Also, $$\pi = \frac{\alpha_1 + \alpha_2}{2},$$

so that $$E_{dc} = \frac{E_m}{4}(\alpha_2 - \alpha_1). \tag{5.44}$$

This result does not give E_{dc} in terms of F_1 and F_2 as desired. Under steady-state operation, the average current through C must be zero. During the period α_1, the charge increases by

$$\Delta q_1 = \frac{\sigma F_1\alpha_1}{\omega}, \tag{5.45}$$

where σ is the sensitivity in amperes per lumen, and F is the flux in lumens. Similarly, during α_2

$$\Delta q_2 = \frac{-\sigma F_2\alpha_2}{\omega}. \tag{5.46}$$

Since the net change in charge must be zero per cycle,

$$\Delta q_1 + \Delta q_2 = 0 = \frac{\sigma F_1\alpha_1}{\omega} - \frac{\sigma F_2\alpha_2}{\omega}. \tag{5.47}$$

Hence
$$F_1\alpha_1 = F_2\alpha_2. \tag{5.48}$$

From this result,
$$F_2\alpha_2 - F_1\alpha_1 = 0 = F_2(\alpha_2 - \alpha_1) - \alpha_1(F_1 - F_2), \tag{5.49}$$

or
$$\alpha_2 - \alpha_1 = \alpha_1\left(\frac{F_1}{F_2} - 1\right). \tag{5.50}$$

Substituting Eq. 5.50 into Eq. 5.44 gives
$$E_{dc} = \frac{E_m\alpha_1}{4}\left(\frac{F_1}{F_2} - 1\right). \tag{5.51}$$

If F_1/F_2 is nearly unity,
$$\alpha_1 \cong \pi, \tag{5.52}$$

since $F_1/F_2 = \alpha_2/\alpha_1$ and $\alpha_1 + \alpha_2 = 2\pi$. Thus, for $F_1/F_2 \cong 1$, Eq. 5.51 becomes
$$E_{dc} = \frac{E_m\pi}{4}\left(\frac{F_1}{F_2} - 1\right). \tag{5.53}$$

Equation 5.53 shows that E_{dc} varies linearly with F_1/F_2 and in proportion to E_m as long as F_1/F_2 is nearly unity. It is usually desired to operate the circuit in this linear region.

It is desirable to design the circuit for the smallest possible ripple voltage Δe in Fig. 5-42. From Eq. 5.45,
$$\Delta e = \frac{\Delta q_1}{C} = \frac{\sigma F_1\alpha_1}{\omega C}. \tag{5.54}$$

Therefore to decrease the ripple, C must be increased. For given values of flux F, sensitivity σ, and allowable voltage ripple Δe, the required capacitance is
$$C = \frac{\sigma F_1\alpha_1}{\omega\,\Delta e},$$

and if $\alpha_1 \cong \pi$,
$$C \cong \frac{\sigma F_1\pi}{\omega\,\Delta e}. \tag{5.55}$$

5.27 Modulated Light Receivers

It is assumed that the reader has a knowledge of audio amplifiers, so that only the means of getting the signal from the phototube to the first grid of an amplifier need be studied. Probably the most common use of the phototube for the detection of modulated light is in the sound motion picture in which the sound tracks are part of the film. The intelligence here is in the audio range, and therefore any conventional amplifier may be used to amplify the signal. The phototube, a load resistance, and a d-c supply are used. However, another circuit element so far neglected becomes of importance in the audio frequency range. This is the interelectrode capacity between the anode and cathode of the phototube. The complete circuit appears in Fig. 5-43. The values of R and C depend upon the circuit and upon how much of it is included.

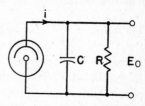

Fig. 5-43. Equivalent circuit of phototube.

R may or may not include the grid resistance of the first amplifier, and C may or may not include the first tube's grid-to-cathode capacitance. Before the output voltage E_o becomes useful, these circuit elements must be considered, but here the analysis will be carried on with the general values R and C.

Consider the light flux F to have the form

$$F = F_c + F_m \sin \omega t. \qquad (5.56)$$

For our purposes only the a-c component need be considered. Therefore

$$F' = F_m \sin \omega t. \qquad (5.57)$$

Since the phototube is essentially a current generator, the current i is equal to the light flux F' multiplied by the sensitivity σ of the phototube; therefore

$$i = \sigma F' = \sigma F_m \sin \omega t. \qquad (5.58)$$

The voltage $\dot{E}_o$ is equal to the product of the effective current $\dot{I}$ and the impedance of the R-C parallel combination.

$$\dot{E}_o = \dot{I}\dot{Z}. \qquad (5.59)$$

Since
$$\dot{Z} = \frac{-jRX_c}{R - jX_c}, \tag{5.60}$$

$$\dot{E}_o = \frac{-j\dot{I}RX_c}{R - jX_c}. \tag{5.61}$$

Equation 5.61 may be squared and expressed as

$$\dot{E}_o{}^2 = \frac{\dot{I}^2 R^2/(\omega^2 C^2)}{R^2 + 1/(\omega^2 C^2)} \, \underline{/2\phi}, \tag{5.62}$$

where $\phi = \tan^{-1}(-R/X_c) = -\tan^{-1} R\omega C$.

Therefore
$$\dot{E}_o = \frac{\dot{I}R}{\sqrt{R^2\omega^2 C^2 + 1}} \, \underline{/\phi}. \tag{5.63}$$

It can be seen from Eq. 5.63 that if R is small compared with X_c, $\dot{E}_o \cong \dot{I}R$, which is the desired condition. Also from Eq. 5.62 the phase shift angle approaches zero as R is made small. Thus the use

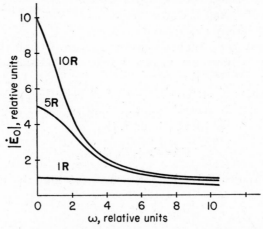

Fig. 5-44.   Response curve of R-C circuit to constant current.

of a large resistance, as was found desirable in the fundamental phototube circuit, is undesirable here because of frequency response and phase shift. A general response curve versus frequency for various values of R is shown in Fig. 5-44. The circuits discussed in this chapter serve only as examples of application of the fundamental principles involved. The engineer may never find use for the circuits as they appear. However, it is hoped that by their study he will become familiar with the methods used and be able to combine them into the type of circuit needed.

PROBLEMS

5.1. A certain cathode material has a work function of 4 electron volts. What is the threshold wavelength?

5.2. A vacuum phototube has a sensitivity of 18 μa per lumen for the light source being used. A resistive load of 10 megohms is used with a power supply of 300 v. What light change is required to produce a change of 4 v across R_L?

5.3. A particular phototube has a cathode area of 1 sq in. and it is found from the characteristic curves that 0.4 lumen is required for operation. The source is to be a 30-cp auto lamp, and is located at a distance of 6 ft from the tube. (a) If no lens, is used, calculate the light falling on the cathode, assuming that no external light is present and the source is a point. (b) Using the same dimensions and a lens whose diameter is 1 in., calculate the maximum focal length of the lens required just to operate the tube, assuming perfect transmission.

5.4. Design a complete circuit for the operation of a 931 multiplier tube including rectifier and an output amplifier. Specify value and wattage of all components.

5.5. A certain photovoltaic cell is being used as a light meter in conjunction with an ammeter of 3 ohms internal resistance. The exposed surface of the cell is a circle of 1-in. radius. In a certain application a beam of light is to be measured that is also circular but has a radius of $\frac{5}{8}$ in. If the meter reads 70 ft-c, what is the actual average light intensity in the measured beam?

5.6. Find the constant by which the current scale of Fig. 5-12 must be multiplied if the light source is changed from tungsten at 2870°K to the following. Assume the response of the eye and the tube are given in Fig. 5-7 and Fig. 5-10.

A	% rel. energy	A	% rel. energy
3000	0	7000	100
4000	6	8000	15
5000	25	9000	2
6000	65		

5.7. In the circuit to the right it is found that F may be conveniently varied from 0.2 to 0.3 lumen. This increase of light is to close the relay R_c, which is to be open at the low value. Suggest values of R_g and E_{cc} if the relay pickup current is 6.5 ma, and the drop-out current is 2.0 ma. Use curves of Fig. 5-12.

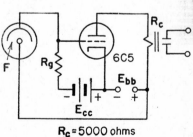

$R_c = 5000$ ohms
$E_{bb} = 300$ volts

Prob. 5.7

5.8. In the circuit below an average current of 0.25 a is required to close the relay. This value includes a safety factor sufficient for design purposes. The gas tube is a 2050. The light flux F when on the tube is 0.3 lumen. If $E_1 = 700$ v and $E_2 = 100$ v, what should be the value of C to just operate the relay?

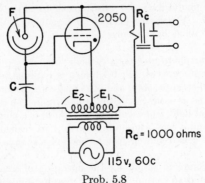

Prob. 5.8

Assume the load on the gas tube to be resistive, neglect the tube drop, and assume the grid firing voltage to be zero. Also assume that the phototube conducts full current as soon as its plate is made positive. Use the characteristics of Fig. 5-12.

5.9. Refer to the circuit of Fig. 5-29. Add a resistor R in parallel with C. For this condition make a careful sketch of the same instantaneous voltages which are shown in Fig. 5-30, taking into account any changes the added resistor may make.

5.10. The interelectrode capacitance of a certain phototube is 30 $\mu\mu$f. A resistive load of 100,000 ohms is to be used. Express the alternating output voltage across this resistor if the light is sinusoidally modulated. F_{max} of the a-c component is 0.2 lumen, and the frequency is f. The tube's sensitivity is 15 μa per lumen. Find the value of f at which the output voltage has dropped to 70.7 per cent of its maximum value.

5.11. In the circuit of Fig. 5-34 assume that $r_{p1} = r_{p2}$, and $R_{L1} = R_{L2}$. Let the resistance of the meter be R and the tube amplification factors be μ. Let the meter current be I. (a) What value of R will make I a maximum? (b) What value of R will make IR a maximum? (c) Show that if R is very small,

$$I \cong \frac{\mu \, \Delta E_g}{2r_p}.$$

(d) Show that if R is very large,

$$IR \cong \frac{\mu \, \Delta E_g R_{L1}}{R_{L1} + r_p}.$$

Here ΔE_g is the difference between the two grid voltages. (e) Show that in general, for any R,

$$I = \frac{\mu R_L \, \Delta E_g}{R(R_L + r_p) + 2R_L r_p}.$$

(f) Show that $\Delta E_g = \sigma R_g(\Delta F_1 - \Delta F_2)$.

5.12. The circuit is to be used to convert light from a source modulated at audio frequencies into a varying voltage. Assuming that the voltage across

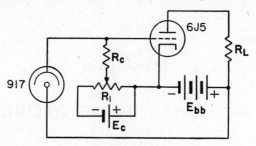

Prob. 5.12

the 917 never falls below 50 v and that the 6J5 operates in the linear region of its characteristics determine: (a) An equation for the a-c voltage across R_L in volts per lumen of incident light to the 917.

If the incident light is $F = 0.3 + 0.2 \sin \omega t$ lumens, find: (b) Suitable values for E_{bb} and E_c. (c) Suitable values for R_c, R_1, and R_L. (d) What should be the value of negative bias on the 6J5?

5.13. Assuming the gas tube to fire when $e_{kg} = 0$, solve for the values of C and C_L if θ_f is to be $65°$.

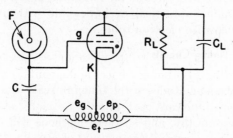

$$R_L = 5000 \; \Omega \qquad F = 0.05 \text{ lumen}$$
$$e_t = 120 \text{ rms} \qquad \sigma = 20 \; \mu a/\text{lumen}$$
$$e_g/e_t = 0.1 \qquad i_{\text{drop out}} = 5 \text{ ma.}$$
$$f = 60 \text{ cps}$$

Prob. 5.13

5.14. Referring to Fig. 5-40, $F_1/F_2 = 1.01$. The sensitivity of the phototubes is 20 μa per lumen, the supply voltage e_p is 200 v rms at 60 c. (a) What is the average value of e_o? (b) What value should C have in order that the ripple factor of e_o be 1 per cent? $F_1 = 0.01$ lumen.

CHAPTER 6

INDUSTRIAL TIMING CIRCUITS

Many electronic circuits used in industrial applications involve timing circuits in one form or another. The fundamental nature of electron tubes makes them naturally adaptable to the measurement or marking off of time intervals which are short by comparison with a period of, say, 1 second. The additional fact that electron tubes can be made to control large amounts of power has permitted the development of control circuits for industrial processes and equipment which were impractical or impossible without the precise control available with electron tubes.

6.1 Types of Timing Circuits

One way to classify timing devices and circuits is to divide them according to the magnitudes of the time intervals which they are to measure. Time intervals of 1 minute or more are usually not measured electronically, and so these methods will be mentioned here only to place them in this method of classification. Usually for such time intervals a mechanical clock or a synchronous motor-driven device is used. Occasionally, where precision is not required, a thermal device can be used, such as a bimetal strip and a heating element. For intervals between 1 minute and 1 second, the synchronous motor, thermal devices, or one of many adaptations of the R-C circuit may be used. Here the R-C circuit may or may not involve vacuum tubes. For intervals from 1 second to 0.01 second duration, R-C circuits involving either high-vacuum or gas tube circuits are widely used, and frequently relays of some kind form part of the timing circuit. Where it is necessary to measure time intervals of the order of 0.01 second or less a number of devices are used.

The multivibrator[1] may be used in this way. It is really, in its simplest forms, a more sophisticated combination of R-C circuits and vacuum tubes. The wave shaping techniques[2] so well developed during World War II can be used in certain types of timing problems. For intervals of the order of 1 to 100 microseconds, techniques involving the velocity of propagation of a wave along a transmission line can be used in some applications.

These are only a few of the devices used for timing purposes, and it will be apparent that to cover them all adequately would require a work of great size. Only the devices involving electron tubes will be discussed here, and of these only the ones most widely used in industry have been chosen.

6.2 Direct Current Operated R-C Circuits

Figure 6-1 shows a very simple time delay relay involving an R-C circuit. Here the relay in the plate circuit is normally open, that is, the contacts are open when no current flows through its winding. With the switch closed the bias voltage E_{cc} is large enough so that little or no plate current flows through the relay. When the switch is opened the bias voltage across R decreases ex-

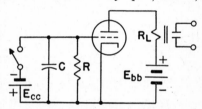

Fig. 6-1.   R-C time delay circuit.

ponentially toward zero, and the anode current increases. If the tube, which may be a triode, tetrode, pentode, or a gas tube, and the other circuit elements and voltages are properly chosen, the relay closes at a time after the opening of the switch which depends upon the product RC. The operation of the circuit and prediction of the time delay is made clear by reference to Fig. 6-2 in the case where the tube used is a high vacuum triode, tetrode, or pentode. Since the tube is a nonlinear element, the simplest procedure is a graphical one. First plot from the plate characteristics of the tube a curve of plate current i_b versus grid voltage e_c for known values of relay resistance and plate supply voltage E_{bb}. The tube and plate supply must be

[1] Reich, H. J., *Theory and Applications of Electron Tubes*, 2d ed., McGraw-Hill Book Company, Inc., New York, 1944, pp. 362–365.
[2] M.I.T. Radar School Staff, *Principles of Radar*, McGraw-Hill Book Company, Inc., New York, 1946, Chapter II.

selected so as to give a current at zero bias larger than the current required to close the relay.   The grid bias supply E_{cc} must be great enough to limit the anode current to a value less than the drop-out current of the relay.   With the switch closed, the plate or relay cur-

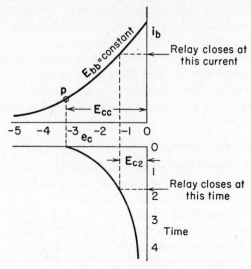

Fig. 6-2.   Method of determining time delay for circuit of Fig. 6-1.

rent is the value at point p.   When the switch is opened the bias voltage decays according to Eq. 6.1.

$$e_c = E_{cc}\epsilon^{-t/RC}. \tag{6.1}$$

As this voltage decays, the plate current increases, and when the current reaches the value indicated, the relay closes.   The value of e_c required to produce the closing current is attained in a time which depends upon the product RC.   Let the closing value of e_c be E_{c2}. Then the time delay T is given by

$$E_{c2} = e_c|_{t=T} = E_{cc}\epsilon^{-T/RC}$$

Solution for T gives

$$T = RC \ln \frac{E_{cc}}{E_{c2}}. \tag{6.2}$$

The above argument is based on the assumption that the relay has negligible inductance, that E_{bb} is constant, and that the relay closing time is either zero or is negligible compared to the total time delay.

If the i_b versus e_c characteristic is assumed to be a straight line in the range of the pickup current, as is shown in Fig. 6-3, a simple mathematical analysis of the problem is possible, which, although not rigorous, is nevertheless useful. The assumption of a straight line for the i_b versus e_c curve implies straight, parallel, equidistant

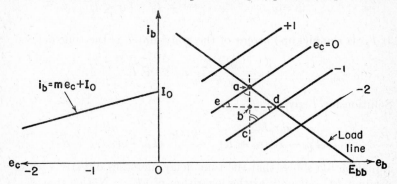

Fig. 6-3.   Approximate analysis of time delay relay.

plate characteristics, several of which are shown. The equation of the i_b versus e_c curve is of the form

$$i_b = me_c + I_0, \tag{6.3}$$

where I_0 is the plate current at zero bias. The slope m can be found from the following analysis:

$$m = \frac{\Delta i_b}{\Delta e_c} = \frac{ab}{1} = ab.$$

Triangle abe is similar to triangle bcd.   Therefore

$$\frac{ab}{be} = \frac{bc}{bd} = \frac{1}{r_p}.$$

Also

$$\frac{ab}{bd} = \frac{1}{R_L},$$

and

$$bc + ab = g_m.$$

$$ab = \frac{bd}{R} = \frac{bc}{R} r_p = \frac{(g_m - ab)r_p}{R_L}.$$

Therefore

$$m = ab = g_m \frac{r_p}{r_p + R_L}. \tag{6.4}$$

Hence $i_b = g_m \dfrac{r_p}{(r_p + R_L)} e_c + I_0$. This result may also be obtained by use of the equivalent a-c plate circuit. Now substitute Eq. 6.1 for e_c:

$$i_b = g_m \frac{r_p E_{cc}}{r_p + R_L} \epsilon^{-t/RC} + I_0 \qquad 0 \le t.$$

If I_{pu} is the pickup current of the relay and T is the time delay,

$$I_{pu} = \frac{g_m r_p E_{cc}}{r_p + R_L} \epsilon^{-T/RC} + I_0.$$

Solution for T gives

$$T = RC \ln \frac{g_m r_p E_{cc}}{(I_{pu} - I_0)(r_p + R)} = RC \ln \frac{\mu E_{cc}}{(I_{pu} - I_0)(r_p + R_L)}. \quad (6.5)$$

Equation 6.5 shows that the time delay increases directly with the product RC but only as the logarithm of μE_{cc}. Notice that E_{cc} is negative, as is the difference $I_{pu} - I_0$. The above analysis is valid only under the assumption that the closure time of the relay is either zero or negligible compared to the total delay. If this assumption is not true, a more careful study including the relay closing time and probably the effect of the inductance of the relay must be made. However, it is unusual to use a relay where precise measurement of short time intervals is necessary. Thyratrons are frequently used in place of the relay contacts for such applications.

Occasionally it is convenient to use a gas tube in the circuit of Fig. 6-1. In that case Eq. 6.2 gives the time delay if E_{c2} is taken to be the grid voltage at which the thyratron fires.

6.3 Alternating Current Operated R-C Circuits

In many applications of time delay circuits it is desirable to eliminate the d-c power supply required in circuits of the type previously discussed. There are many such a-c operated circuits in use in industrial equipment, and they have proved to be rugged, simple in construction, and reliable. Figure 6-4 shows the basic elements required for one such circuit. Many actual circuits differ from this in detail and complexity, but most of them operate on the same fundamental principles that apply here. The circuit is shown with a thyratron, because the analysis of this circuit is somewhat simpler than if the tube were a high-vacuum type. The operation of the circuit will be described with the aid of Fig. 6-5. All voltages in Fig. 6-5 are referred to point k. For simplicity it is assumed that when either the grid or the anode conducts there is no drop from the conducting electrode to the cathode. As long as

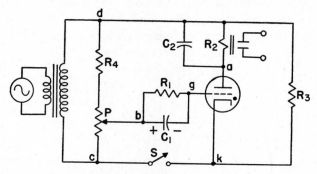

Fig. 6-4. Simple a-c operated time delay circuit. (From G. M. Chute, *Electronics in Industry*, McGraw-Hill Book Company, Inc., New York, 1946.)

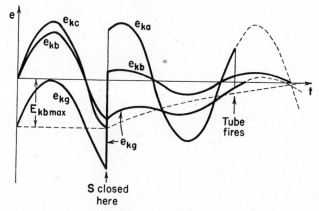

Fig. 6-5. Voltages of various points on Fig. 6-4.

switch S is open, capacitor C_1 is charged to the polarity shown in Fig. 6-4 by current flowing from grid to cathode of the thyratron. Again for simplicity it is assumed that R_3 is negligible compared with R_1, and that R_1 does not discharge C_1 appreciably in one cycle as long as S is open. These assumptions later are abandoned, and the resulting complexities of the circuit analysis are discussed in Sec. 6.4.

It is also assumed that the potential of the tap on potentiometer P remains unchanged by the transient. Under these assumptions, the potentials of points c, b, and g vary as shown in Fig. 6-5. The potential across C_1 is constant and equal to the maximum value of e_{kb} before S is closed. Since the tube cannot carry current, and since R_3 is assumed small compared to R_1, point a is at cathode potential before S is closed. If S is closed at some random point in the cycle, the voltages with respect to k of points a, b, c, and g change. The potential of the anode a now varies sinusoidally with respect to k. At first the tube cannot fire, however, because the

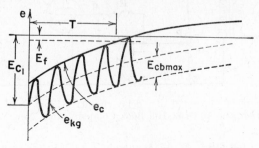

Fig. 6-6.   Variation of thyratron grid voltage during time delay period.

grid is biased negatively by the charge on C_1. In addition to this charge the a-c voltage e_{cb} is present. Immediately after S closes, the grid charging of C_1 ceases, and C_1 begins to discharge exponentially through R_1. Hence the grid voltage consists of a negative and exponentially decreasing component plus an a-c component. When the d-c component of bias gets small enough, the thyratron fires, the relay closes, and the grid loses control. The capacitor C_2 is connected across the relay coil R_2 to prevent chatter of the relay. It should be large enough to maintain some current through the relay during the half cycle when the thyratron is not conducting.

For the purpose of analyzing the circuit, Fig. 6-5 has been re-drawn in Fig. 6-6 with time counted from the moment the switch is closed. The rate of discharge of C_1 is assumed smaller than in Fig. 6-5. The critical firing voltage of the grid is E_f, and the time delay is T. *T is assumed to be the time at which the envelope of the a-c voltage e_{kg} intersects the curve of critical firing voltage E_f.* Although this is not actually the case, T computed in this way is as accurate as the performance of the circuit, since there is no way of knowing where in the cycle the switch S is closed. This fact limits the accuracy with which this circuit can repeat itself to $\pm\frac{1}{2}$ cycle of the supply voltage. Therefore the shortest time delay for which this circuit is suitable is of the order of two or three periods of the supply voltage alternation, and even here the percentage variation of delay in a number of operations may be quite large. The tolerable variation is of course determined by the application. The equation for the envelope voltage e_c is

$$e_c = -E_{C1}\epsilon^{-t/R_1C_1} + E_{cb\ max},$$

where E_{C1} is the initial voltage of C_1. T may be found by setting this equation equal to $-E_f$:

$$-E_f = -E_{C1}\epsilon^{-T/R_1C_1} + E_{cb\ max},$$

$$T = R_1C_1 \ln \frac{E_{C1}}{E_f + E_{cb\ max}}. \tag{6.6}$$

Under the assumptions stated in this section, E_{C1}, the initial d-c voltage across C_1, is equal to the maximum value of e_{kb} before S is closed, or $e_{db\ max}$. A more realistic computation of E_{C1} is carried out in Sec. 6.4.

    With the above circuit a given time delay may be achieved with a large R_1C_1 product and a small value of initial bias voltage E_{C1}, or by a small R_1C_1 product and a large value of E_{C1}. For practical reasons the latter is preferable, because if a given time delay is achieved with a large voltage E_{C1}, the slope of the envelope e_g at the intersection of the envelope with the critical firing voltage curve is greater than if the same delay is achieved with a small voltage E_{C1} and a large product R_1C_1. The greater the slope at the intersection, the less do variations in line voltage (and hence in the a-c component of e_{kg}) affect the delay time. Consider again the equation for the envelope voltage e_g:

$$e_g = -E_{C1}\epsilon^{-t/R_1C_1} + E_{cb\ max}. \tag{6.7}$$

The slope m of this curve may be found for any time t by differentiating Eq. 6.7 with respect to time. Thus

$$\frac{de_g}{dt} = m = \frac{E_{C1}}{R_1C_1}\epsilon^{-t/R_1C_1}.$$

If this is evaluated at time T,

$$m|_T = \frac{E_{C1}}{R_1C_1}\epsilon^{-T/R_1C_1}. \tag{6.8}$$

Now from Eq. (6.7),

$$E_{C1}\epsilon^{-T/R_1C_1} = E_f + E_{cb\ max}.$$

Thus by combining the last two equations,

$$m|_T = \frac{E_f + E_{cb\ max}}{R_1C_1}. \tag{6.9}$$

From Eq. (6.9) it is apparent that the slope m at the time T is inversely proportional to R_1C_1. Thus R_1C_1 should be as small as is practical and still satisfy Eq. (6.6), which indicates that E_{C1} must be increased as R_1C_1 is decreased to maintain a constant value of T.

At this point it is desirable to digress from the discussion of the timing circuit as a whole and examine in detail a method of calculating the bias voltage appearing across C_1 of Fig. 6-4.

6.4 Analysis of Grid Biasing Circuits

In the circuit of Fig. 6-4 the capacitor C_1 is charged through a series circuit consisting of R_3 and the rectifier. This combination is found in some form in a great many industrial circuits, and so a careful analysis has been made.[3] The circuit may be resolved into the one shown in Fig. 6-7. The battery voltage V represents the magnitude of the tube drop, such as the constant drop across a gas tube. The voltage e is the source voltage, an alternating electromotive force. R represents any series resistance, and may include, in addition to any series resistance deliberately introduced into the circuit, a fictitious resistance added to approximate the volt-ampere characteristic of the grid and cathode of a high-vacuum tube. In many instances it may be unnecessary to add the tube resistance or the voltage V in order to obtain a sufficiently accurate result, because often these quantities are negligible compared with other resistances and voltages. The rectifier element is considered to be an ideal rectifier in Fig. 6-7.

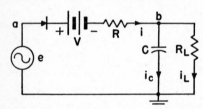

Fig. 6-7. Equivalent circuit of grid rectifying circuit.

[3] The analysis of grid biasing circuits is based upon a thesis by H. R. Weed, submitted in partial fulfillment of the M.Sc. requirements at the Ohio State University, Electrical Engineering Department, 1948.

In Fig. 6-8 are sketched the wave forms of voltages at points a and b of Fig. 6-7. In the sketch the effect of V was neglected. The angles α_1 and α_2 are the angles, measured from zero value of e_a, where the rectifier starts and stops conducting, respectively. It will be noticed that because of the voltage dividing action of R and R_L, the peak value of e_b is always less than the peak value of e_a, even

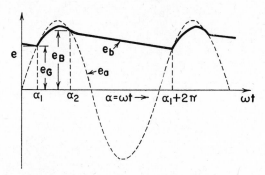

Fig. 6-8.   Voltage wave forms for Fig. 6-7.

for a perfect rectifier. In the interval between α_1 and α_2 when C is being charged, e_b depends in a complicated way on R, R_L, C, and frequency. In the interval between α_2 and $\alpha_1 + 2\pi$, the voltage e_b is simply an exponential decay curve.

The analysis may be divided into two parts, one for the period when the tube is not conducting and one for the period when the tube is conducting. For the period when $\alpha_2 \leq \alpha \leq \alpha_1 + 2\pi$:

Let e_B = initial voltage across C at $\alpha = \alpha_2$,

$$e_a = E_m \sin \alpha,$$

$$\alpha = \omega t = 2\pi f t.$$

Then $i_L = -i_c.$ $\hspace{3cm}$ (6.10)

$$i_L R_L = \frac{1}{C} \int_{\alpha_2/\omega}^{\alpha/\omega} i_c \, dt + B. \hspace{2cm} (6.11)$$

$$i = 0. \hspace{3cm} (6.12)$$

Simultaneous solution of these equations for i_L gives

$$i_L = \frac{e_B}{R_L} \epsilon^{-(\alpha - \alpha_2)/\omega C R_L}. \hspace{2cm} (6.13)$$

Now define
$$\omega C R_L = \frac{R_L}{X_c} = \tan \lambda_2, \qquad (6.14)$$

and note that $e_B = E_m \sin \alpha_2 - V$. Then

$$i_L = \frac{E_m \sin \alpha_2 - V}{R_L} \epsilon^{-(\alpha - \alpha_2) \cot \lambda_2}. \qquad (6.15)$$

Now consider the period when $\alpha_1 \leq \alpha \leq \alpha_2$. Let G be the capacitor voltage when $\alpha = \alpha_1$.

$$E_m \sin \alpha = iR + i_L R_L + V. \qquad (6.16)$$

$$i_L R_L = \frac{1}{C} \int_{\alpha_1/\omega}^{\alpha/\omega} i_c \, dt + G. \qquad (6.17)$$

$$i = i_L + i_c. \qquad (6.18)$$

The solution of these equations is conveniently carried out by use of the Laplace transform, but it may also be done by classical methods. By differentiating Eq. 6-17 and by proper substitutions into Eq. 6.16 we get an equation involving only i_L.

$$\frac{di_L}{dt} + \frac{R + R_L}{R R_L C} i_L = \frac{E_m}{R R_L C} \sin \omega t - \frac{V}{R R_L C}. \qquad (6.19)$$

Solution of Eq. 6.19 gives

$$i_L = \frac{E_m}{Z_1} \sin (\alpha - \alpha_1) - \frac{V}{Z_1 \cos \lambda_1}$$

$$+ \left[i_1 + \frac{V}{Z_1 \cos \lambda_1} - \frac{E_m}{Z_1} \sin (\alpha_1 - \lambda_1) \right] \epsilon^{-(\alpha - \alpha_1) \cot \lambda_1} \qquad (6.20)$$

where $\tan \lambda_1 = \dfrac{\omega C R R_L}{R + R_L}$.

$$Z_1 = [(\omega C R R_L)^2 + (R + R_L)^2]^{1/2}.$$

$$i_1 = \frac{E_m \sin \alpha_1 - V}{R_L}.$$

Equations 6.15 and 6.20 give the current i_L in the load resistance R_L in the two intervals which comprise the cycle. If α_1 and α_2 were known, i_L would be known, and the average voltage across C or R_L could be computed. Two equations involving α_1 and α_2 may be obtained by setting Eqs. 6.15 and 6.20 equal to each other at $\alpha = \alpha_2$ and $\alpha = \alpha_1 + 2\pi$. If this is done and certain rearrangements are made the following two equations result.

$$\frac{\sin \alpha_1 - V/E_m}{\sin \alpha_2 - V/E_m} = \epsilon^{(\alpha_2 - \alpha_1 - 2\pi) \cot \lambda_2}. \tag{6.21}$$

$$\frac{\sin \alpha_1 \tan \lambda_2 - \dfrac{V}{E_m} \tan \lambda_1 - \dfrac{K}{2} [\cos (\alpha_1 - 2\lambda_1) - \cos \alpha_1]}{\sin \alpha_2 \tan \lambda_2 - \dfrac{V}{E_m} \tan \lambda_1 - \dfrac{K}{2} [\cos (\alpha_2 - 2\lambda_1) - \cos \alpha_2]}$$

$$= \epsilon^{(\alpha_2 - \alpha_1) \cot \lambda_1} \tag{6.22}$$

Here
$$K = \frac{R_L}{R}. \tag{6.23}$$

Solution of Eqs. 6.21 and 6.22 for α_1 and α_2 in terms of circuit parameters is impossible. Certain simplifications can be made, however, which permit a solution to be obtained by plotting. The voltage V is almost always either zero or small in comparison, say, to E_m. Hence to a good approximation it may be considered zero. With this assumption, and with the definition $\delta = \alpha_2 - \alpha_1$, which is the conduction angle, Eqs. 6.21 and 6.22 may be manipulated so that each yields an expression for $\tan \alpha_1$,

$$\tan \alpha_1 = \frac{\sin \delta}{\epsilon^{-(\delta - 2\pi) \cot \lambda_2} - \cos \delta}. \tag{6.24}$$

$$\tan \alpha_1 =$$
$$\frac{K \sin^2 \lambda_1 [\cos \delta - \epsilon^{-\delta \cot \lambda_1}] + \sin \delta [\tan \lambda_2 - K \sin \lambda_1 \cos \lambda_1]}{K \sin^2 \lambda_1 \sin \delta - [\tan \lambda_2 - K \sin \lambda_1 \cos \lambda_1][\cos \delta - \epsilon^{-\delta \cot \lambda_1}]}. \tag{6.25}$$

Equating these two expressions for $\tan \alpha_1$ gives Eq. 6.26.

$$\frac{\sin \delta (1 + \epsilon^{(\delta K + 2\pi) \cot \lambda_2})}{\cos \delta (1 + \epsilon^{(\delta K + 2\pi) \cot \lambda_2}) - \epsilon^{\delta(1+K) \cot \lambda_2} - \epsilon^{-(\delta - 2\pi) \cot \lambda_2}}$$
$$= \frac{K \tan \lambda_2}{\tan^2 \lambda_2 + 1 + K}. \tag{6.26}$$

This equation is of the form

$$f(\delta, \lambda_2, K) = g(\lambda_2, K). \tag{6.27}$$

Since λ_2 and K are determined by circuit parameters, Eq. 6.27 becomes, for any particular set of parameters,

$$f(\delta) = \text{a constant.} \tag{6.28}$$

Equation 6.28 may be solved for δ by plotting $f(\delta)$ against δ and determining in this way the value of δ for which Eq. 6.28 is satisfied. With the conduction angle δ known for a given set of parameters, α_1 may be found from Eq. 6.24. Hence $\alpha_2 = \delta + \alpha_1$.

Equations 6.15 and 6.20 now give the value of i_L in the two intervals $\alpha_2 \leq \alpha \leq \alpha_1 + 2\pi$ and $\alpha_1 \leq \alpha \leq \alpha_2$, respectively. The average or d-c voltage across C or R_L can then be found from $I_{L\,dc}$.

$$E_{dc} = I_{L\,dc}R_L = \frac{R_L}{2\pi} \left(\int_{\alpha_1}^{\alpha_2} i_{L_1}\, d\alpha + \int_{\alpha_2}^{\alpha_1+2\pi} i_{L_2}\, d\alpha \right) \tag{6.29}$$

Here i_{L_1} is current through R_L in interval $\alpha_1 \leq \alpha \leq \alpha_2$, and i_{L_2} is current through R_L in interval $\alpha_2 \leq \alpha \leq \alpha_1 + 2\pi$. After integration and simplification, Eq. 6.29 becomes

$$\frac{E_{dc}}{E_m} = \frac{1}{2\pi}\left(\frac{K}{1+K}\right)[\cos \alpha_1 - \cos \alpha_2 + \tan \lambda_2(\sin \alpha_2 - \sin \alpha_1)]. \tag{6.30}$$

The use of the ratio E_{dc}/E_m gives an equation involving only dimensionless ratios, so results obtained from Eq. 6.30 are applicable to any circuit of the type for which this result was obtained and for any supply voltage. Equation 6.30 is plotted in Fig. 6-9 against λ_2 for various values of K. This figure displays very well the effects of varying one or more of the parameters. Increasing ω and increasing $R_L C$ both have the same effect of increasing the d-c bias voltage. Increasing the ratio $R_L/R = K$ also increases the d-c bias voltage, but increasing K beyond about 10 does not result in much increase in bias. At this point the product $\omega C R_L$ becomes the most important factor in determining the bias. It will be noticed that when $R = 0$, or $K = \infty$, and $C = 0$, $E_{dc} = 0.317 E_m$ which is the average value E_m/π of a half-rectified sine wave of voltage. It will also be noticed that for $K = \infty$ and $R_L = \infty$, $E_{dc}/E_m = 1$. This is the familiar case in which there is no series impedance and no load in parallel with the capacitor, which therefore charges to the peak value of the supply voltage.

With the aid of the curves of Fig. 6-9 the average d-c voltage across the parallel R-C circuit may be obtained. This information, however, is sometimes not all that must be known about the circuit. It is sometimes necessary to know the ripple voltage across C. The true peak-to-peak value of the ripple may of course be obtained from Eq. 6.20 for i_L, the load current. To evaluate this equation requires a knowledge of α_1, the firing angle, which is difficult to calculate.

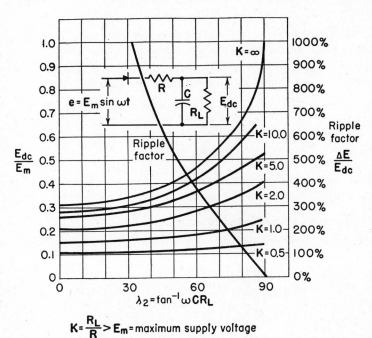

Fig. 6-9.   Calculated voltage, E_{dc}.

However, if an approximation is made, the ripple voltage may be estimated very easily. The approximation amounts to assuming that the wave form of the voltage across C is a sawtooth. This assumption implies that during the discharge period the exponential decay can be approximated by a straight line, and that the charging period is short enough so that the charging can be assumed to be instantaneous. Under these assumptions all the current supplied to the load must come from the capacitor. If ΔE is the peak-to-peak value of the sawtooth voltage, then

$$I_{L\,dc} = C\,\frac{\Delta E}{T} = \frac{E_{dc}}{R_L}.$$

Here T is the period of one complete cycle of the sawtooth, and in the case of a half wave rectifier, $T = 1/f$. Hence

$$\frac{\Delta E}{E_{dc}} = \frac{1}{fR_LC}. \tag{6.31}$$

Equation 6.31 gives a ripple larger than the true value, because it is based on the assumption that the capacitor discharges for a longer time per cycle than it actually does. If the ratio $\Delta E/E_{dc}$ is to be equal to or less than some maximum value r, then

$$r \geqq \frac{1}{fR_LC} = \frac{2\pi}{\omega CR_L}$$

and

$$\omega CR_L \geqq \frac{2\pi}{r}. \tag{6.32}$$

Thus, if the ripple voltage is to be no more than 10 per cent of E_{dc}, $\omega CR_L \geqq 62.8$, or in Fig. 6-9, $\lambda_2 \geqq 89.1°$.

6.5   Practical A-C Operated Time Delay Circuit

We may now proceed with a discussion of a less idealized and more practical a-c operated time delay circuit. Figure 6-10 shows such a circuit. It operates on the same principle as that of Fig. 6-4, which has been discussed in detail. The operation is as follows. With switch S open neither time delay relay $TD1$ nor $TD2$ is energized, but C_1 is charged by the grid biasing action previously described. The capacitor between grid and cathode is a surge-suppressing device to prevent spurious firing of the thyratron by line surges or electrostatic pickup from external sources. It is very small compared to C_1 and may be neglected in calculating circuit performance. R_2 is added to limit grid current to safe values. When the slider on potentiometer P is as far toward R_3 as possible, C_1 charges to its greatest voltage, and maximum time delay results. Also the amplitude of the a-c component of the cathode-to-grid voltage during the time delay is minimum, a factor which tends to increase the delay. When switch S is closed, relay coil $TD1$ is energized, thus closing both sets of contacts marked $TD1$. One of these connects the cathode to one side of the line, and the other connects to any circuit to be controlled by the time delay circuit. The time delay action as described in Sec. 6.3 starts as soon as *TD1* is energized. When the thyratron fires at the end of the time delay, relay *TD2* is energized, thus closing contact *TD2* in parallel with *TD1* contact, and de-energizing *TD1*. As soon as *TD1* is de-energized, both its contacts open, thus ending the time delay period.

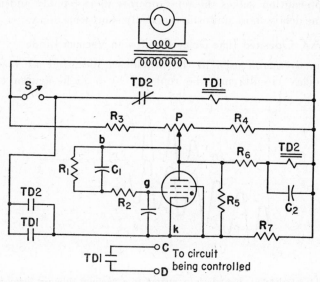

Fig. 6-10. A-c operated time delay circuit. (*Electronics Laboratory Manual for Educational Institutions,* Westinghouse Electric Corporation, East Pittsburgh, Pennsylvania, 1945.)

The thyratron is still conducting, however, and can be stopped only by opening switch *S*. Thereupon *TD2* is de-energized, and the circuit returns to its initial or "ready" condition. Resistor R_6 is used to limit the initial thyratron current, which would otherwise be quite large because of the large capacitor C_2. C_2 serves to maintain a more nearly constant current through the relay *TD2* to prevent chatter. Examination of the thyratron plate circuit shows that exactly the same procedure may be used to design C_2 as was used in computing the bias voltage across C_1, since the circuits are similar. This statement is true if the relay *TD2* be a pure resistance, in which case the method of Sec. 6.4 applies. C_2 should be designed to give an average voltage across $TD2$ equal to the d-c voltage required for reliable operation of the relay. Any inductance which may be present in the relay winding would make the current ripple even smaller, so neglecting the inductance in designing C_2 gives a conservative design. Resistor R_5 is used to provide a small alternating relay current during the time delay period to minimize any residual magnetism in the relay remaining from the previous operation. This precaution makes the relay operate more reliably and makes the time delays more uniform, especially short time delays.

6.6   A-C Operated Time Delay Circuit with Vacuum Triode

The thyratron used in the previously discussed a-c operated time delay circuits may be replaced by a high-vacuum triode,

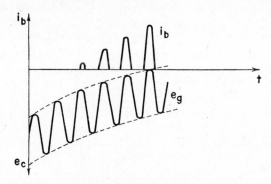

Fig. 6-11.   Grid voltage and plate current in a vacuum tube a-c delay circuit.

tetrode, or pentode. The grid voltage during the time delay period is the same as that of the thyratron. The plate current is a series of pulses which increase, as shown in Fig. 6-11, from low amplitude and duration pulses to larger and longer pulses as the grid bias decreases. When the average plate current becomes large enough, the relay closes. Calculation of the time delay is then largely a matter of determining the average value of plate current at any time. This is a rather complicated problem for several reasons. In the first place the characteristics of the tube are not likely to be linear in the region near cutoff. The anode supply voltage is not constant, but varies sinusoidally with time. If a capacitor is used to smooth the relay current, the computation of the average relay current is still further complicated. For these reasons it is not

considered worth the effort to attempt even an approximate solution
of the problem of determining the time delay in such a circuit. The
designer faced with this problem might best produce a preliminary
design based on the theory for a thyratron, build the circuit using a
vacuum tube, and then make adjustments of circuit parameters
based on a few measurements of time delays. Indeed, the experimental method of circuit design is frequently resorted to in electronics, and it may in many cases be the most practical way to find
suitable answers, because of the ease and speed with which circuit
parameters may be changed.

6.7 Another A-C Operated Time Delay Relay

A slightly different a-c operated relay circuit is shown in Fig. 6-12.
When switch S is open, only transformer $T1$ is energized. Its

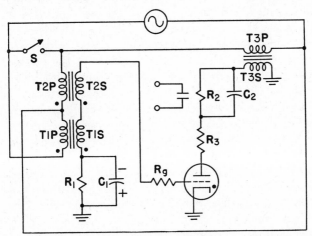

Fig. 6-12. A-c operated time delay relay. (From G. M. Chute, *Electronics in
Industry*, McGraw-Hill Book Company, Inc., New York, 1946.)

secondary, $T1S$, supplies energy to charge C_1 by grid current flow to
the polarity shown. The calculation of this bias voltage has been
discussed in Sec. 6.4. When switch S is closed, transformers $T2$ and
$T3$ are energized. The secondary windings $T1S$ and $T2S$ are
identical and are series connected so that their net voltage is zero.
Thus when S closes, the thyratron anode has applied to it an alternating voltage, and the grid is made negative to the cathode by the
amount of bias on C_1. At the same time the a-c voltage which was

charging C_1 is opposed by the equal and opposite voltage of $T2S$, so that the charging action ceases. Thus the grid voltage consists only of the voltage across C_1. This voltage decays exponentially until the thyratron fires, the time delay being controlled by the product R_1C_1. In this circuit, the only way to change the time delay is to vary R_1, C_1, or both.

6.8   Applications to Resistance Welding—Introduction

Resistance welding embraces that branch of the art of welding in which the heat required for welding is produced by the passage of an electric current through the metals to be welded. In most cases no additional materials such as filler rods or flux are used, although occasionally certain metals are used as a flux to aid in welding difficult materials. Almost all commonly used metals can be resistance welded, although in some cases the difficulties involved make the process commercially impractical. The shapes and sizes of parts which may be resistance welded vary widely from very small wires and thin sheets with dimensions of the order of a few thousandths of an inch to very large sections with diameters or thicknesses of the order of 0.3 inch or more. In every case the resulting weld is a forge weld, that is, a weld resulting from mechanical working of the metal by pressure from the electrodes while the metal is hot. The resulting fine grain structure produces a weld whose strength is at least equal to, if not greater than, that of the parent metal. Because of the flexibility and versatility of resistance welding, and because by proper control great speed and reproducibility can be attained, this method of joining metals has become widespread in a great variety of industries. This wide adoption of resistance welding has been greatly accelerated by the use of precise electronic control of welding equipment. Indeed, the mass production of welded aluminum parts was not practical at all until the development of electronic controls.

6.9   Factors Affecting a Resistance Weld

If an electrical engineer is to design an electronic control for a welder he should have some appreciation of the factors involved in making a successful weld. It is the purpose of this section to outline very briefly some of these factors.

Obviously, if the weld is made by heating the material to be welded by passage of an electric current, the electric resistivity affects the weld. In general, it is true that the greater the resistivity, the more easily a metal can be welded. Thus copper, silver, and aluminum, which have low resistivities, are difficult to weld, whereas most ferrous metals and many of their alloys are relatively easily welded. The thickness and shape of the parts to be joined is of great importance. In general, the thicker the parts to be joined, the more weld current is required. On the other hand, for very thin sheets or small wires, a small current whose duration is precisely controllable is necessary to prevent spattering or exploding the metal. The relative sizes of the parts to be joined constitute a factor affecting the weld. For example, it is in general easier to weld sheets of equal thickness than to weld a very thin sheet to a very thick one. The thermal conductivity of the material is one factor in determining how rapidly heat is carried away from the weld volume. In general, high thermal conductivities are bad. Surface condition is an extremely important factor, since it affects the surface resistance between the metals being welded. A further complication is added by the fact that surface or contact resistance varies with pressure. Finally, the specific heats and heats of fusion of the materials are properties of the material which influence the weld to some extent.

Electrode pressure is found to be quite critical in making reproducible and reliable welds, and in most automatic and semiautomatic welding equipment, the electrode pressures are carefully controlled. Pressure cycling may be necessary. For example, the work may be squeezed for a definite time before weld current flows. Pressure must be exerted during the weld to forge the weld, and there is usually a squeeze period after welding current ceases, to permit cooling without distortion. Pressure and heating cycles may be combined in much more complicated sequences.

The material and shape of the electrodes are very important factors in making successful welds. Usually copper is used. Its high thermal and electric conductivities, the properties which make it difficult to weld, also prevent the electrodes from sticking to the work piece. In large machines the electrodes are usually water cooled when high production rates are necessary.

Other factors must sometimes be considered in making successful welds. The mass of the moving electrode parts must not be so great that the electrodes fail to maintain the proper pressure on the work during the deformation or forging period of the cycle. Thermal expansion and contraction of the work pieces may cause difficulties, such as warping, during the cooling period. Surface dissipation of heat is one of the methods by which heat is carried away from the weld, and it may sometimes affect the success of the weld.

Obviously the magnitude and duration of the weld current and its wave form during the weld are of the greatest importance in making successful welds. In any process which involves as many factors as those mentioned above which may contribute to the success or failure of the process, it is desirable to have as many as possible of these factors under control. Many of the factors in resistance welding are fixed by the materials being welded and by their shape and size. Here a limited control is possible. Such conditions as contact resistance are occasionally difficult to control, but with care fairly reproducible results may be obtained. The duration, magnitude, and shape of welding currents can be controlled to any desired degree of precision by means of electronic devices. This is also true of the automatic control of electrode position and pressure. In such control circuits timing devices play an important part.

6.10   Fundamental Resistance Welding Circuit

Since in any but the smallest resistance welds very large currents at low voltages are required, a transformer is usually used in which the welding electrodes are connected to a 1- or 2-turn secondary winding. Welding is done by connecting the primary to a source of energy, usually a 60-c power line, for the required length of time. Figure 6-13 shows the elements of such a circuit. This circuit uses ignitrons to control the primary transformer current, because in any but small welders the primary current is beyond the range of the largest thyratrons. This connection is called a back-to-back connection.

The operation of the circuit is simple. Neither ignitron can fire until terminals A and B are connected together. When A and B are connected, suppose that terminal M is positive to N, and current then flows through rectifiers 2 and 3 to ignite tube 2. At first the ignitor circuit has the full a-c supply voltage between K_1 and K_2

across it, but as soon as tube 2 fires, the ignitor circuit voltage drops to a small value equal to the drop across tube 2.   The average ignitor current is thus kept low.   The full supply voltage, less tube drop, then appears across the welding transformer primary, and welding current flows.   During this half cycle, rectifier 1 serves to prevent reverse current from flowing through the ignitor of tube 1, since reverse current will damage the ignitor and shorten its life.   The cycle of operation when N is positive to M is apparent.   Thus as

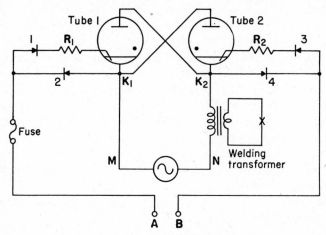

Fig. 6-13.   Ignitron controlled resistance welder circuit.

long as terminals A and B are connected, welding current flows.   It is the function of the timing circuit to close and open the connection between A and B.   The circuit of Fig. 6-10 may be used very well for this purpose.   The terminals marked C and D would connect to terminals A and B of Fig. 6-13.

The fuse in Fig. 6-13 is to protect the ignitor circuits.   If, for example, one of the ignitrons should fail to fire for one or more cycles, the full supply voltage would be applied to the ignitor circuit for one or more complete cycles.   The resulting ignitor current would damage the ignitor, so the fuse is inserted in the ignitor circuit as protection against this possibility.   As an ignitron ages it becomes more and more difficult to ignite, and as it approaches the end of its life it actually refuses to ignite, occasionally at first and then more and more frequently.   Thus frequent blowing of the fuse is usually a sign that an ignitron may soon have to be replaced.

It has already been stated that one of the simplest types of timer for ignitron control is the one shown in Fig. 6-10. As applied to the welder, it is called a nonsynchronous semiautomatic timer. It is called semiautomatic because it merely controls the duration of the weld and does not provide automatic control of the electrodes. It is called nonsynchronous because it does not start the weld at the same point in the cycle of the supply voltage every time a weld is made. The next refinement in the welder control is to provide automatic electrode sequencing. A typical sequence provides a squeeze period before welder current flows, a period during which current flows, a period during which the weld cools before the electrodes open, and a period during which the work is moved into position for another weld. Such a circuit is called an automatic sequence timer. When very short duration welds are required, synchronous control is necessary, and a circuit for this purpose will be discussed. Finally, it may be desirable to limit welding current to a definite part of each cycle in order to control the amount of heat generated in the weld. Such a control is called a heat control. The above devices may be used in various combinations, depending upon the job to be done.

The operation of the nonsynchronous semiautomatic timer has already been discussed in Sec. 6.5.

6.11 Simple Automatic Sequence Timer

Figure 6-14 shows a simple automatic sequence timer. This device utilizes four identical time delay circuits to perform the timing functions of (1) squeezing the work between the electrodes, (2) timing the weld current duration, (3) holding the electrodes against the work until the weld cools, and (4) timing the interval between the end of one welding cycle and the start of the next. Since these four timers are identical, they are shown only in block form, and a detail of them is shown at the lower right of Fig. 6-14. It is the same as the timer of Fig. 6-10 whose operation was discussed in detail in Sec. 6.5.

The sequence of operations is as follows. Closing the starting switch $S1$ excites relay coil $CR1$, which closes all contacts marked $CR1$. One of these excites the solenoid operated air valve which closes the electrodes on the work. Another seals around switch S, which may then be released or not, at the choice of the operator.

The third contact connects point $K1$ of the time delay circuit marked "Squeeze" to the a-c supply, thus initiating its timing operation.   At the end of the squeeze period time delay relay $TD1$ closes both contacts marked $TD1$.   One of these excites relay $CR2$, which closes contacts which initiate the firing of the welding circuit

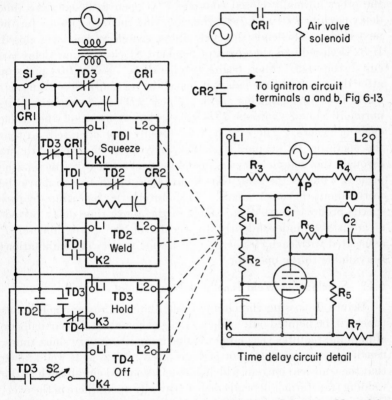

Fig. 6-14.   Automatic sequence timer.   (*Electronics Laboratory Manual for Educational Institutions,* Westinghouse Electric Corporation, East Pittsburgh, Pennsylvania, 1945.)

ignitron contactors.   (Ignitrons are often called contactors because they serve the same function as electromechanical contactors.) The other contacts initiate the timing action of the "Weld" timer by connecting $K2$ to the a-c line.   The weld period ends when relay $TD2$ picks up, thus opening the normally closed contacts $TD2$ in series with the relay coil $CR2$ which initiated and maintained welding current. At the same time the normally open contacts $TD2$ close to initiate the "Hold" time delay circuit. During this period the electrodes are still closed, but when relay $TD3$ picks up, the normally closed contacts $TD3$ in series with $CR1$ open, thus allowing the pneumatically controlled electrodes to open. At the same time the other normally closed contacts $TD3$ open to de-energize time delay circuits $TD1$ and $TD2$, thus allowing them to "reset" for the next cycle. This ends the cycle unless switch $S2$ has been closed. If $S2$ is closed and the operator has kept $S1$ closed, time delay circuit 4, the "Off" timer, begins its operation. When $TD4$ picks up after the required time delay, it opens the normally closed contacts $TD4$, thus de-energizing $TD3$. When $TD3$ is de-energized, its normally closed contacts $TD3$ close, thus reinitiating the whole cycle of events. The switch $S1$ is usually foot operated, so that the operator, by keeping $S1$ closed, may allow the welder to run through the complete cycle just described as many times as he pleases, while at the same time he has both hands free to move the work about between welds. This automatic repeating feature speeds production welding. Each of the above time delay periods is adjustable independently by means of the potentiometer P associated with each circuit, so that a wide variety of combinations is available to the operator.

6.12 Synchronous Weld Timer with Heat Control

Before discussing the circuit itself, the need for a synchronous timer will be pointed out. The welding of some metals, particularly aluminum, requires very large welding currents for very short times, usually one or two cycles, or perhaps a few more. It is well known that the transient current which flows in a coupled circuit such as the welding transformer depends rather critically upon where in the cycle the circuit is closed. If the circuit is closed very early or very late in the cycle, large current transients result, and if the circuit is closed at random for each weld the amount of heat produced in successive welds varies from weld to weld so much that consistent welds cannot be obtained. It is therefore important that the weld always be started at the same phase angle, and it is one purpose of the synchronous timer to close the circuit always at the same phase angle in the cycle, and to allow the operator to adjust this angle at will. This function is carried out by the heat control circuit used in conjunction with the synchronous timer. Its purpose is to allow the operator to control at will the point in the cycle where the ignitron contactors fire so as to control the average current per cycle. In this way the amount of heat generated per cycle is controlled. A further function of the synchronous timer is to determine precisely the number of cycles during which current is to flow. In addition it insures that an even number of half cycles of welding current flow each time a weld is made. This precaution prevents

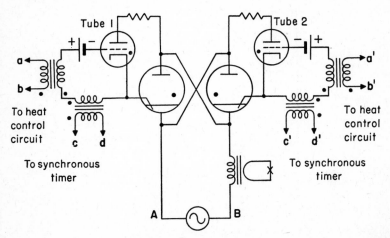

Fig. 6-15. Ignitron contactor circuit for synchronous and heat controls. (From Electronics Engineers of the Westinghouse Electric Corporation, *Industrial Electronics Reference Book*, John Wiley & Sons, Inc., New York, 1948.)

the saturation of the welding transformer which would occur if two or more successive half cycles of welding current were in the same direction.

A circuit is shown in Fig. 6-15 which may be used with synchronous control and heat control. Here the ignitrons are fired by thyratrons whose grids are controlled by three components of voltage, a d-c bias, a component from the heat control circuit, and a component from the synchronous control circuit. These voltages are shown in their proper relation to the line voltage in Fig. 6-16. The voltage from the heat control consists of a sequence of spikes whose phase with respect to the line voltage is variable. The voltage from the synchronous control is a sine wave 180° out of phase with the supply voltage. As long as this sine wave is present the

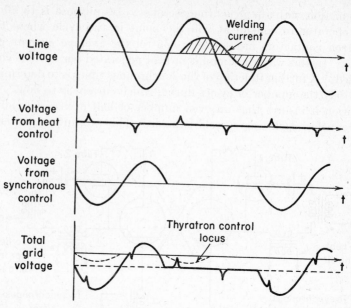

Fig. 6-16.   Voltages in ignitron contactor circuit of Fig. 6-15.   (From Electronics Engineers of the Westinghouse Electric Corporation, *Industrial Electronics Reference Book*, John Wiley & Sons, New York, 1948.)

thyratrons cannot fire, as will be seen by examination of the total grid voltage curve.   If the sine wave is removed, the thyratrons, and hence the ignitrons, fire. This condition is shown for one cycle in Fig. 6-16.

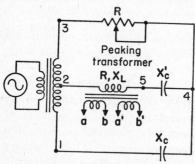

Fig. 6-17.   Heat control circuit. Terminals a,b and a',b' connect to corresponding points in circuit of Fig. 6-15.

A heat control circuit is shown in Fig. 6-17. It is a phase shifting circuit of the type discussed in Chapter 2. If the peaking transformer, which is nearly a pure reactance, were connected directly across terminals 4 and 2, and if X_c were small compared to X_L, then the phase of the voltage across the peaking transformer would, in accordance with Eq. 2.8, be variable from 0° to 180° with respect to $\dot{V}_{21}$. If the phase shifting circuit is excited from the same source which supplies the line voltage for the welder of Fig. 6-15, the peaks of the transformer output shift between 90° and 270° with respect to the line voltage. This condition, shown in Fig. 6-18, permits control of the thyratrons of Fig. 6-15 only between 90° and 180°. It is then necessary to shift the peaking transformer primary voltage forward or backward 90° in order to obtain the peaks within the correct range. This shift is obtained by putting a capacitive reactance X'_c in series with the transformer primary, as is shown in Fig. 6-17, and adjusting it so that the voltage across the transformer

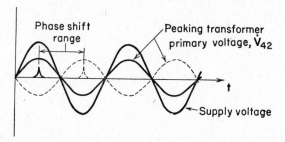

Fig. 6-18.   Phase shift of peaking transformer output without tuning reactance

is exactly 90° out of phase with the voltage $\dot{V}_{24}$. In this way the phase shift range of the voltage peaks is changed so that thyratron control from 0° to 180° is attained.

The assumption is now made that X_c is small compared with the total impedance of the peaking transformer and tuning capacitor, so that the voltage from 2 to 4 is essentially constant in magnitude and adjustable from 0 to 180° with respect to $\dot{V}_{12}$. This matter was discussed in connection with Eq. 2.8. The circuit and phasor diagrams for the desired conditions are shown in Fig. 6-19. The capacitive reactance X'_c is adjusted so that $\dot{I}_{24}$ leads $\dot{V}_{24}$ by an angle θ. The angle θ is adjusted so that ϕ is 90°. In the series R-L-C circuit,

$$\theta = \tan^{-1} \frac{X'_c - X_L}{R_L}.$$

From the phasor diagram,

$$\theta = \tan^{-1} \frac{R_L}{X_L}.$$

Hence
$$\frac{X'_c - X_L}{R_L} = \frac{R_L}{X_L},$$

and
$$X'_c = \frac{R_L{}^2 + X_L{}^2}{X_L}. \tag{6.33}$$

In many peaking transformers, $X_L > 10R_L$, so that to a good approximation,

$$X'_c \cong X_L. \tag{6.34}$$

The approximate design of peaking transformers is discussed in Sec. 2.14, and factors controlling X_L are discussed. In making a

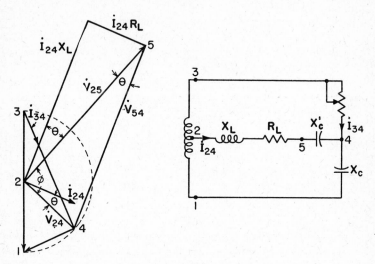

Fig. 6-19.   Phase relations in heat control circuit.

design, R_L should be known approximately, since it limits the current and hence the voltages developed across X_L and X'_c. Design of the phase shifting circuit is discussed in Sec. 2.12, where conditions of pure resistance load and pure inductance load are considered. In the heat control circuit of Fig. 6-17 the load may, to a good approximation, be considered a pure resistance equal to R_L, because the circuit is nearly in series resonance. Here is another reason why R_L should be known.

The synchronous timer circuit is shown in Fig. 6-20. Tubes 5 and 6 are connected back to back and so may be considered equiva-

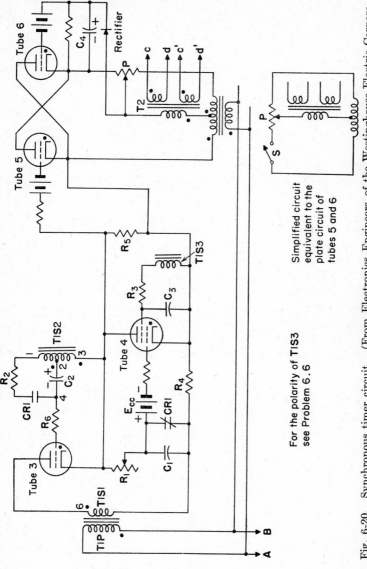

Fig. 6-20. Synchronous timer circuit. (From Electronics Engineers of the Westinghouse Electric Corporation, *Industrial Electronics Reference Book*, John Wiley & Sons, Inc., New York, 1948.)

lent to a switch, neglecting tube drop. The simplified equivalent circuit is also shown. The potentiometer P is center tapped, so that with switch S open there is a voltage across the transformer to provide the necessary sine waves of voltage in the grid circuits of Fig. 6-15. These voltages must be in phase opposition to their respective anode voltages in Fig. 6-15. If points similarly labeled in Figs. 6-15 and 6-20 are connected, and if transformer polarity markings are as indicated, this condition is fulfilled. In Fig. 6-20, when tubes 5 and 6 fire, or in effect when S is closed, there is no voltage across the transformer $T2$, and, according to Fig. 6-16, the ignitrons fire. As long as tubes 5 and 6 conduct, the ignitrons also conduct. When the grid of tube 5 is made positive by a voltage across R_5, tube 5 fires. When tube 5 conducts, a voltage is developed across the upper half of potentiometer P, which charges C_4 through the rectifier, which may be a copper oxide type. The rectifier prevents reversal of the charge on C_4, so that tube 6, whose grid is now positive, fires on the succeeding half cycle. This circuit is known as a follow-through circuit, since it insures that if tube 5 fires, tube 6 also fires on the following half cycle. In fact the firing of tube 6 depends on the firing of tube 5. In this way the welder current is sure to flow for an even number of half cycles, which is one of the requirements of this type of circuit.

The firing of tube 5 is controlled by tubes 3 and 4. Contacts $CR1$ are the initiating contacts. Before the normally open contact $CR1$ closes, capacitor C_2 charges by grid-charging action so as to bias tube 3 negatively and prevent firing. The voltage of point 4 with respect to point 3 is shown in detail in Fig. 6-21. When the contactor closes, C_2 rapidly discharges its d-c component of charge through R_2, and the voltage of the grid then becomes the sum of the voltages $\dot{E}_{32}$ and $\dot{E}_{24}$. For clarity it is here assumed that the grid draws no current when point 4 becomes positive, and the voltage curves of Fig. 6-21 are drawn on this basis. This is nearly true if R_g is 10 times the larger of R_2 or X_{c_2}. The voltage $\dot{E}_{24}$ is phased by means of R_2 and C_2 so that it lags $\dot{E}_{32}$ by an angle θ. Therefore the sum $\dot{E}_{32} + \dot{E}_{24} = \dot{E}_{34}$ also lags $\dot{E}_{32}$ by a small angle, so that the grid of tube 3 is positive during only the first part of the cycle when the anode is positive. Thus tube 3 can fire only at the beginning of a cycle, so that tube 5 also fires at the beginning, regardless of where in the cycle the starting contacts are closed.

Tube 4, Fig. 6-20, is held nonconducting by the control grid as long as the normally closed contacts $CR1$ are closed.   When they open, capacitor C_1 begins to charge through tube 3 and R_1, thus increasing the voltage of the grid of tube 4.   The voltage of the

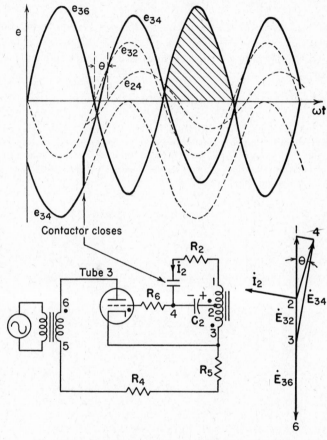

Fig. 6-21.   Details of operation of tube 3 in Fig. 6-20.

shield grid is phased by R_3 and C_3 in the same way as the grid voltage of tube 3, so that tube 4 can be fired only at the beginning of a cycle.   Thus tube 4 fires at the beginning of the cycle following the one in which its control grid becomes sufficiently positive.   As soon as tube 4 fires, it short-circuits R_5, so that tubes 5 and 6 no longer fire. Thus the weld duration is controlled by the timing circuit consisting of R_1 and C_1. By selecting a high-quality mica capacitor for C_1 and a wire-wound resistor of low temperature coefficient of resistance for R_1, it is possible to obtain exactly any even number of half cycles of weld current from two to the upper limit of the equipment, usually about 16 to 20 half cycles. Such precision is not needed for welds longer than this. Resistor R_4 limits the current through both tubes 3 and 4 when tube 4 fires. Both tubes stop firing when contacts $CR1$ are returned to their normal positions as shown.

PROBLEMS

6.1. In this circuit, when the switch is moved from a to b, the relay contacts open for a definite time and then reclose. If the relay pickup current is 6 ma, find R and C for an open period of 1 sec. Assume zero relay pickup time, and assume that the potentials of points a and b stay at their steady-state values during the transient period.

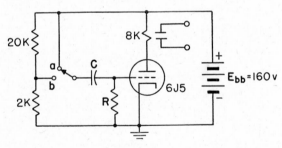

Prob. 6.1

6.2. Obtain the equation following Eq. 6.4 by use of the equivalent a-c plate circuit theorem.

6.3. Refer to Fig. 6-12. Design R_g, R_1, C_1, and the voltages of $T1S$ and $T2S$ for a time delay of 0.5 sec. Assume the tube to be a 2050. What should be the polarity of transformer $T3$?

6.4. In the accompanying circuit the thyratron conducts until a certain delay time after switch S opens, at which time the relay TD drops out. Voltage E_{AK} is 110 v rms and E_{KB} is 10 v rms. (a) Determine suitable values of R_2, C_2, and P for a time delay of 1 sec. (b) What maximum powers must P and R_2 be able to dissipate? (c) Plot a curve of time delay against the resistance of P as P is varied from maximum to zero. (d) What is the minimum allowable value of R_3?

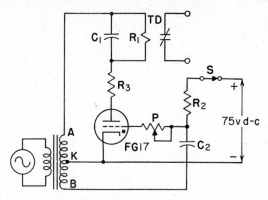

Prob. 6.4

6.5. It is desired to operate a small shunt motor from an a-c source as shown in the figure. The motor is connected to a load which requires a torque proportional to speed N. Let the load torque be $T_L = K_3 N$. Let the motor torque be $T_m = K_2 i$, where i is the armature current. Let the motor back emf be $K_1 N$. Assume no motor losses. Angular moment of inertia of motor and load is J. (a) Show that the motor and load is equivalent to a capacitor and resistor in parallel, and that the equivalent C and R will be

$$C = \frac{J}{K_1 K_2} \text{ and } R = \frac{K_1 K_2}{K_3}.$$

(b) If the supply voltage is 115 v rms and $J = 0.00015$ lb ft (sec)^2/radian, $K_1 = 0.6$ v/radian/sec, $K_2 = 0.4$ lb-ft/a, $K_3 = 0.00435$ lb-ft/radian/sec, what will be the motor speed? Neglect tube drop, and assume the tube fires when the anode goes positive to the cathode.

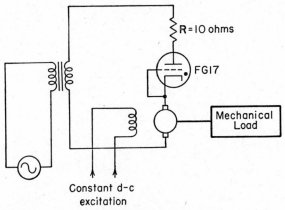

Prob. 6.5

6.6. (a) In Fig. 6-20 determine the correct polarity of transformer winding $T1S3$. (b) If tube 4 is a type 2050, design R_3 and C_3 and select a suitable voltage for $T1S3$.

6.7. In the accompanying circuit, when contactor A is closed the thyratron is cut off for a time T. (a) Find T. (b) Explain the purposes of R_g and R_2.

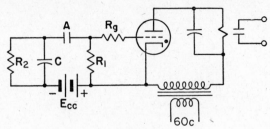

Prob. 6.7

(c) With what accuracy can the time delay T of this circuit be predicted?
(d) Discuss the effect of R_2 on the time delay.

$$R_2 = 10 \text{ megohms} \qquad C = 2\mu\text{f}$$

$$R_1 = 500K \qquad E_{cc} = 25v$$

$$R_g = 1 \text{ megohm}$$

Assume the thyratron fires at $e_{kg} = -3v$.

6.8. Assume an ideal rectifier in the circuit shown. (a) Calculate the average or d-c voltage across R_L for the following combinations.

R	R_L	C
0.1 megohm	1 megohm	0.01 μf
1	1	0.01
2	1	0.01
1	1	0.1
1	1	1.0

Prob. 6.8

(b) Calculate the d-c voltage across R for the first set of parameters of (a). (c) Calculate the d-c voltage across the rectifier for the first set of parameters. (d) Estimate the ripple voltage, peak to peak, for all the data sets of part (a).

6.9. Design C_2 and R_2 of Figs. 6-20 and 6-21 so that tube 3 can fire not later than $10°$ after its anode swings positive. Discuss factors influencing the choice of voltages E_{32} and E_{21}. Assume critical firing voltage of zero.

6.10. In Fig. 6-20, $R_4 = 1000$ ohms, $R_5 = 10000$ ohms, $R_1 = 1$ megohm, the voltage of winding $T1S1$ is 110 v rms. Design C_1 for a maximum time delay of *approximately* 10 cycles of a 60-c supply voltage, assuming $E_{cc} = 22$ v and that tube 4 will fire at $e_{kg} = -2$ v. State carefully all assumptions.

6.11. What factors will influence the design of the bias cell voltage in the grid circuit of tube 5, Fig. 6-20?

CHAPTER 7

SERVOMECHANISMS

7.1 Introduction

Many designations have been given to the great variety of systems used for automatically controlling physical operations. If they are to control a furnace or to keep the voltage of a generator constant, they may be called regulators. If they are to regulate the speed of the rolls in a steel mill or correlate the color printing of the comics, they are known as industrial control equipment. Many other terms and applications will come to the reader's mind. Whether or not these various names are advantageous is questionable. At least from the theoretical point of view all such systems may be grouped under one classification. The term that is generally used for this is *servomechanism*.

A servomechanism is fundamentally any closed cycle system. A closed cycle system is any system that compares some quantity with a reference and then takes steps to correct the quantity if a difference exists. In comparison, an open cycle system is one in which the output quantity is changed without reference to how much it differs from the desired value before or after the change. It is possible for a man to be the difference between an open and a closed cycle system. For example, suppose that a certain d-c generator is supplying power to a laboratory. It has been adjusted to some desired value when the laboratory is not operating. No voltmeter is connected to read the terminal voltage. Under operation, one of the laboratory personnel decides that the voltage is undoubtedly low and turns the field rheostat to increase it. Having turned it, he is content and does not check the voltage. This is an example of an open cycle system. For all the man knew the generator might have had a rising characteristic and already have had too high a voltage under load.

However, if the man had read a voltmeter connected to read the terminal voltage and upon observing that it had dropped, he had increased the voltage until he observed that the meter read the desired value, the whole system including the man would have been a closed cycle system. The man is not necessary. If some device is used which continually compares the actual voltage to some desired reference and tends to correct any error, it is just as good as the man standing continually at the field rheostat. We are particularly interested in the automatic type of system, and the chapter will be devoted to its analysis.

The example mentioned was for controlling the output voltage of a generator. It should be clear that the basic idea of a closed cycle system applies equally well to any system regardless of the regulated quantity so long as the link between actual and desired output is maintained. The regulated quantity might be the temperature of a home or of a stove. It might be the speed of a milk separator or the position of the rudder on a large ship. All fit basically into the same class.

7.2 Terminology and Essential Components

Properly it would be most desirable to use a separate set of symbols for each problem attacked. For example, if the problem were that of a voltage regulator it would seem reasonable to solve the problem in terms of the output and reference voltages and the circuit constants, probably electrical. It would be similarly true for any other particular system. However, from a theoretical point of view and for ease in generalizing the various types of system components and their effects, it becomes necessary to approach the problem from a more general point of view.

Those quantities which are present in most systems will be given symbolic representations, and their exact units will depend upon the application. In each system there will be a controlled quantity such as position, speed, temperature, or voltage. This will be represented by θ_o. Usually there will be some reference quantity to which the system tends to align itself. This may or may not have the same units as the controlled quantity. In the general analysis the reference quantity will be represented by θ_i. In general, a difference or error will exist from time to time between θ_o and θ_i. The difference $\theta_i - \theta_o$ will be symbolized by ϵ. It will often prove advantageous to refer to two definite ratios of the system. One is the complex ratio between the controlled quantity θ_o and the reference quantity θ_i. The ratio θ_o/θ_i will be thought of as the closed cycle gain A_f and may be real or complex depending on the quantities involved. The second useful quantity is the ratio of output to input signals with the feedback disconnected. This ratio is referred to as the open cycle gain A. Other symbols used will be introduced as they are needed in the course of the text.

It is evident from a study of the work thus far that certain elements or processes are essential to a closed loop system or servomechanism. Briefly, they may be summarized as follows. There must be some means of measuring the controlled quantity and of comparing it with the reference. There must be some method of obtaining a signal proportional to any error existing and of applying it in such a manner as to reduce this error. As will be seen later, it is occasionally desirable to use a signal equal to the time derivative or integral of the error or output as well as the proportional signal. And finally, there must be some source of power which is controlled by the system and is used to produce the desired results.

7.3 Desired Results and Methods of Analysis

There are basically two reasons for studying a servomechanism from the theoretical point of view. First, it is desirable to know the important factors or constants of any system in order to design systematically an operable unit or to make logical corrections or additions to an existing system. Second, it is essential in many instances to have some criterion for comparison of quality for systems already built or designed or of required qualities in a system to be designed.

Several useful methods exist for the correlation of these facts. However, all the practical methods, other than experimental, stem basically from the system's differential equations. Thus the ability to write the differential equations relating two or more variables after having made reasonable simplifying assumptions is of prime importance. Once the equations are written, the analysis becomes almost a matter of routine, and therefore it is often felt that obtaining the equations constitutes at least half of the problem solution.

The various systems of analysis are based largely on the form in which the differential equations are written and upon the types of solution obtained. It might be well to mention a few of the more important methods of solution that will be used in this chapter.

(a) *The transient solution.* This consists of the solution for the output variation as a function of time for a particular input signal. Usually the input signal used is a unit function type of change. Thus the input, or reference, is suddenly changed from one steady-state value to another, and the solution indicates how well and how quickly the output follows this change. With this solution it is easy to determine whether the output oscillates about its new value, approaches it exponentially, or approaches by a damped oscillation. Although very useful, this process has several inherent disadvantages, among which are the comparative length of time required to determine the roots of the equation which are necessary for a time solution, the usual complexity of the forms of the relations between system constants, and the somewhat dubious validity of the relations when used with any other particular type of input function.

(b) *Frequency response, steady-state.* This method is based upon the fact that any normal input function can be represented by a Fourier series. Thus the question is one of determining the system's response to sinusoidal input variations consisting of any frequency from zero to infinity. If there is neither magnitude nor phase change in the ratio of the output function to the input function, the output is always a perfect reproduction of the input. It can be shown that a phase change proportional to frequency results in similar input and output waves, but slides the entire output wave along the time axis. A frequency plot similar to that used for communication amplifiers will show how well this requirement is met. Perhaps the chief advantage of this method is that it is the result of a steady-state solution and is thus comparatively easy to obtain, particularly for the electrical engineer who is already very well aware of the possible short cuts in the solution of sinusoidal, steady-state problems. Fortunately, too, considerable information can be obtained about the fundamental relations of the system when in this form. Both rectangular and polar plots can be made, and there are useful applications of both.

(c) *LaPlace and Fourier transform.* These advanced methods of writing differential equations in terms of $j\omega$ or a complex variable s

serve to introduce the initial conditions, simplifying the time solution
as well as giving the frequency response. However, these useful
results are not particularly different from those already mentioned
for the frequency response.

7.4 First-order System

Having the general ideas of the previous three sections in mind,
consideration will now be given to particular types of systems. The
first to be considered consists of any system, electrical, mechanical,
or other, that leads to a differential equation of the first order.
Again it should be noted that it is the form of the differential
equation that is important and not the use or units of the system in
question.

Consider first a simple mechanical system. It consists of a
reference position θ_i; a mechanical differential which gives a dis-

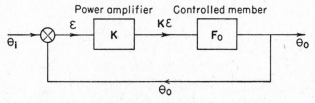

Fig. 7-1. Simplified mechanical servomechanism.

placement output equal to the difference $\theta_i - \theta_o$ between θ_i and the
system displacement output θ_o; an amplifier which gives a torque
output that is proportional to this error, $K\epsilon$; and a mechanical
member with a coefficient of friction F_o,[1] and negligible inertia.
This hypothetical system is shown in Fig. 7-1.[1]

There are probably few practical systems of this simplicity, but
an example is shown in Fig. 7-2. In Fig. 7-2, as long as θ_i and θ_o are
equal, no voltage is applied to the motor. However, if one is
changed, say θ_i, a voltage exists until the motor has corrected the
error. The system is oversimplified, but an understanding of the
simple system is helpful.

The problem of writing the differential equations for such a
system is apparently easier when the system is generalized in the

---

[1] The subscript "o" here represents output, thus F_o is the friction coefficient
as seen from the output. This permits the consideration of gear trains, etc.
without further complexity.

form of Fig. 7-1. Torque is chosen as the dependent variable. The torque required to rotate the motor must be equal to the torque

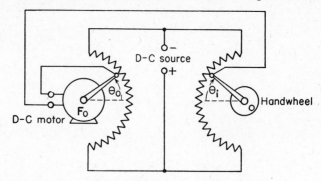

Fig. 7-2.　Example of system generalized in Fig. 7-1.

supplied. Therefore, in operational form,

$$(F_o p)\theta_o = K\epsilon. \tag{7.1}$$

This form will be found useful, but it may also be expressed in terms of θ_o and θ_i. Thus

$$(F_o p)\theta_o = K(\theta_i - \theta_o). \tag{7.2}$$

This equation may be rewritten as

$$(K + F_o p)\theta_o = K\theta_i. \tag{7.3}$$

In this form, the equation expresses the relation that must exist between θ_o and θ_i at all times. Other simple systems result in similar differential equations.

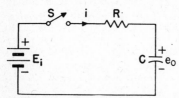

Fig. 7-3.　Simple R-C circuit.

As far as the transient solution is concerned there are many systems whose time solution and differential equation are similar in form to those of this servomechanism. It is not always necessary that a system have all the elements required by the definition of a servomechanism in order that the equation fit this form.

For example, consider the electric system of Fig. 7-3. Writing the loop equation when S is closed gives

$$E_i = Ri + e_o \tag{7.4}$$

or

$$Ri = E_i - e_o.$$

Since $$e_o = \left(\frac{1}{Cp}\right) i,$$

$$RCpe_o = E_i - e_o,$$

or $$(Rp)e_o = \frac{E_i - e_o}{C}. \qquad (7.5)$$

If

$$e_o = \theta_o, \qquad E_i = \theta_i,$$

this becomes $$(Rp)\theta_o = \frac{\epsilon}{C} = \frac{\theta_i - \theta_o}{C}. \qquad (7.6)$$

Here is an example of an electric system whose differential equation has the same form as that of the mechanical system of Fig. 7-1. However, this would not be considered to be a servomechanism.

The simple voltage regulator of Fig. 7-4 might also be considered. The following relations determine its operation:

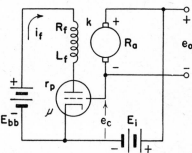

Fig. 7-4. Simple voltage regulator.

$$e_c = E_i - e_o,$$

$$E_{bb} + \mu e_c - E_x$$
$$= (R_f + r_p + L_f p)i_f,$$

$$e_g = e_o = ki_f,$$

$$E_x \cong \mu E_{cc},$$

for an ideal triode.   Thus

$$[(R_f + r_p) + L_f p]\frac{e_o}{k} = E_{bb} - E_x + \mu(E_i - e_o). \qquad (7.7)$$

By rewriting,

$$[(R_f + r_p + \mu k) + L_f p]e_o = k\mu(E_i) + k(E_{bb} - E_x). \qquad (7.8)$$

Since $E_{bb} - E_x$ can affect only the steady state, the form of the transient solution of Eq. 7.8 is identical with that of either of the other two systems.

As the system becomes more complex, the differential equation contains more terms and may be the result of the simultaneous solution of many relationships to obtain the dependence of one particular variable on another.

Consider the solution of Eq. 7.2 for the transient of θ_o if θ_i is changed suddenly from its original value to a new steady-state position. Using the form of Eq. 7.3,

$$(F_o p + K)\theta_o = K\theta_i.$$

The solution for θ_o consists of two parts, the transient and the steady state. Thus

$$\theta_o(t) = \theta_{o\,t} + \theta_{o\,ss}. \tag{7.9}$$

Since both θ_i and θ_o are constant after an infinite time, $\theta_{o\,ss}$ can be found by setting p equal to zero in Eq. 7.3 and solving for θ_o. Thus

$$\theta_{o\,ss} = \theta_i.$$

The transient solution for θ_o is exponential and of the form

$$\theta_{o\,t} = K_1 \epsilon^{m_1 t},$$

where m_1 is root of the characteristic equation

$$(F_o p + K) = 0.$$

Thus
$$\theta_o = K_1 \epsilon^{-Kt/F_o} + \theta_i. \tag{7.10}$$

It is now necessary to evaluate K_1 and θ_i. If it is assumed that θ_i was changed from θ_{i_1} to θ_{i_2}, then at $t = \infty$, $\theta_o = \theta_{i_2}$. Thus, substituting into Eq. 7.10 gives $\theta_i = \theta_{i_2}$. At $t = 0$, $\theta_o = \theta_{i_1}$. Thus

$$\theta_{i_1} = K_1 + \theta_{i_2},$$

or
$$K_1 = \theta_{i_1} - \theta_{i_2}.$$

Substituting into Eq. 7.10 gives

$$\theta_o = (\theta_{i_1} - \theta_{i_2})\epsilon^{-Kt/F_o} + \theta_{i_2}. \tag{7.11}$$

This is the expression of θ_o as a function of time for a step input. It is of interest to see what information can be determined from this solution. First, θ_o approaches θ_{i_2} exponentially, reaching it after infinite time, but being very nearly equal to it in a length of time determined by the ratio F_o/K. The ratio F_o/K will be referred to as the time constant T. Thus, the smaller T, the less time is required for θ_o to accomplish a certain percentage of the change in θ_i. If T is to be small, F_o should be as small as possible and K as large as possible.

For comparison, consider the results that could be obtained from a steady-state sinusoidal solution. Refer again to Eq. 7.3:

$$(F_o p + K)\theta_o = K\theta_i. \tag{7.3}$$

If the system is linear and θ_i is sinusoidal, θ_o also is sinusoidal in the steady state. Thus let

$$\theta_i(t) = \Re(\dot{\theta}_i \epsilon^{j\omega t}) \tag{7.12}$$

and

$$\theta_o(t) = \Re(\dot{\theta}_o \epsilon^{j\omega t}) \tag{7.13}$$

where $\dot{\theta}_i$ and $\dot{\theta}_o$ are complex as a function of ω. Then

$$p\theta_o(t) = j\omega\Re(\dot{\theta}_o \epsilon^{j\omega t}) = j\omega\theta_o(t) \tag{7.14}$$

since

$$p = j\omega \text{ in the steady state.} \tag{7.15}$$

This will be true of p for any application so long as the variation is sinusoidal. Substitute into Eq. 7.3 and rearrange.

$$\frac{\theta_o}{\theta_i}(j\omega) = \frac{K}{K + j\omega F_o} = \frac{1}{1 + j\omega F_o/K}. \tag{7.16}$$

If F_o/K is considered to equal T,

$$\frac{\theta_o}{\theta_i}(j\omega) = \frac{1}{1 + j\omega T}. \tag{7.17}$$

It is obvious that this ratio approaches unity as ωT approaches zero. Also, it is nearly unity for large values of ω if T is small. Equation 7.17 is plotted in magnitude and phase versus ω in Fig. 7-5.

From Fig. 7-5 it can be seen that the frequency response improves as T decreases, and thus the same information is available as from the transient solution. For the simple circuit there is little advantage in either solution over the other. This is the closed-loop solution since it relates the actual output and input for the system under normal operation.

It is often desirable in the more complex systems to obtain as much information as possible from the open-loop solution. This is the relation between the output and input functions with the loop open, or without feedback. Feedback is considered to exist when some portion of the output or some function of the output is used to alter the input. In terms of this system it would be the relation between θ_o and ϵ. Begin with Eq. (7.1).

$$(F_o p)\theta_o = K\epsilon \qquad (7.1)$$

Assuming both functions to be sinusoidal in the steady state,

$$\frac{\theta_o}{\epsilon}(j\omega) = \frac{K}{j\omega F_o}, \qquad (7.18)$$

or

$$\frac{\theta_o}{\epsilon}(j\omega) = \frac{1}{j\omega T}. \qquad (7.19)$$

Since it is desirable in the closed loop solution for θ_o to exist with no error, or $\epsilon = 0$, it is necessary that this ratio approach infinity.

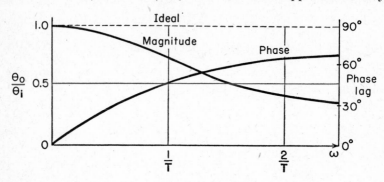

Fig. 7-5.   Sinusoidal response of first-order system.

This condition is best approached at high frequencies when $T \to 0$. Thus the same information is available from the open cycle solution as from the closed cycle or transient solutions.

It is often desirable to know the variation of ϵ, either as a function of time or in terms of ω. Rewriting Eq. 7.1 gives

$$(F_o p)(\theta_i - \epsilon) = K\epsilon$$

or

$$(K + F_o p)\epsilon = (F_o p)\theta_i. \qquad (7.20)$$

This relation may now be subjected either to the transient type of solution or the sinusoidal, steady-state solution. The two results are,

$$\epsilon = (\theta_{i_2} - \theta_{i_1})\epsilon^{-t/T} \qquad (7.21)$$

or

$$\frac{\epsilon}{\theta_i}(j\omega) = \frac{j\omega F_o}{K + j\omega F_o} = \frac{1}{1 - j/\omega T}. \qquad (7.22)$$

Only the first circuit was analyzed, and the results obtained are in terms of that system's constants. Comparison of Eq. 7.3, simplification of Eq. 7.6, and Eq. 7.8 show that the following analogs exist between the various system constants.

$$F_o \sim R \sim L_f$$

$$K \sim \frac{1}{\mu C} \sim R_f + r_p + \mu k.$$

It should be noted that in the last system the steady-state value is affected by the constant $(E_{bb} - E_x)$, and thus the right-hand side of the equation is not completely analogous to the simple system. However, the left-hand side of the equation, usually referred to as the characteristic equation, is analogous to the general system and specifies that the transient behaviors of all three systems are identical.

It will be left to the reader to show that the complete time solution of the third system results in

$$e_o = \frac{k\mu}{R_f + r_p + k\mu} (E_{i_1} - E_{i_2})\epsilon^{-t/T} + \frac{k\mu E_{i_2} + (E_{bb} - E_x)k}{R_f + r_p + k\mu} \quad (7.23)$$

where
$$T = \frac{L_f}{R_f + r_p + k\mu}.$$

7.5 Second-order System

The systems discussed in Sec. 7.4 were similar in that their differential equations were of the same form, with the one exception of steady-state constants. They were all of the oversimplified, linear type with one time delay or time constant. Consideration will now be given to those systems whose equation has two time delays or time constants. These circuits are more practical in that it is often possible to simplify a real system to this form by good and valid approximations.

As a first example, consider again the system of Fig. 7-1. Previously, it was assumed that the system had negligible inertia, generally a poor assumption. Suppose that the system's equations be written assuming a total output inertia J_o.[2] Again, writing the

___

[2] The term J_o is not to be confused with the similar notation used for Bessel functions.

torque equation gives

$$(J_o p^2 + F_o p)\theta_o = K(\theta_i - \theta_o). \tag{7.24}$$

Rearrange and divide by J_o:

$$\left(p^2 + \frac{F_o}{J_o} p + \frac{K}{J_o}\right)\theta_o = \left(\frac{K}{J_o}\right)\theta_i. \tag{7.25}$$

It is apparent that the left-hand side of the equation is of the second order in p. Thus the complete solution of θ_o as a function of time is

$$\theta_o(t) = K_1 \epsilon^{t/T_1} + K_2 \epsilon^{t/T_2} + \theta_{o\,ss}, \tag{7.26}$$

where $1/T_1$ and $1/T_2$ are the two roots of p in the characteristic equation

$$\left(p^2 + \frac{F_o}{J_o} p + \frac{K}{J_o}\right) = 0. \tag{7.27}$$

A second example of this second-order system might be found in a voltage regulator with load. Consider the circuit of Fig. 7-6. This system is similar to that of Fig. 7-4 but has a definite load R_L, and the field supply is more general. For example, the amplifier shown could be a vacuum tube so biased that no current flows when $\epsilon = 0$. The reader will be able to imagine many other circuits that fit this general case.

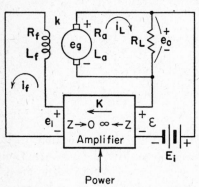

Fig. 7-6. Closed loop voltage regulator resulting in a second-order equation.

Let us write the differential equations of the system by breaking the loop at some point and writing all the existing relations around the loop from that point. Let us start on the right side of the amplifier and go clockwise.

$$e_1 = K\epsilon. \qquad\qquad e_g = (R_a + R_L + L_a p)i_L.$$
$$e_1 = (R_f + L_f p)i_f. \qquad e_o = i_L R_L.$$
$$e_g = k i_f. \qquad\qquad \epsilon = E_i - e_o.$$

Simultaneous solution of these equations for the relation between

e_o and E_i results in

$$(p^2 + a_2 p + a_1)e_o = (b_1)E_i \tag{7.28}$$

where
$$a_2 = \frac{(R_a + R_L)L_f + (R_f)L_a}{L_a L_f},$$

$$a_1 = \frac{(R_a + R_L)R_f + (R_L kK)}{L_a L_f},$$

$$b_1 = \frac{(R_L kK)}{L_a L_f}.$$

Equation 7.28 is easily seen to be of the same form as Eq. 7.25.

Many other examples could be shown. Again, consideration will be given to the two general types of solution, transient and sinusoidal steady state. Let us first consider the transient solution that would result from a sudden change in θ_i from one steady-state value to another.

As was stated in Eq. 7.26, the complete time solution consists of two exponential terms and the steady-state term. The actual values of the three constants of course depend upon the system constants and upon the boundary conditions. Thus any particular solution would be of little use in a general study. However, it is apparent that regardless of the values of K_1 and K_2, it is generally desirable that both exponential terms die out as quickly as possible and that $\theta_{o\ ss}$ approach θ_i in the steady state.

Let us consider first the value of $\theta_{o\ ss}$ at $t = \infty$, or the steady-state value. In the system represented by Eq. 7.25, $p\theta_o = p^2\theta_o = 0$ at $t = \infty$, if $p\theta_i = p^2\theta_i = 0$. Thus

$$\theta_{o\ ss}(t = \infty) = \theta_{i\ ss}(t = \infty), \tag{7.29}$$

or
$$\theta_{o\ ss} = \theta_i. \tag{7.30}$$

This system has zero error at $t = \infty$, and of course closely approaches this condition in a finite time determined by T_1 and T_2. On the other hand, the system represented by Eq. 7.28 does not have zero error at $t = \infty$. Consider the value of $\theta_{o\ ss}$ for the system represented by Eq. 7.28. Again at $t = \infty$, $p\theta_o = p^2\theta_o = 0$, if $p\theta_i = p^2\theta_i = 0$. Thus

$$\theta_{o\ ss} = \frac{b_1}{a_1}\theta_{i\ ss}. \tag{7.31}$$

Evaluating b_1 and a_1 gives

$$\theta_{o\,ss} = \frac{R_L k K}{R_L k K + R_f (R_a + R_L)} \, \theta_{i\,ss}.$$

$$\theta_{o\,ss} = \frac{R_L k K / [R_f (R_a + R_L)]}{1 + R_L k K / [R_f (R_a + R_L)]} \, \theta_{i\,ss}. \qquad (7.32)$$

The reader will find it easy to show that the term $R_L k K / [R_f (R_a + R_L)]$ is A, the d-c open cycle gain around the system loop, so that

$$\frac{\theta_{o\,ss}}{\theta_{i\,ss}} = \frac{A}{1 + A} = A_f. \qquad (7.33)$$

Since all of the output term θ_o was fed back for comparison, the feedback factor B appears to be unity, and Eq. 7.33 is really a special case of the general feedback amplifier relation

$$A_f = \frac{A}{1 + BA}, \quad \text{with} \quad B = 1. \qquad (7.34)$$

It is apparent that $\theta_{o\,ss}$ could exactly equal $\theta_{i\,ss}$ only if $A = \infty$. This will later be shown to be impractical, as this system always results in some steady-state error. There is some feeling at this time that the study of servomechanisms should be split over this point, calling servomechanisms those systems with zero error, and those with error, regulators. This text does not make such a distinction, but only points out the two possibilities.

Thus the steady-state value of θ_o may or may not approach equality with θ_i, depending upon the system. However, the time required for it to reach its steady-state value and the way in which it approaches steady state are entirely determined by T_1 and T_2, and are referred to as the transient part of the solution, $\theta_{o\,t}$. It was mentioned previously that the right-hand side of the differential equation, called the driving function, served to determine the steady-state conditions, and this statement was borne out in the two examples discussed. In the same manner, the left-hand side of the equation, or the "characteristic equation," determines the transient solution. This of course is the reason that all systems with similar characteristic equations have similar transient solutions independent of their steady-state solutions. Let us investigate this transient solution by referring again to Eqs. 7.25, 7.26, and 7.27. Solve Eq. 7.27 for the two roots of p.

$$p_{1,2} = -\frac{F_o}{2J_o} \pm \frac{1}{2}\sqrt{\frac{F_o^2}{J_o^2} - \frac{4K}{J_o}}. \tag{7.35}$$

These two roots may be real and equal, real and unequal, or complex conjugates, depending upon the value of the terms under the radical.

In terms of Eq. 7.28,

$$p_{1,2} = -\frac{a_2}{2} \pm \frac{1}{2}\sqrt{a_2^2 - 4a_1}. \tag{7.36}$$

If the roots are real and equal, the value of the radical must equal zero. The solution then has the form:

$$\theta_o(t) = K_1\epsilon^{-pt} + K_2t\epsilon^{-pt} + \theta_{o\,ss} \tag{7.37}$$

where $p = F_o/2J_o$.

At first this might not seem to agree with the requirement of this system that $\theta_o(t = \infty)$ be finite because of the term $K_2t\epsilon^{-pt}$. However, if p is positive, this term can be shown to approach 0 as t approaches ∞. In fact, if θ_o is to approach $\theta_{o\,ss}$ as $t \to \infty$, p must be positive in both expressions. If this is not true, the system is considered unstable, since it never settles down to a finite steady-state value.

If the two roots are real, but unequal, the solution has the form

$$\theta_o(t) = K_1\epsilon^{-p_1t} + K_2\epsilon^{-p_2t} + \theta_{o\,ss} \tag{7.38}$$

where

$$p_1 = -\frac{F_o}{2J_o} + \frac{1}{2}\sqrt{\frac{F_o^2}{J_o^2} - \frac{4K}{J_o}} \quad \text{and} \quad p_2 = -\frac{F_o}{2J_o} - \frac{1}{2}\sqrt{\frac{F_o^2}{J_o^2} - \frac{4K}{J_o}}.$$

It is again true that both p_1 and p_2 must be positive if the system is to be stable. If the two roots are complex, the solution has the form

$$\theta_o(t) = K_1\epsilon^{(-a+jb)t} + K_2\epsilon^{(-a-jb)t} + \theta_{o\,ss} \tag{7.39}$$

where

$$a = \frac{F_o}{2J_o}; \qquad b = \frac{1}{2}\sqrt{\frac{4K}{J_o} - \frac{F_o^2}{J_o^2}}.$$

It is convenient to rewrite this expression as

$$\theta_o(t) = \epsilon^{-at}(K_1\epsilon^{jbt} + K_2\epsilon^{-jbt}) + \theta_{o\,ss}. \tag{7.40}$$

Substituting for ϵ^{jbt} and ϵ^{-jbt} gives

$$\theta_o(t) = \epsilon^{-at}[K_1(\cos bt + j \sin bt) + K_2(\cos bt - j \sin bt)] + \theta_{o\ ss}$$

$$= (K_1 + K_2)\epsilon^{-at} \cos bt + j(K_1 - K_2)\epsilon^{-at} \sin bt + \theta_{o\ ss} \quad (7.41)$$

and $\qquad \theta_o(t) = \theta_{o\ ss} + K_4\epsilon^{-at} \cos (bt - \beta)$

where $\qquad K_4 = \sqrt{(K_1 + K_2)^2 + [j(K_1 - K_2)]^2}$,

and $\qquad \beta = \tan^{-1} \dfrac{j(K_1 - K_2)}{(K_1 + K_2)}$.

Thus $\theta_o(t)$ is the steady-state term plus a damped oscillation. It can be seen that for the system to be stable, a must be positive. These three solutions correspond to the three conditions of critical, over- and underdamping, respectively. The various constants may be calculated by introduction of boundary conditions. For the system of Eq. 7.25, this would result in the three following solutions:

(a) Critical damping:

$$\theta_o(t) = \theta_i(1 - \epsilon^{-pt} - at\epsilon^{-pt}). \qquad (7.42)$$

(b) Overdamping:

$$\theta_o(t) = \theta_i \left(1 + \frac{p_2}{p_1 - p_2} \epsilon^{-p_1 t} - \frac{p_1}{p_1 - p_2} \epsilon^{-p_2 t} \right). \qquad (7.43)$$

(c) Underdamping:

$$\theta_o(t) = \theta_i \left[1 - \frac{\sqrt{a^2 + b^2}}{b^2} \epsilon^{-at} \cos (bt - B) \right] \qquad (7.44)$$

where $B = \tan^{-1} a/b$.

The verification of these is left to the reader. Plots of Eqs. 7.42, 7.43, and 7.44 appear in Fig. 7-7. It can be seen from Fig. 7-7 that if a certain amount of overshoot can be tolerated, the underdamped case permits the output to reach the new requirement more quickly than the critically or overdamped systems. Of course, too wild an oscillation is generally unacceptable. Most practical systems are slightly underdamped.

Although this procedure of solving the differential equation and plotting the result gives the exact response, it is usually difficult to use this method for circuit design since it requires at best some very judicious guessing as far as component values are concerned to solve a particular problem with three or four such calculations. It is desirable that some measure or criterion of the output behavior be established that can be solved for directly or that leads to a direct solution for the circuit or system components.

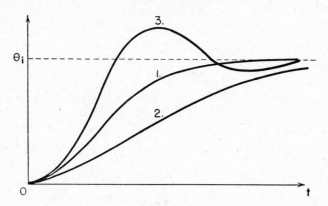

Fig. 7-7. Relative response of second-order system with three values of damping.

One practical method involves two new terms, ζ the damping ratio, and ω_n, the natural frequency of the system.

$$\zeta = \frac{\text{actual damping}}{\text{critical damping}}. \tag{7.45}$$

The term ω_n is the natural frequency of the system if it had no damping at all. Assuming that the system is going to be operated somewhat underdamped, ζ will be less than unity, since $\zeta = 1$ corresponds to the critically damped case. Let us see how these terms fit into a simple mechanical system.

The differential equation 7.25 for the system of Fig. 7-1 was

$$(J_o p^2 + F_o p + K)\theta_o = K\theta_i. \tag{7.25}$$

Here F_o is the actual damping. Solving the characteristic equation for its roots gives

$$p_{1,2} = -\frac{F_o}{2J_o} \pm \frac{1}{2}\sqrt{\frac{F_o{}^2}{J_o{}^2} - \frac{4K}{J_o}}. \tag{7.36}$$

For critical damping the value of the radical must be zero. From this relation the value of F_o for critical damping F_c may be found.

$$\frac{F_c^2}{J_o^2} - \frac{4K}{J_o} = 0. \tag{7.46}$$

$$F_c = 2\sqrt{KJ_o}. \tag{7.47}$$

Thus the value of ζ for this system is

$$\zeta = \frac{F_o}{F_c} = \frac{F_o}{2\sqrt{KJ_o}}. \tag{7.48}$$

The solution for ω_n is merely the value of the imaginary part of the roots with $F_o = 0$. Thus

$$\omega_n = \sqrt{\frac{K}{J_o}}. \tag{7.49}$$

It is now possible to rewrite the original equation in terms of ζ and ω_n.

$$\left(p^2 + \frac{F_o}{J_o}p + \frac{K}{J_o}\right)\theta_o = \frac{K}{J_o}\theta_i \tag{7.26}$$

$$\left[p^2 + 2\frac{F_o}{2\sqrt{KJ_o}}\sqrt{\frac{K}{J_o}}p + \left(\sqrt{\frac{K}{J_o}}\right)^2\right]\theta_o = \left(\sqrt{\frac{K}{J_o}}\right)^2\theta_i$$

$$(p^2 + 2\zeta\omega_n p + \omega_n^2)\theta_o = \omega_n^2\theta_i \tag{7.50}$$

Thus when the differential equation of the system relating θ_o and θ_i has been written, the *left-hand side* only, or "characteristic equation," may immediately be put into this form if it is a second-order equation. The right-hand side, or "driving function," does not necessarily have a coefficient equal to ω_n^2. The actual frequency of oscillation may also be found in terms of these factors. It is the value of the imaginary part of the root. Thus

$$\omega = \frac{1}{2}\sqrt{\frac{4K}{J_o} - \frac{F_o^2}{J_o^2}} = \sqrt{\frac{K}{J_o} - \frac{F_o^2}{4J_o^2}} = \sqrt{\frac{K}{J_o}\left(1 - \frac{F_o^2}{4KJ_o}\right)},$$

which may be written in terms of ζ and ω_n as

$$\omega = \omega_n\sqrt{1 - \zeta^2}. \tag{7.51}$$

The behavior of a system in many cases can be sufficiently well predicted from these relations. Suppose that a system is too wild, oscillating for long periods and badly overshooting. An increase in ζ would be indicated from Fig. 7-7. This could be accomplished by increasing F_o, decreasing K, or decreasing J_o or their equivalents. If at the same time it is desired to speed up the system or reduce the time of correction, which corresponds to an increase in ω, it would seem that a decrease in J_o would accomplish both ends. If this is not practical, ω may be increased by increasing K, but this requires a still further increase in F_o or its equivalent to increase ζ.

A second and perhaps more practical criterion placed on a system, assumed to be somewhat underdamped, is the decrement, or ratio of α to ω. Consider the general form of the time solution for the second-order system.

$$\theta_o = \theta_{o\ ss} + K_4\epsilon^{-\alpha t} \cos\ (\omega t - \theta). \tag{7.41}$$

Here $-\alpha \pm j\omega$ corresponds to $-a \pm jb$ of Eq. 7.39, and α is called the damping coefficient and ω the angular frequency. The angular period between peaks of the transient can be shown to be 2π radians by setting the derivative of Eq. 7.41 equal to zero.

$$0 = \frac{d}{dt}\ [K_4\epsilon^{-\alpha t} \cos\ (\omega t - \theta)]$$
$$= K_4[-\epsilon^{-\alpha t}\omega \sin\ (\omega t - \theta) - \alpha\epsilon^{-\alpha t} \cos\ (\omega t - \theta)]. \tag{7.52}$$
$$\omega \sin\ (\omega t - \theta) = -\alpha \cos\ (\omega t - \theta).$$

$$\tan\ (\omega t - \theta) = -\frac{\alpha}{\omega}.$$

It is also apparent that

$$\tan\ (\omega t - \theta + \pi n) = -\alpha/\omega \tag{7.53}$$

where n is any integral number. Thus the alternate maxima and minima of the transient are π radians apart, and hence corresponding peaks are 2π radians apart.

In the general equation then, the time T for one cycle is $2\pi/\omega$, and thus in the first cycle the transient is damped or reduced by the factor $\epsilon^{-\alpha 2\pi/\omega}$. The larger the ratio α/ω the more completely the transient dies out in one period.

It is sometimes desirable to determine the damping achieved in the first half cycle. If the slope of the output function is zero at $t = 0$, and if this is also a negative peak of the transient, the angular period to the first positive peak is π radians, and the amplitude of the transient component has been reduced by the factor $\epsilon^{-\alpha\pi/\omega}$. In either case the ratio α/ω is the important factor.

Suppose, as an example, that the system is required to have a maximum overshoot of 10 per cent which it must attain in 0.1 sec. The value of ω for this condition can be found from the fact that the time given is one half cycle. Thus the period of one cycle is 0.2 sec. and the frequency is 5c. Or

$$\omega = 5 \times 2\pi = 31.40 \text{ radians per sec.} \tag{7.54}$$

From the maximum overshoot, $\epsilon^{-\alpha\pi/\omega} = 0.1.$ (7.55)

From Eq. 7.54, $\omega/\pi = 10$, and thus $\epsilon^{-\alpha/10} = 0.1.$

Therefore $\alpha = 10 \ln 10$

and

$$\frac{\alpha}{\omega} = \frac{1}{\pi} \ln 10 = 0.732. \tag{7.56}$$

If this ratio α/ω can also be used so effectively to determine a system behavior it seems reasonable that there should be some direct relation between α/ω and ζ. From our simple system,

$$\alpha = \frac{F_o}{2J_o} \quad \text{and} \quad \omega = \omega_n \sqrt{1 - \zeta^2},$$

so

$$\frac{\alpha}{\omega} = \frac{F_o/2J_o}{\omega_n \sqrt{1 - \zeta^2}} = \frac{\zeta \sqrt{K/J_o}}{\omega_n \sqrt{1 - \zeta^2}} = \frac{\zeta \omega_n}{\omega_n \sqrt{1 - \zeta^2}} = \frac{\zeta}{\sqrt{1 - \zeta^2}}. \tag{7.57}$$

Thus we see that specifying either α/ω or ζ also determines the other.

This knowledge of the general form of the equation and the system components that affect it is all that many practical engineers use for system design. It gives a means whereby the behavior of a system can be predicted from its differential equation or permits the specification of the constants for design purposes.

Consideration will now be given to the second method of solution, that of sinusoidal steady state. As was mentioned before, it is sometimes advantageous to work with the closed loop, or the expression between θ_o and θ_i, and at other times it is preferable to work with the open loop, which is usually the same as the expression between θ_o and ϵ in the closed system. Both will be considered briefly.

Refer again to Eqs. 7.24 and 7.25

$$(J_o p^2 + F_o p)\theta_o = K(\theta_i - \theta_o) \tag{7.24}$$

and

$$\left(p^2 + \frac{F_o}{J_o} p + \frac{K}{J_o}\right) \theta_o = \left(\frac{K}{J_o}\right) \theta_i. \tag{7.25}$$

Equation 7.24 is in open-loop form while Eq. 7.25 is the closed-loop relation. If the system is assumed to be linear and θ_i is sinusoidal in the steady state, then of course, both θ_o and ϵ vary sinusoidally in the steady state. Thus,

$$\frac{\theta_o}{\theta_i} (p) = \frac{1}{1 + F_o p/K + J_o p^2/K} \tag{7.58}$$

and

$$\frac{\theta_o}{\epsilon} (p) = \frac{1}{p(F_o/K + J_o p/K)}. \tag{7.59}$$

Since $p = j\omega$ in the steady state,

$$\frac{\theta_o}{\theta_i} (j\omega) = \frac{1}{1 - J_o \omega^2/K + jF_o \omega p/K} \tag{7.60}$$

and

$$\frac{\theta_o}{\epsilon} (j\omega) = \frac{1}{j\omega(F_o/K + jJ_o \omega/K)}. \tag{7.61}$$

It must be remembered that the constants involved in these equations are related to a special system, but the method is general. Let us attempt to utilize a more general form for three relations.

Use will be made of the system of Fig. 7-6 since it is electrical in nature and may prove less confusing. Simultaneous solution of the system equations resulted in the following relation between E_o and ϵ:

$$(R_a + R_L + pL_a)(R_f + pL_f)E_o = (KkR_L)\epsilon. \tag{7.62}$$

Examination of the circuit immediately makes evident two electric loops and their associated time constants. Let $T_1 = L_f/R_f$ and $T_2 = L_a/(R_a + R_L)$. These may be incorporated into Eq. 7.62 with the following result.

$$(1 + T_1 p)(1 + T_2 p)E_o = \left[\frac{KkR_L}{(R_f)(R_a + R_L)}\right] \epsilon, \tag{7.63}$$

or

$$(1 + T_1 p)(1 + T_2 p)\theta_o = (K')\epsilon. \tag{7.64}$$

Equation 7.64 is a general form which expresses a relation between θ_o and ϵ for any second-order system, whether the system be electrical or otherwise. In general the open-loop expression consists of products of terms, each utilizing one time constant of the system. Thus Eq. 7.64 can be written as

$$\frac{\theta_o/\epsilon}{K'}(j\omega) = \frac{1}{(1 + j\omega T_1)(1 + j\omega T_2)}, \qquad (7.65)$$

or
$$\frac{\theta_o/\theta_i}{K'/(1 + K')}(j\omega) = \frac{1}{1 - \omega^2 T_1 T_2/(1+K') + j\omega\ (T_1+T_2)/(1+K')}, \qquad (7.66)$$

where T_1 and T_2 are the two loop time constants and K' is the open cycle d-c gain of the system. See Eq. 7.32. Equations 7.65 and 7.66 may be plotted directly if T_1, T_2, and K' are known. A still more general result is obtained if Eq. 7.66 is expressed in terms of ζ and ω_n. Rewriting Eq. 7.64 gives

$$[(1 + T_1 p)(1 + T_2 p) + K']\theta_o = K'\theta_i, \qquad (7.67)$$

or
$$\left[p^2 + \left(\frac{T_1 + T_2}{T_1 T_2}\right)p + \frac{1 + K'}{T_1 T_2}\right]\theta_o = \frac{K'}{T_1 T_2}\theta_i. \qquad (7.68)$$

In the general form of Eq. 7.50,

$$(p^2 + 2\zeta\omega_n p + \omega_n^2)\theta_o = \frac{K'}{T_1 T_2}\theta_i. \qquad (7.69)$$

It is obvious from Eqs. 7.68 and 7.69 that

$$\omega_n^2 = \frac{1 + K'}{T_1 T_2}.$$

Now divide both sides of Eq. 7.69 by ω_n^2:

$$\left(-\frac{\omega^2}{\omega_n^2} + j2\zeta\frac{\omega}{\omega_n} + 1\right)\theta_o = \frac{K'}{1 + K'}\theta_i. \qquad (7.70)$$

Therefore

$$\frac{\theta_o/\theta_i}{K'/(1 + K')}(j\omega) = \frac{1}{1 - \omega^2/\omega_n^2 + j2\zeta\omega/\omega_n}. \qquad (7.71)$$

A plot of Eq. 7.71 is shown in Fig. 7-8. It can be seen immediately from Fig. 7-8 that the frequency response that best approximates the ideal is for $\zeta \cong 0.4$. It is also apparent that the frequency response is better for any particular ζ, the higher ω_n. Both ζ and ω_n are dependent upon T_1, T_2, and K' and are specified by them.

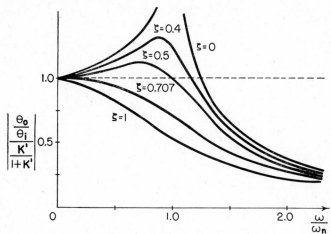

Fig. 7-8.   Plot of Eq. 7.71.

Thus from Eqs. 7.68 and 7.69

$$\omega_n = \sqrt{\frac{1 + K'}{T_1 T_2}} \tag{7.72}$$

and

$$\zeta^2 = \frac{(T_1/T_2 + T_2/T_1 + 2)}{4(1 + K')}. \tag{7.73}$$

Hence Eqs. 7.71, 7.72, 7.73 and Fig. 7-8 are general for all second-order systems with a steady-state d-c gain of $K'/(1 + BK')$ for a closed system.

Consider briefly the other type of system with a steady-state d-c closed cycle gain of unity, such as the mechanical system of Eqs. 7.24 and 7.30.

$$p(F_o + J_o p)\theta_o = K\epsilon.$$

Let $T_1 = J_o/F_o$ and $K' = K/F_o$.

Then $p(1 + T_1 p)\theta_o = K'(\theta_i - \theta_o), \tag{7.74}$

or $\left(p^2 + \frac{1}{T_1} p + \frac{K'}{T_1}\right)\theta_o = \frac{K'}{T_1}\theta_i.$

In the general form,

$$(p^2 + 2\zeta\omega_n p + \omega_n{}^2)\theta_o = \omega_n{}^2\theta_i. \tag{7.75}$$

Thus $\qquad \dfrac{\theta_o}{\theta_i}(j\omega) = \dfrac{1}{1 - \omega^2/\omega_n{}^2 + j2\zeta\omega/\omega_n}.$ $\qquad$ (7.76)

This is identical in form to Eq. 7.71 except that the left-hand side of Eq. 7.76 is not divided by $K'/(1 + BK')$, and thus Fig. 7-8 is also applicable to this type of system as well. It can be seen from Fig. 7-8 that the peak value of the curves as a function of ω depends upon ζ. This relation is easily expressed mathematically by use of Eq. 7.71, or Eq. 7.76.

$$\left|\frac{\theta_o}{\theta_i}(j\omega)\right| = \frac{1}{[(1 - \omega^2/\omega_n{}^2)^2 + 4\zeta^2(\omega/\omega_n)^2]^{1/2}}. \qquad (7.77)$$

Taking the derivative with respect to ω and equating to zero gives

$$\frac{d\left|\frac{\theta_o}{\theta_i}(j\omega)\right|}{d\omega} = 0 = +\frac{1}{2}\left[2\left(1 - \frac{\omega^2}{\omega_n{}^2}\right)\left(-2\frac{\omega}{\omega_n{}^2}\right) + 8\zeta^2 \frac{\omega}{\omega_n}\left(\frac{1}{\omega_n}\right)\right].$$

Rearranging and solving for ω,

$$\omega = \omega_n \sqrt{1 - 2\zeta^2}. \qquad (7.78)$$

By substitution of Eq. 7.78 into Eq. 7.77,

$$\left|\frac{\theta_o}{\theta_i}(j\omega)\right|_{max} = \frac{1}{2\zeta\sqrt{1 - 2\zeta^2}}. \qquad (7.79)$$

Thus the specification of $\left|\dfrac{\theta_o}{\theta_i}(j\omega)\right|_{max}$ for a second-order system also specifies the damping ratio ζ. As will be shown later, this ratio is often used as a design criterion. The relation between the two is not exactly the same for all order systems but is sufficiently close to serve for design.

Again ζ and ω_n depend upon T_1 and K', and from Eq. 7.75 and its preceding form, we get

$$\omega_n = \sqrt{\frac{K'}{T_1}} \qquad (7.80)$$

and $\qquad\qquad\qquad \zeta = \dfrac{1}{2}\dfrac{1}{\sqrt{T_1 K'}}. \qquad\qquad (7.81)$

Up to this point the important study of steady-state error has been omitted. There were two reasons for delaying its consideration until this time. First it was felt that its omission would be more than compensated for by reducing the number of complex factors to be studied simultaneously. Second, certain general quantities have now been defined that will help in understanding the problem of steady-state error.

The only system studied so far that has resulted in any steady-state error was the regulator. It will be recalled that this error was necessitated by the demand for a continuous corrective effort in order to maintain an increased field current. In the proportional system studied this could be accomplished only by a continuous error. All position systems mentioned appeared to have zero steady-state error, but this was possible only by assuming such systems and such input signals that no steady-state torque was required. If the position system studied were to have added to it the requirement of a constant torque load independent of position, this torque could be balanced only by a constant-magnitude steady-state error independent of position. Also, if the input signal were considered to be a constant-velocity function, then a constant-output torque would be required of sufficient magnitude to overcome the viscous friction, and thus the steady-state error would be directly proportional to the friction coefficient F_o and the output velocity. The same methods of analysis used previously could be utilized here and the above results shown mathematically. This will be left as a project for the reader which will serve as an opportunity to check his understanding of the fundamental methods of analysis.

Perhaps one important relation should be pointed out. The damping ratio ζ is directly proportional to the friction coefficient F_o. However, steady-state error due to the torque required to overcome friction in the steady state, which is probably the most often encountered, is also directly proportional to F_o. Thus any increase in damping accomplished by increased friction is gained by the reducing of steady-state accuracy and by loss of power. Sections 8 and 9 will be devoted to the study of ways and means of achieving both good damping and good accuracy.

7.6 Higher-order Systems

So far only those systems that resulted in a first- or second-order differential equation have been considered. In most instances this was made possible by the use of simplifying assumptions that are more or less valid. This method is indeed a powerful tool and is resorted to frequently. It is often possible to see which terms can best be neglected after the differential equation has been written. As an example suppose that the following differential equation was found to express the relation between the output and error function of some system:

$$(1 + 0.01p)(1 + 0.05p)(1 + 0.002p)(1 + 0.0006p)\theta_o = 500\epsilon. \quad (7.82)$$

This is perhaps the most convenient form since each of the parentheses includes a time constant of some electric loop or mechanical combination of the system. It is apparent from the following discussion that the values $T_3 = 0.002$ and $T_4 = 0.0006$ are relatively unimportant compared with the other two time constants. If this differential equation were to be solved for some unit function error, there would be four exponential terms of the form

$$K_n\epsilon^{-t/T_n}. \quad (7.83)$$

Thus if T_n is very small compared with other values of T in similar terms, the effect of the K_n term will have almost entirely died out while the others are still large.

In terms of steady-state frequency response, these terms in Eq. 7.82 of the form

$$(1 + T_np) = (1 + j\omega T_n) \quad (7.84)$$

are very nearly unity until the frequency is very high and the response has fallen to a low value. The solutions of Eq. 7.82 are plotted in Fig. 7-9 with and without the two small time constants for comparison. The error involved in neglecting the two small time constants is obviously small. A good approximation to a system can sometimes be made even when the time constants are not so obviously negligible. However, many systems are found whose differential equations cannot be so easily approximated or that have three or four time constants of equivalent importance. Consider a system with the following relation between θ_o and ϵ:

$$p(p + 10)(p + 5)(p + 2)\theta_o = 20,000\epsilon. \quad (7.85)$$

It is immediately apparent that all three time constants must be considered if the results are to be at all reliable. Therefore the system does not fall into any of the general types so far discussed.

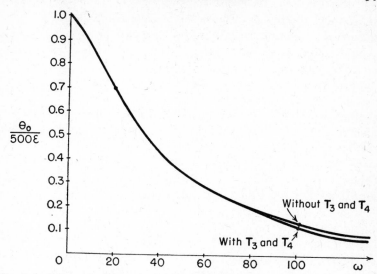

Fig. 7-9.   Plot of Eq. 7.82 with and without the two small time constants T_3 and T_4.

The apparent solution is to proceed with a new analysis on either the transient or sinusoidal steady-state basis.   The main purpose of this section is to point out some of the steps and general procedures to follow with these higher-order systems.

Consider first the possibility of solving the system for its transient solution resulting from a unit function input.   The first step is to rewrite the differential equation in terms of θ_o and θ_i.   Thus

$$[p(p + 10)(p + 5)(p + 2) + 20{,}000]\theta_o = 20{,}000\theta_i. \quad (7.86)$$

Rewritten, this becomes

$$(p^4 + 17p^3 + 80p^2 + 100p + 20{,}000)\theta_o = 20{,}000\theta_i. \quad (7.87)$$

The transient part of the solution is of the form

$$\theta_{ot} = K_1\epsilon^{p_1t} + K_2\epsilon^{p_2t} + K_3\epsilon^{p_3t} + K_4\epsilon^{p_4t}. \quad (7.88)$$

However, any numerical evaluation of these terms requires a knowledge of the roots of the characteristic equation of Eq. 7.87, which is a fourth-order equation.   It is of course clear that although the solution of a second-order equation is comparatively easy, solution of third and higher order becomes increasingly difficult. This difficulty of determining the roots of higher-order equations is probably the chief reason for the development of other methods of determining the characteristics of a system.

The first and most important factor to determine about a system from its differential equation is whether or not the system is stable. In other words, will the system settle down to some steady-state value or will it oscillate? If it is stable, the terms in the transient solution must all eventually reach zero. Reference to Eq. 7.88 shows that such a requirement imposes the condition that all roots of the characteristic equation be negative, or if a complex conjugate pair exists, they must have negative real parts.

Routh's criterion offers a simple and accurate method of determining how many roots are positive or have positive real parts. If all are negative, further consideration can be given the system to determine more of its characteristics. For those not already familiar with it, Routh's criterion may be stated as follows:

Arrange the characteristic equation into the following form:

$$p^n + a_1 p^{n-1} + a_2 p^{n-2} + \cdots + a_{n-1} p + a_n. \qquad (7.89)$$

With the equation in this form, construct an array of the constants. The first two rows consist of two series made up of alternate constants from the equation until all terms are exhausted.

$$1 \qquad\qquad a_2 \qquad\qquad a_4 \cdots\cdots\cdots\cdots 0$$

$$a_1 \qquad\qquad a_3 \qquad\qquad a_5 \cdots\cdots\cdots\cdots 0$$

$$\frac{a_1 a_2 - a_3}{a_1} \qquad\qquad \frac{a_1 a_4 - a_5}{a_1} \cdots\cdots\cdots\cdots 0$$

$$a_3 - \frac{a_1(a_1 a_4 - a_5)}{(a_1 a_2 - a_3)} \cdots\cdots\cdots\cdots\cdots\cdots 0$$

Each following row is made up of cross products of the last two rows previously formed, as indicated, and divided by the first term of the last row formed. Continue this construction until all terms so formed are zero. The number of roots with positive real parts is the same as the number of changes in sign of the elements in the first column. Consider as an example the solution of Eq. 7.87:

$$p^4 + 17p^3 + 80p^2 + 100p + 20{,}000 = 0.$$

Form the array as stated by Routh's rule,

$$
\begin{array}{cccc}
1 & 80 & 20{,}000 & 0 \\
17 & 100 & 0 & 0 \\
74.1 & 20{,}000 & 0 & \\
-4488 & 0 & 0 & \\
20{,}000 & 0 & & \\
0 & 0 & &
\end{array}
$$

Observation of the first column shows two changes of sign. Thus two roots of the four have positive real parts. Generally speaking, the system would be unsuitable and would not be considered further in this form. However, sometimes it is necessary to attempt to alter the differential equation until its form indicates that the system is stable. Such processes will be discussed in Sec. 7.8.

7.7 Transfer and Inverse Transfer Loci

The results of Routh's criterion often indicate that all roots have negative real parts, and then it is desirable to continue the examination of the system to determine as much about it as possible. The time transient solution has already been ruled out by algebraic difficulties; thus the sinusoidal steady-state solution is the next consideration.

In the brief treatment of this type of solution carried out in Sec. 7.4 and 7.5, use was made of the relation between θ_o and ϵ as well as the one between θ_o and θ_i. As was shown in Sec. 7.5, the relation between θ_o and ϵ, which is usually referred to as the "transfer function," is in simpler mathematical form than the one between θ_o and θ_i. Thus it is usually the transfer function θ_o/ϵ, or the inverse transfer function ϵ/θ_o, that is studied.

Consider the ratio θ_o/θ_i.

$$
\frac{\theta_o}{\theta_i} = \frac{\theta_o}{\epsilon + \theta_o} = \frac{\theta_o/\epsilon}{1 + \theta_o/\epsilon} = \frac{1}{1 + \epsilon/\theta_o}. \tag{7.90}
$$

The relation between θ_o and θ_i can be completely expressed in terms of θ_o/ϵ, or in terms of ϵ/θ_o. Thus, in general terms, the characteristic equation relating θ_o and θ_i can be expressed as

$$
\frac{\theta_i}{\theta_o} = 1 + \frac{\epsilon}{\theta_o}\,(p) = 1 + Y_o(p) \tag{7.91}
$$

where $Y_o(p) = \dfrac{\epsilon}{\theta_o}\,(p).$

The requirement of stability in the system demands that Eq. 7.91, which is the characteristic equation, have no roots with positive real parts.   If all possible roots are considered points in the complex plane, the above requirement specifies no roots in the positive half plane.

It is assumed that the characteristic equation, $1 + Y_o(p)$, can be expressed as a polynomial; thus

$$1 + Y_o(p) = \frac{A_0 + A_1p + A_2p^2 + \cdots A_np^n}{B_0 + B_1p + B_2p^2 + \cdots B_mp^m}. \qquad (7.92)$$

Equation 7.92 may then be rewritten as

$$1 + Y_o(p) = \frac{A_n(p - a_1)(p - a_2) \cdots (p - a_n)}{B_m(p - b_1)(p - b_2) \cdots (p - b_m)}. \qquad (7.93)$$

The roots $a_1, a_2, \cdots, a_n, b_1, b_2, \cdots, b_m$ may be either real or complex, and thus may be represented by points in the complex plane.   The variable p is a general point, $\alpha + j\omega$.   The points in the complex plane may be thought of as representing vectors as shown in

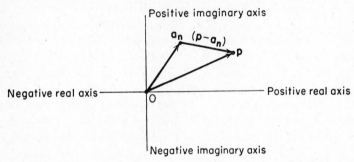

Fig. 7-10.   Complex plane representation of roots of Eq. 7.93.

Fig. 7-10.   Thus each term of the polynomial of Eq. 7.93 is represented by a vector such as the one $(p - a_n)$ shown.   The points a_n, etc. are fixed for any particular equation, but the general point p may be any point in the plane.

If the point p is allowed to move in any path whatsoever in the plane so long as it always returns to its original starting point, the final magnitude of a vector such as $(p - a_n)$ is the same as at the start, but its total angle is increased by 2π times the net number of times the point p encircles the point a_n in the counterclockwise direction.

By the same reasoning, the total angle of $1 + Y_o(p)$ in Eq. 7.93 would be increased by 2π times the net number of times the point p encircled the roots $a_1, a_2, \cdots, a_n$ and decreased by 2π times the net number of times the point p encircled the roots $b_1, b_2, \cdots, b_m$. Therefore the net angular change of $1 + Y_o(p)$ is equal to 2π times the number of roots of the numerator enclosed minus 2π times the number of roots of the denominator enclosed. A root of the numerator is called a "zero," since it results in a value of zero for the function, and a root of the denominator which results in a value of infinity, is a "pole." The net number of times the function's angle is increased by 2π indicates the number of "zeros" minus the number of "poles" of the characteristic equation enclosed by the path of the point p.

As was mentioned before, it is desirable to determine if the characteristic equation has any roots in the positive half plane. Thus the path of the general point p should be such as to include *the entire positive half plane and no more.*

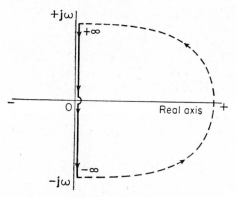

Fig. 7-11. Path of the point p which includes positive half plane.

The variable point p may be made to enclose the entire positive half plane by moving it in a counterclockwise sense along the imaginary axis from $+\infty$ to 0 to $-\infty$ and then close back to $+\infty$ as shown in Fig. 7-11. Such a path would obviously include the origin. It will be found that many practical applications deal with functions that have the origin as a perfectly good stable root. Thus, the path of p must be made to avoid 0 as shown in Fig. 7-11.

The variation of p along the imaginary axis is the variation of ω

for the special condition of $\alpha = 0$. Since ω is the angular frequency, it is easily varied over a range of positive values for sinusoidal steady-state operation. From Eq. 7.90,

$$\frac{\theta_i}{\theta_o} = 1 + Y_o(p). \qquad (7.94)$$

The polar plot of $1 + Y_o(p)$, magnitude and phase versus ω, for ω from $+\infty$ to $-\infty$ plots out the loci of all the possible vector positions representing the function as ω is varied. If the net vector rotation

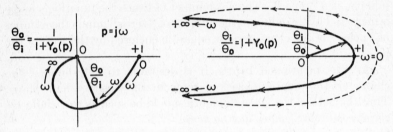

Fig. 7-12. Polar plots of θ_o/θ_i and θ_i/θ_o versus ω.

is zero, the number of zeros minus the number of poles in the positive half plane is zero. A typical example is shown in Fig. 7-12.

$$1 + Y_o(p) = \frac{\theta_i}{\theta_o} = \frac{(J_o p^2 + F_o p + K)}{K} \qquad (7.95)$$

It must be noted that the two points at $\omega = \pm \infty$ are closed by a curve back through the positive real axis at infinite magnitude. It is obvious that this is necessary when it is remembered that the point p was taken from $-\infty$ to $+\infty$ through the positive real axis to include the entire half plane.

The characteristic equation was expressed in the form $1 + Y_o(p)$ and the zeros were shown by the rotation of the function about the origin. If only the function $Y_o(p)$ is plotted, $1 + Y_o(p)$ is also plotted if the origin is considered to be at -1. Thus

$$Y_o(p) = \frac{p(J_o p + F_o)}{K} = \frac{\epsilon}{\theta_o}(p). \qquad (7.95a)$$

Equation 7.95a is plotted in Fig. 7-13, which is the same as Fig. 7-12 except for a shift of origin, and can thus be used to determine the same information if rotation is considered about the point

−1 instead of about zero. This is usually referred to an the "inverse transfer function" or "inverse open cycle plot," since it is the plot of the reciprocal of the open cycle transfer function or open cycle gain. This procedure is often very desirable practically, since the relation between θ_o and ϵ can be written with comparative ease. It is also easily obtainable by experiment.

Similar information can also be obtained from a plot of $1/Y_o(p)$ or $\theta_o/\epsilon(p)$, known as the "transfer function plot" since from Eq.

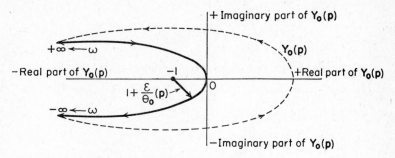

Fig. 7-13.   Plot of the inverse transfer function.

7.90 the poles of Eq. 7.90, which are zeros of the denominator of Eq. 7.90, may be accurately found from the roots of $1 + \theta_o/\epsilon$ as from $1 + \epsilon/\theta_o$.

Consider the same example:

$$\frac{1}{Y_o(p)} = \frac{\theta_o}{\epsilon}(p) = \frac{K}{p(J_o p + F_o)}. \tag{7.96}$$

The complete polar plot is shown in Fig. 7-14. The closing of the curve of Fig. 7-14 for $\omega = 0$ through the positive real axis is necessitated by the irregularity of the path of p around the origin in Fig. 7-11, so as not to include the origin in its area. Thus Eq. 7.96 becomes a very large positive real number when p is a very small positive real number. For clarification, a second example will be discussed for both methods of plotting. Assume that the transfer function has the form

$$\frac{\theta_o}{\epsilon} = \frac{K}{p(p - a_1)(p - a_2)}. \tag{7.97}$$

Plotted, this might appear as shown in Fig. 7-15. Figure 7-15

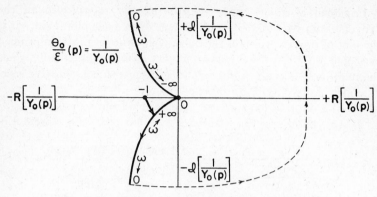

Fig. 7-14.   Plot of direct tranfer function $(\theta_o/\epsilon)(p)$.

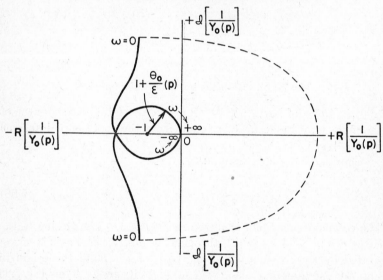

Fig. 7-15.   Direct transfer plot, Eq. 7.97.

indicates that this particular system is unstable, since the locus
rotates twice about the point -1.

   The inverse function is plotted in Fig. 7-16.   It should be noted
that the closing process of Fig. 7-16 is opposite to what might be
expected, but it can be checked easily by substituting values of p of
the proper angle into Eq. 7.97 as the point p goes from $+\infty$ to $-\infty$.
It should also be noted that the curves between $\omega = 0$ and $\omega = \pm\infty$

cross the negative real axis at a value less than unity, since the
direct transfer plot crossed with a value greater than unity.

In general, for either type of transfer plot, if in going from $\omega =$
$+\infty$ to $\omega = 0$, the point -1 is to the right of the locus of the transfer
function as viewed by an observer moving along the path, the sys-
tem is stable.   If -1 appears on the left, the system is unstable.

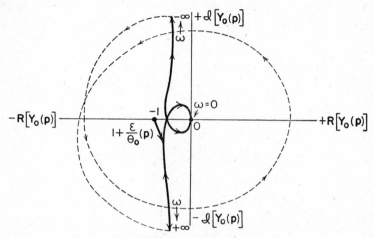

Fig. 7-16.   Plot of inverse of Eq. 7.97.

One of the obvious advantages of this method is that it is possible
to determine experimentally whether a closed system is stable or
unstable by means of the open cycle system, which is stable.

In addition to determining stability, some measure of the damping ratio may also be obtained.   Consider a typical plot of $Y_o(p) =$
$\epsilon/\theta_o(p)$ as shown in Fig. 7-17.   The phasors of Fig. 7-17 show that
the distance from -1 to the curve is the magnitude of $\left|\dfrac{\theta_i}{\theta_o}\right|$, which
therefore varies with ω exactly as did the same relation when con-
sidered as part of the frequency response in Eq. 7.71.   It will be
remembered that the maximum value of $\left|\dfrac{\theta_o}{\theta_i}(j\omega)\right|_{max}$ in Eq. 7.79 was
directly related to the damping ratio ζ, and that either one specified
the other in the second-order system.   Although the relation
between them is not the same for systems of any order, it is similar,
and $\left|\dfrac{\theta_o}{\theta_i}(j\omega)\right|_{max}$ is often used as a design criterion.

For convenience and for agreement with other literature, let

$$\left|\frac{\theta_o}{\theta_i}(j\omega)\right| = M. \tag{7.98}$$

It can be seen from Fig. 7-17 that the phasor from -1 to the curve is $1/M$, and therefore $1/M_{max}$ is shown graphically by the shortest distance from -1 to the curve. Thus the plot of $Y_o(p)$ gives almost directly a measure of damping. A value of $M_{max} = 1.3$ is a common design figure. In the second-order system this can be shown to correspond to $\zeta = 0.404$ by use of Eq. 7.79.

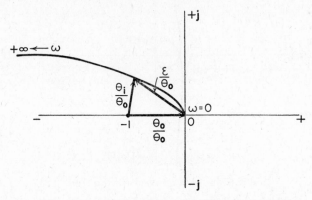

Fig. 7-17.   Typical inverse transfer function plot.

The plot of $Y_o(p)$ is particularly well adapted for determining the maximum gain with which a system can operate and still maintain a certain specified stability or M rating.

Suppose the curve of $Y_o(p)$ is plotted without the effect of K, or with only the effect of the system's unadjustable gain. It is helpful to express $Y_o(p)$ as $\dfrac{1}{KG(p)}$, where K is the constant value of gain and $G(p)$ is the system behavior with the gain removed. Thus if only $\dfrac{1}{G(p)}$ is plotted, the critical point about which rotation is determined and to whose nearness stability is determined, is now $-K$. The distance from $-K$ to the curve is $\dfrac{K}{M}$. To aid in determining the proper K and M circle, it can be easily shown that the M circle must be tangent to a straight line through the origin, which makes an angle of ψ with respect to the negative real axis, where

$$\psi = \sin^{-1} \frac{1}{M}.$$

After constructing this line it is easy to construct a circle tangent to both this line and the curve, with its center on the negative real axis. The center of this circle is the new, required gain K of the system.

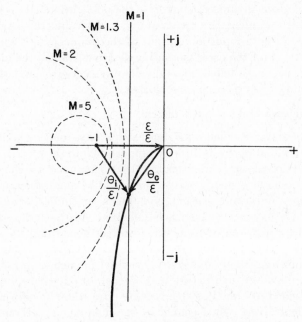

Fig. 7-18.   Plot of constant M circles for $(\theta_o/\epsilon)(j\omega)$.

Similar relations exist between M and the curve of $1/Y_o(p) = \theta_o/\epsilon(p)$. However, they are not as convenient and will be mentioned here only for completeness. The constant values of M appear as circles of varying radii and center, and the one tangent to the curve determines the value of M for that system. An example is shown in Fig. 7-18.

The requirement of constant M requires a constant ratio between θ_o and θ_i, so that the important segments of the curves can be constructed easily from the phasor relations shown in Fig. 7-18. Use will be made of the transfer plots in following sections, and a more complete treatment may be obtained from a text on the subject of servomechanisms.

It should be mentioned that this type of plotting is very useful in determining some measure of the quality of a system too complex to analyze mathematically. It requires only that sufficient experimental data be obtained to plot the transfer curve. This is usually accomplished by disconnecting the feedback circuit and applying as input an artificial sinusoidal error at the point where the system is open. Measurements are then required to determine the magnitude and phase of both input and output as the frequency is varied. If the sensitivity of the error measuring device is known, the artificial error can be correlated to an equivalent system error and the system's transfer function may be plotted.

7.8 Derivative Control and Its Effects

The systems studied thus far have always depended upon a corrective signal that was directly proportional to the error. In the case of the regulator it was this fact that demanded a steady-state error, since no new steady-state value could be maintained unless a continuous effort were exerted, and thus a continuous error maintained. In the position systems studied, no steady-state error was found if no steady-state torque was required to maintain the system in its new position once it was attained. However, a few changes in the assumptions about the system resulted in such an error. For example, a load of such nature that a constant output torque must be maintained resulted in a steady-state error whose magnitude was independent of the size of change in the input signal. If the input was considered to be a constant velocity, there resulted a steady-state error directly proportional to the torque required to overcome the viscous friction. It is the purpose of this and the following section to introduce methods and circuits which tend to reduce these errors, while still maintaining a satisfactory transient response.

The effects will be studied from two points of view, although several other approaches are also useful. The first method will deal with the system's differential equations and the effects on the general coefficients ζ, ω_η, and ω. The second method will be the application of the transfer plot, which will lend itself more readily to experimental procedure. Consider again the typical second-order system. If it is a mechanical rotating system, the differential equation is of the form

$$(J_o p^2 + F_o p)\theta_o = (K)\epsilon. \tag{7.99}$$

Suppose that the system is altered so that the corrective torque is proportional to the derivative[3] of the error as well as to the error itself. The equation then is of the form

$$(J_o p^2 + F_o p)\theta_o = (Lp + K)\epsilon. \tag{7.100}$$

If Eq. 7.100 is rearranged to express the relation between θ_o and θ_i, it becomes

$$(J_o p^2 + [F_o + L]p + K)\theta_o = (Lp + K)\theta_i. \tag{7.101}$$

Since the left side of the equation determines the transient response, it is immediately obvious that the damping coefficient F_o has in effect been altered by the addition of the constant L. Since the damping ratio, ζ, is directly proportional to the damping coefficient, Eq. 7.48 becomes,

$$\zeta = \frac{F_o + L}{2\sqrt{KJ_o}}. \tag{7.102}$$

The result of adding the positive derivative signal has been to increase the damping of the system. Oftentimes in practical circuits the actual value of F_o introduced by the system is far too small to provide a satisfactory damping ratio, and the addition of the term $Lp\epsilon$ serves in preference to added friction which consumes steady-state power. This is particularly desirable from the point of view of the steady-state error due to constant velocity inputs.

The relation between θ_i and ϵ, obtained from Eq. 7.101, is

$$[J_o p^2 + (F_o + L)p + K]\epsilon = (J_o p^2 + F_o p)\theta_i. \tag{7.103}$$

After the steady state has been reached, and both $p^2\epsilon$ and $p\epsilon$ equal zero,

$$K\epsilon = (J_o p^2 + F_o p)\theta_i. \tag{7.104}$$

If the input is a constant velocity, $\omega_i = p\theta_i$, $p^2\theta_i = 0$, and

$$\epsilon_{ss} = \frac{F_o p\theta_i}{K} = \frac{F_o \omega_i}{K}. \tag{7.105}$$

---

[3] Methods of introducing derivative feedback will be discussed later in this chapter.

As would be expected, the steady-state error is inversely proportional to the system gain K, but directly proportional to the friction
coefficient F_o.   However, the term L is absent from the relation and
does not contribute to the steady-state error even though it does
help determine ζ.   Thus if F_o is made very small, perhaps negligible,
the steady-state error approaches zero, and ζ is kept at the required
value by the addition of L.

It is apparent in this system that the required system gain constant K is determined by the allowable steady-state error, the coefficient of friction, and the input signal.   The damping ratio ζ is
determined by the allowable overshoot, which in turn dictates the
relation between $F_o + L$, K, and J_o.   This leaves no freedom in the
choice of ω_n or ω, which together with ζ determine both the frequency of oscillation and the time duration of the transient.   The
natural frequency is of course expressed by

$$\omega_n = \sqrt{\frac{K}{J_o}}. \tag{7.106}$$

If J_o were variable, the specification of the third parameter, ω_n,
would be possible, and all three constants in the characteristic
equation could then be controlled.

The variation of J_o, usually to be decreased, may be accomplished
by the addition of a second derivative term to the corrective effort.
Thus from Eq. 7.100,

$$(J_o p^2 + F_o p)\theta_o = (M p^2 + L p + K)\epsilon. \tag{7.107}$$

Rearrange Eq. 7.107 in terms of θ_o and θ_i:

$$[(J_o + M)p^2 + (F_o + L)p + K]\theta_o = (M p^2 + L p + K)\theta_i. \tag{7.108}$$

If the constant M is made either positive or negative, it is possible to
adjust the total inertia term to any required value.   With these
changes, it is possible to take any second-order system with given
values of J_o and F_o or their equivalents, and adjust the system to
have any desired steady-state error, approaching zero as a limit, and
any desired transient response.   Problem 7.4 is particularly designed
to demonstrate these possibilities.

The problem of derivative control can also be approached from
the frequency response or transfer function point of view.   The
error signal can always be represented by the Fourier transform, and

may thus be considered as the superposition of many sinusoids over a wide frequency band. This view is convenient because it permits application of the theory developed for steady-state sinusoidal input.

For the ideal proportional-plus-derivative type of rotational system, the relation between corrective torque and error should be

$$\frac{T}{\epsilon}(p) = K + Lp, \tag{7.109}$$

or

$$\frac{T}{\epsilon}(j\omega) = K + j\omega L. \tag{7.110}$$

The polar plot of this function is shown in Fig. 7-19.

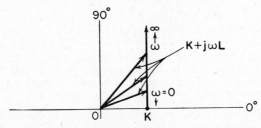

Fig. 7-19.   Polar plot of perfect proportional-plus-derivative signal.

The magnitude varies from K to infinity, and the phase angle is leading, varying from $0°$ to $90°$ if L is positive. This is of course the basis for the common term, "phase lead network." This relation appears as a series factor in the open-loop system, and thus $K + j\omega L$ becomes a multiplying factor on any previous open-loop transfer function. A typical plot of a second order system with and without the derivative signal is shown in Fig. 7-20. From the general application of the M circles of Sec. 7.7 it can be seen that the system with derivative control is appreciably more stable than the one without it. It has been assumed so far that it was possible to obtain a signal or function that was exactly $(K + Lp)\epsilon$. This is not usually possible in practice. A few practical circuits will be discussed and their approximation to the ideal relation shown.

Consider first the circuit of Fig. 7-21. It will be noticed that the circuit is electric in nature both at the input and the output terminals. Practically, therefore, the system error would be converted to a voltage signal and utilized in this form if this is not already the case.   This is by no means a necessity for derivative control, but merely a convenience.

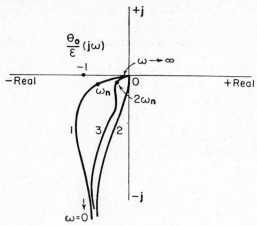

Fig. 7-20.   Plot of second-order system transfer function.   (1) Proportional control only.   (2) Proportional-plus-ideal derivative control.   (3) Proportional-plus-approximate derivative control (Fig. 7-21).

Since it is difficult to specify the exact form of the error function, it will be represented by a Fourier transform, so that the steady-state sinusoidal response may be studied.   For sinusoidal variations, the steady-state complex ratio of the output to input voltage in the circuit of Fig. 7-21 is represented by

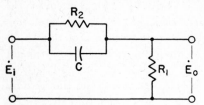

Fig. 7-21.   Passive circuit for producing approximately a proportional-plus-derivative signal.

$$\frac{\dot{E}_o}{\dot{E}_i}(j\omega) = \frac{R_1}{R_1 + \dfrac{R_2/(j\omega C)}{R_2 + 1/(j\omega C)}}$$

$$= \frac{R_1 + R_1 R_2 j\omega C}{R_1 + R_2 + R_1 R_2 j\omega C}. \quad (7.111)$$

For convenience let

$$\frac{R_1}{R_1 + R_2} = \frac{1}{\alpha_d}, \quad \text{and} \quad R_2 C = T_d. \quad (7.112)$$

By substitution and rearrangement,

$$\frac{E_o}{E_i}(j\omega) = \frac{1}{\alpha_d}\frac{1 + j\omega T_d}{1 + j\omega T_d/\alpha_d}. \quad (7.113)$$

The polar plot of this ratio is shown in Fig. 7-22. Comparison of Fig. 7-22 with Fig. 7-19 shows that the plot of Fig. 7-22 duplicates reasonably well the ideal curve of Fig. 7-19 for low frequencies. As the frequency increases the approximation becomes poorer.

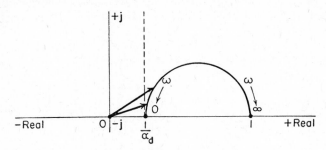

Fig. 7-22. Polar plot of Eq. 7.113.

This fact could also be recognized from Eq. 7.113 if $\omega \dfrac{T_d}{\alpha_d} \leqq 0.2$, so that Eq. 7.113 becomes approximately

$$\frac{\dot{E}_o}{\dot{E}_i}(j\omega) \cong \frac{1}{\alpha_d}(1 + j\omega T_d), \qquad (7.114)$$

which is of the same form as the ideal. It will be remembered from Fig. 7-8 of Sec. 7.5 that the frequency response curve was rapidly approaching zero for values of ω greater than $2\omega_n$, and thus it makes little difference what the frequency response of the circuit of Fig. 7-21 is above this value since the system does not follow.

Thus it seems practical to specify that the maximum frequency which must satisfy the relation

$$\omega \frac{T_d}{\alpha_d} \leqq 0.2$$

be $2\omega_n$. Therefore

$$\frac{\dot{E}_o}{\dot{E}_i} j\omega \cong \frac{1}{\alpha_d}(1 + j\omega T_d) \qquad (7.114)$$

if

$$\frac{2\omega_n}{\alpha_d} T_d \leqq 0.2. \qquad (7.115)$$

The use of this system requires an additional system gain equal to α_d to compensate for the loss across the system of Fig. 7-21.   The effect of this approximate proportional-plus-derivative control is also shown in Fig. 7-20.   It will be left to the reader to show that the circuit of Fig. 7-23 will produce a similar response.   The two circuits mentioned are passive and thus could approach but never attain

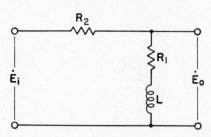

Fig. 7-23.   Circuit for producing approximately a proportional-plus-derivative signal.

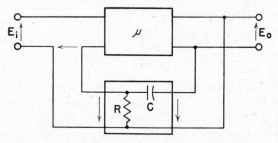

Fig. 7-24.   Active circuit for production of proportional-plus-derivative signal.

perfection.   An active circuit is shown in Fig. 7-24, which theoretically could produce the exact desired signal.   Practically, it too is limited.   This circuit is a feedback amplifier, so that

$$\frac{\dot{E}_o}{\dot{E}_i} = \frac{\mu}{1 - B\mu}, \qquad (7.116)$$

where μ is the gain of the amplifier without feedback. The feedback ratio B is given by

$$B = \frac{R}{R + 1/(Cp)} = \frac{RCp}{RCp + 1}. \qquad (7.117)$$

Thus $\dfrac{\dot{E}_o}{\dot{E}_i}(p) = \dfrac{\mu}{1 - \mu RCp/(RCp + 1)} = \dfrac{\mu(RCp + 1)}{1 + RCp(1 - \mu)}.$

$$(7.118)$$

If μ is adjusted to exactly unity, $\mu \equiv 1$,

$$\frac{\dot{E}_o}{\dot{E}_i} j\omega = (1 + j\omega RC). \qquad (7.119)$$

This is of course the form of the ideal relation.

The passive feedback factor determined by the R-C combination in Fig. 7-24 and the relations of the passive circuits of Fig. 7-19 and Fig. 7-23 all were dependent upon an input circuit of zero impedance and output circuit of infinite impedance, neither of which can be entirely realized. In the active circuit of Fig. 7-24 this condition would require the amplifier with a gain of μ to have infinite input impedance, zero output impedance, and unity gain at all frequencies. Although a cathode follower approaches these conditions, it is not perfect and thus the circuit is not ideal, although practically it is very good.

In addition to the electric circuits discussed, it is sometimes more convenient to use other components to produce the deriva-
tive signal. A transformer is
very often practical since its
output voltage is proportional
to the rate of change of the
input current and contains no
d-c component. Thus if the
primary in series with a resistance is placed across the error

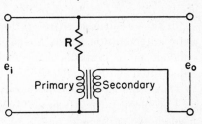

Fig. 7-25. Use of a transformer for derivative signal.

signal and the secondary in series, the total output contains components proportional to the error and its derivative. The circuit is shown in Fig. 7-25. The series resistance is large to prevent saturation and to ensure that the primary current is nearly proportional to e_i.

If the system is rotational, a tachometer is often convenient for producing a signal proportional to the derivative of the *output* position. This serves the same purpose as a signal proportional to the derivative of the error if θ_i is constant. If this is not the case, the slight differences in the effect of derivative of the error or derivative of the output can be worked out by the methods already utilized in this chapter. If the system is rotational and uses a d-c motor, the armature voltage of the motor often serves as the derivative signal, since the electromotive force is nearly proportional to speed in the much-used shunt motor. One important use of derivative control has not yet been mentioned, and it is perhaps of sufficient importance to warrant consideration.

The imperfect circuit of Fig. 7-19 may often serve to replace an unwanted time constant by a more desirable one. For example, the general form of the relation between θ_o and ϵ is often

$$(1 + T_1 p)[1 + (T_2 + T_3)p + (T_2 T_3)p^2]\theta_o = K(1 + T_4 p)\epsilon. \quad (7.120)$$

If the proportional-plus-derivative term appearing on the right were being approximated by a circuit such as that of Fig. 7-19, Eq. 7.120 would have the form

$$(1 + T_1 p)[1 + (T_2 + T_3)p + (T_2 T_3)p^2]\theta_o = K\left(\frac{1}{\alpha_d}\right)\left(\frac{1 + T_4 p}{1 + T_4 p/\alpha_d}\right)\epsilon. \quad (7.121)$$

If the circuit is so adjusted that $T_1 = T_4$, the fourth-order characteristic equation, 7.120, has been reduced to third order, and the smaller, more desirable time constant T_4/α_d has in effect been substituted for $T_1 = T_4$.

The other effects on the system of such a substitution will be left as a problem to the student. Again the methods of analysis already used should prove adequate.

In summation, the effects of derivative control are basically two-fold. First, the addition of derivative control to a system tends to increase the damping or stability of that system if all other parameters are maintained constant. Thus if no other system alterations are made, the effect of derivative control is entirely on the transient response.

Second, if the stability of the system without derivative control were already satisfactory, the addition of derivative control would produce more damping than is required. In this situation the total system gain may be increased, thus decreasing the steady-state error and bringing the damping back to the original value.

7.9 Integral Control and its Effects

As was shown in the preceding section, the basic effect of derivative control is to reduce the transient oscillation, with no effect on steady-state error if all other terms remain unchanged. In other words, the differentiating circuit may be thought of as an anticipation network which foresees or anticipates an error before it exists. In comparison, the integral control attempts to improve the steady-state condition. So far, a steady-state error has been necessary because there was no other way to produce a steady-state output power or torque. The integral control, however, works basically as a memory device, producing an output torque, voltage, or other corrective effect as a result of an error in the past but not dependent on a present error. In fact, since the integration is with respect to time, any present error of necessity is either increasing or decreasing the corrective output, depending upon its relative direction. The analysis of integral control will be carried out from both the differential equation point of view and the frequency or transfer plot method.

Let us first consider the effect of adding to the general system a corrective effort proportional to the time integral of the error. Thus, Eq. 7.100 would then become

$$(J_o p^2 + F_o p)\theta_o = \left(K + Lp + \frac{N}{p}\right)\epsilon. \qquad (7.122)$$

As before, the differential equation may be expressed in terms of θ_o and θ_i or in terms of θ_i and ϵ, depending upon which is the more convenient. Differentiating and rewriting both sides of Eq. 7.122 gives

$$(J_o p^3 + (F_o + L)p^2 + Kp + N)\epsilon = (J_o p^3 + F_o p^2)\theta_i. \qquad (7.123)$$

The time solution for $\epsilon(t)$ is again the sum of the steady-state and transient solutions:

$$\epsilon(t) = \epsilon_t + \epsilon_{ss}. \qquad (7.124)$$

Next consider the steady-state solution. For comparison with previous functions, assume that the input is a unit function of constant velocity. Thus, at $t \geqq 0+$

$$p^2\theta_i = p^3\theta_i = 0; \qquad p\theta_i = \omega_i.$$

A very long time after $t = 0$, the transient has died out so that in

Eq. 7.123,

$$p^3\epsilon = p^2\epsilon = p\epsilon = 0.$$

Thus $\epsilon_{ss} = 0.$

Therefore the addition of integral control to this particular system has resulted in reducing the steady-state error to zero from the constant value of $\epsilon_{ss} = F_o\omega_i/K$ as found in Sec. 7.5. However, it is not correct to say that the addition of integral control always reduces the steady-state error to zero. The steady-state error obviously depends upon the system and the input function. It is correct to say that for any particular system the addition of integral control reduces the steady-state error to zero for one higher time derivative of input displacement than that for which the system could originally have had zero error. For example, the basic system previously studied had zero steady-state error for a unit function of input position, but a finite steady-state error for a unit function of input velocity. The addition of integral control reduced to zero the steady-state error for a unit function of input velocity, but a glance at Eq. 7.123 indicates that there is a constant steady-state error for a unit function of input acceleration.

A method for determining these steady-state relations for any general system will be introduced at this point. It is first essential to realize that the *steady-state* operation and the *zero frequency* response are identical for the two methods of approach. Thus in Eq. 7.123 the steady-state error was evaluated by letting $p \to 0$ in the characteristic equation. Since $p = j\omega$ in the steady state for a sinusoidal input, letting $p \to 0$ corresponds to allowing ω to approach zero. If it is assumed that the output function is eventually of the same form as the input, i.e., constant output position for constant input position, constant output velocity for constant input velocity, etc., then the following three terms can be defined in terms of output conditions and error rather than input and error:

$$K_\theta = \text{position constant} \quad = \lim_{p \to 0} \frac{\theta_o}{\epsilon}(p),$$

$$K_\omega = \text{velocity constant} \quad = \lim_{p \to 0} \frac{p\theta_o}{\epsilon}(p),$$

$$K_\alpha = \text{acceleration constant} = \lim_{p \to 0} \frac{p^2\theta_o}{\epsilon}(p).$$

Since $p \to 0$, these are obviously steady-state relations. Consider the second term, K_ω. If this limit approaches a finite value different from zero, there is finite steady-state error for a finite steady-state output velocity. If the limit approaches infinity, there is zero steady-state error for a finite steady-state output velocity. If the limit approaches zero, there is an infinite steady-state error for a finite steady-state output velocity, or an ever-increasing error. Similar interpretations can be made for K_θ and K_α as associated with constant position output and constant acceleration output.

Let us apply these general relations to a particular system. Rewrite Eq. 7.122 in different form:

$$\frac{\theta_o}{\epsilon}(p) = \frac{(Lp^2 + Kp + N)}{p^2(J_o p + F_o)}. \tag{7.125}$$

$$K_\theta = \lim_{p \to 0} \frac{(Lp^2 + Kp + N)}{p^2(J_o p + F_o)} = \frac{N}{0(F_o)} = \infty.$$

$$K_\omega = \lim_{p \to 0} \frac{(Lp^2 + Kp + N)}{p(J_o p + F_o)} = \frac{N}{0(F_o)} = \infty.$$

$$K_\alpha = \lim_{p \to 0} \frac{(Lp^2 + Kp + N)}{(J_o p + F_o)} = \frac{N}{F_o}.$$

It is therefore apparent that the steady-state error for this system is zero for both position and velocity inputs, but finite for a constant acceleration input.

Let us consider now the effect of integral control on the transient response. As before, the transient response is determined by the characteristic equation. Reference to Eq. 7.123 shows that a second-order system has been increased to a third-order system by the simple addition of integral control. Unfortunately there is no simple form for the solution of a cubic equation in general, and thus the exact effects of integral control on the transient response are more or less obscure from this approach. It is possible to develop the equation in terms of the constants of the second-order system and thus have some measure of the effect of the change. The procedure is long and arduous and thus will not be attempted here.[4]

[4] For the complete solution see, H. Lauer, R. Lesnick, and L. E. Matson, *Servomechanism Fundamentals*, McGraw-Hill Book Company, Inc., New York, 1947.

It is sufficient to say that the effect is dependent upon the relative magnitude of the various component terms, but in general tends to make the system somewhat less stable. This will become apparent in connection with the frequency response.

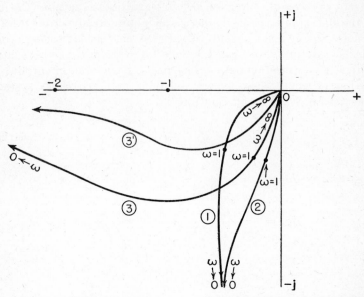

Fig. 7-26. Comparison of system transfer functions with proportional, proportional-plus-derivative, and proportional-plus-derivative-plus-integral control.

(1) $\dfrac{\theta_o}{\epsilon}(p) = \dfrac{10^2}{p(100p + 100)}$, $L = N = 0$, proportional control.

(2) $\dfrac{\theta_o}{\epsilon}(p) = \dfrac{10^2 + 50p}{p(100p + 100)}$, $N = 0$, proportional-plus-derivative control.

(3) $\dfrac{\theta_o}{\epsilon}(p) = \dfrac{50p^2 + 10^2p + 10}{p^2(100p + 100)}$,   proportional-plus-derivative-plus-integral control.

Let us now consider the general transfer or frequency response relations. Begin with Eq. 7.125:

$$\frac{\theta_o}{\epsilon}(p) = \frac{(Lp^2 + Kp + N)}{p^2(J_o p + F_o)}. \tag{7.125}$$

Since $p = j\omega$ for sinusoidal variations, the shape of the curve and the magnitude of the function at any particular value of ω depend directly upon the relative magnitudes of L, K, and N. The term Lp^2 becomes increasingly important as ω increases, and finally predominates in determining the phase angle of the function as $\omega \to \infty$. On the other hand the constant N requires that the numerator be nonzero even when $\omega = 0$, and thus N serves to determine the phase angle of the function as $\omega \to 0$.

Figure 7-26 shows three plots of Eq. 7.125 one with L and N zero, one with N zero, and one with all three constants finite. The actual values were chosen arbitrarily and of course could be altered to fit any system. The relative effects of the three terms are immediately obvious from Fig. 7-26. As shown, the integral control does not appreciably affect the damping by bringing the curve closer to -1, but shifts the curve by 90° as $\omega \to 0$, thus indicating the shift of zero steady-state error to one higher-time derivative input. The effect of adding integral control could just as easily have produced the curve 3′ which is appreciably less damped than curves 2 or 3. These effects will be considered again later in the light of practical circuits for production of the integral signal.

7.10 Circuits for Integral Control

Consider now the circuits that are available for production of this integral signal. It is first desirable to examine the type of response a perfect circuit would have and then see how closely this ideal can be approached. For convenience, consideration will be given only to circuits for the production of proportional-plus-integral control or for the production of integral control alone. Combinations of all three effects are usually produced by tandem or series operation of several such networks. In terms of our mechanical system we need a torque that satisfies the relation:

$$T = \left(K + \frac{N}{p} \right) \epsilon, \tag{7.126}$$

or
$$\frac{T}{\epsilon}(p) = K + \frac{N}{p}. \tag{7.127}$$

In terms of $j\omega$,
$$\frac{T}{\epsilon}(j\omega) = K - j\frac{N}{\omega}. \tag{7.128}$$

The polar plot of Eq. 7.128 is shown as the solid curve in Fig. 7-27. It is therefore desirable that any practical circuit used should have a

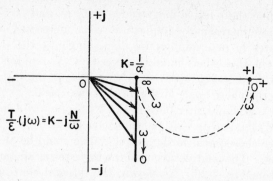

Fig. 7-27. Polar plot of Eq. 7.128 and circuit of Fig. 7-28.

frequency response between output and input that approximates the

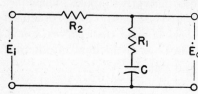

Fig. 7-28. Passive network for production of proportional-plus-integral control.

straight-line plot of Fig. 7-27. As before, this is most easily accomplished with electric quantities such as voltages, and thus requires suitable transducers to fit the system on either side of the network.

As a first consideration, let us examine the circuit of Fig. 7-28. The relation between $\dot{E}_o$ and $\dot{E}_i$ is

$$\frac{\dot{E}_o}{\dot{E}_i}\,(p) = \frac{R_1 + 1/Cp}{R_1 + R_2 + 1/Cp} = \frac{R_1}{R_1 + R_2} \cdot \frac{1 + 1/(R_1 Cp)}{1 + R_1/[(R_1 + R_2)R_1 Cp]}. \tag{7.129}$$

Let $$\frac{R_1}{R_1 + R_2} = \frac{1}{\alpha_i} \quad \text{and} \quad T_i = R_1 C. \tag{7.130}$$

Substituting into Eq. 7.129 gives

$$\frac{\dot{E}_o}{\dot{E}_i}\,(p) = \frac{1}{\alpha_i} \cdot \frac{1 + 1/(T_i p)}{1 + 1/(\alpha_i T_i p)}. \tag{7.131}$$

A glance at Eq. 7.131 indicates that the circuit whose response it represents would be a nearly perfect proportional-plus-integral controller if it were always true that

$$\frac{1}{\alpha_i T_i p} \ll 1. \tag{7.132}$$

Again, since a general error function can be analyzed by a Fourier transform, we make the simplification of setting $p = j\omega$ so that Eq. 7.132 becomes

$$\frac{1}{\alpha_i T_i \omega} \ll 1,$$

or
$$\omega \gg \frac{1}{\alpha_i T_i}. \tag{7.133}$$

Equation 7.133 specifies that the frequency of the incoming error signal must be greater than some minimum value if the circuit under consideration is to produce an essentially proportional-plus-integral signal. However, it must be remembered that the magnitude effect of the integral control is greatest at values of $j\omega$ approaching zero. The condition of Eq. 7.133 and the desired operating range are obviously contradictory. Thus, here again, as was found in connection with the derivative control, it is impossible to produce a perfect network with passive elements. In the case of the derivative signal, conditions could be so imposed that the circuit was operative over the frequency range that was important. This seems impossible here. The polar plot of the circuit of Fig. 7-28 appears as the dotted curve in Fig. 7-27. However, the circuit can be of use but from a slightly different point of view. Suppose that over a certain frequency range,

$$\frac{1}{\omega T_i} \leqq 0.2. \tag{7.134}$$

In this range Eq. 7.131 would specify that the network would approximate a true proportional control with a direct gain of $1/\alpha_i$. Thus if the total system gain is to be maintained at its value previous to the addition of the integrating circuit in that range, an additional stage of d-c amplification equal to α_i must be introduced into the system. This frequency range can easily be made to include the frequency range in which $\left|\frac{\theta_o}{\theta_i}(j\omega)\right|_{max}$ of the system occurs, which is the frequency range that determines the transient response.

The necessary conditions can be established as follows. In most practical circuits ω_p is just slightly less than ω_n. Thus if the relation of Eq. 7.134 holds for frequencies down to approximately $\omega_n/2$, the integral controller would have no appreciable affect on the transient response *if* the overall gain were adjusted to equal the original value without integral control by means of an amplifier as previously discussed.

Thus a practical design condition for the integral network may be

$$\omega \gtreqqless \frac{5}{T_i}.$$ (7.135)

Substituting $\omega = \omega_n/2$ yields

$$T_i \gtreqqless \frac{1}{0.1\omega_n}.$$ (7.136)

If all these conditions are met and a satisfactory transient response exists, consider the effect on the steady state.

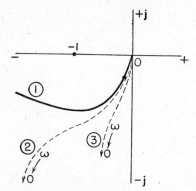

Fig. 7-29. Comparison of perfect and approximate integral control. (1) Perfect integral control added to proportional-plus-perfect derivative control. (2) Approximate integral control added to proportional-plus-perfect derivative control. (3) System without integral control.

Referring again to Eq. 7.131 we see that as $p \to 0$, the relation of Eq. 7.133 or Eq. 7.134 no longer holds, and the integral controller gain alone approaches unity. This is α_i times the gain of the controller in the transient range. Thus if the gains of the other elements in the system including the d-c amplifier remain constant, the *over-all* system gain increases by a factor of α_i as ω decreases from $\omega_n/2$ to 0. Since this is the frequency range determining the steady-state response, the system has a higher gain for the steady state than it has for the transient response. Thus although the passive system is incapable of completely eliminating steady-state error, it can reduce it by the factor α_i. The comparative effect of perfect and approximate integral control is shown in Fig. 7-29.

It will be left to the reader to show that the negative *real* value which the transfer function approaches as $\omega \to 0$ is inversely proportional to the steady-state error, and thus curve 2 of Fig. 7-29 represents a smaller steady-state error than curve 3.

Again, as was true of the derivative signal, the required mathematical form can be approached by several passive networks and perfectly reproduced by an active network similar to that of Fig. 7-24.

The design criteria for both derivative and integral control have been based on a knowledge of ω_n, which may be affected itself by changes in the system. It is usually satisfactory to use the value of ω_n determined before either integral or derivative controls are added. A typical example follows.

Example. Consider a mechanical system with the constants: $J_o = 200$ slug-ft²; $K_o = 100$ ft-lb per radian; $F_o = 100$ ft-lb-sec per radian. To this system is to be added the following controller network:

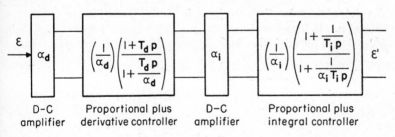

D-C amplifier	Proportional plus derivative controller	D-C amplifier	Proportional plus integral controller

$$\omega_{no} = \sqrt{\frac{K_o}{J_o}} = \sqrt{\frac{10^2}{200}} = 0.707,$$

$$\frac{T_d}{\alpha_d} \leqq \frac{0.2}{2\omega_n} = \frac{0.1}{\omega_n} = \frac{0.1}{0.707} = 0.141,$$

$$T_i \geqq \frac{1}{0.1\omega_n} = \frac{1}{0.0707} = 14.14.$$

Suppose $\alpha_i = \alpha_d = 5$; then $T_d = 5 \times 0.141 = 0.707$, and

$$\frac{\theta_o}{\epsilon} = \frac{K_o \cdot \dfrac{K'}{K'} \cdot \dfrac{K'}{K'} \cdot \dfrac{1 + T_d p}{1 + T_d p/K'} \cdot \dfrac{1 + 1/(T_i p)}{1 + 1/(K' T_i p)}}{p(J_o p + F_o)}$$

Evaluation:
Without added network, $\zeta = 0.353$,

ω	$\left|\dfrac{\theta_o}{\epsilon}\right|$	$\angle$
10	0.0050	−178
5	0.02	−174
1	0.447	−153.5
0.5	1.41	−135
0.1	9.80	−101.5

With added network,

ω	$\left|\dfrac{\theta_o}{\epsilon}\right|$	$\angle$
1	0.5540	−126
0.5	1.5	−123
0.1	11.9	−128
0.05	28.2	−116

The plots of these functions are drawn in Fig. 7-30, on polar graphs as functions of ω. It is apparent that the complete system is appreciably more damped than the original and also has a much smaller steady-state error.

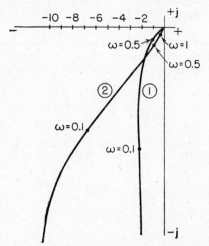

Fig. 7-30. Polar plot of example. (1) System without derivative or integral control. (2) Complete system.

7.11 Other Systems

The discussion of this chapter has been limited to the type of system classified as linear and continuous. This means a system in which the correcting effort is always operative and is always some direct function of the error signal. Many other types of system exist in practice, such as dead zone, on-off, modulated, etc. Each of these would require special handling mathematically as dictated by the system. Most of the general concepts, however, are still valid. No attempt will be made here to discuss these systems. It is hoped that the present work may serve as an introduction to the subject and create an active interest in the topic. A more detailed and complete coverage is left for the many complete books now available on the subject.

PROBLEMS

7.1. A certain system is found to have the following differential equation:

$$(p^2 + 9.6p + 144)\theta_0 = 143\theta_i$$

(a) At what frequency will the output oscillate about its new value after a sudden change in requirement? (b) If the initial value of $d\theta_0/dt = 0$, how long will it be before the overshoot peaks have decayed to less than 1 per cent of the difference between the initial and final value of θ_0? (c) What is the value of the maximum overshoot?

7.2. Show mathematically the value of the steady-state error in a second-order system for: (a) Constant velocity input and no output load. (b) Constant velocity input with constant torque load. (c) Constant velocity input with output load torque proportional to speed. (d) Parts (a), (b), and (c) with constant position input.

7.3. This circuit is designed as a light level regulating circuit.

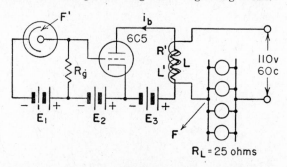

Prob. 7.3

$$F = 1.2\ E^2 \text{ lumens} \qquad R_g = 10^6 \text{ ohms}$$

$$F' = 10^{-5}\ F \qquad\qquad R' = 5000 \text{ ohms}$$

$$\sigma = 20\ \mu\text{a/lumen} \qquad L' = 1h$$

$$E_1 = E_3 = 300 \text{ v} \qquad L = 2000\ (0.005 - i_b)h$$

$$E_2 = 10.4 \text{ v} \qquad\qquad (i_b \text{ in milliamperes})$$

(a) Obtain the differential equation for changes from the normal operating point. (b) Determine the expression of $F(t)$ for a sudden drop in line voltage of 10 per cent.

7.4. A second-order mechanical servo system has a corrective effort torque expressed by

$$T = (K + Lp + Mp^2)\epsilon.$$

It has a moment of inertia J_o and a friction coefficient F_o. So specify K, L, and M that the system has the following response to a constant velocity input of 200 radians per sec: $\epsilon_{ss} = 0.01$ radian; $\omega = 100$ radians per sec. The transient exponential has been reduced to 1 per cent or less of its maximum value in one cycle of oscillation. $J_o = 100$ ft-lb-sec^2 per radian; $F_o = 1$ ft-lb-sec per radian.

7.5. A second-order system has the differential equation

$$(200p^2 + 10p)\theta_o = (10^4 + 10^2p)\epsilon.$$

It is suggested that a term N/p be added inside the brackets of the right side to introduce integral control. (a) Since this addition tends to make the system less stable, what is the maximum value of N that can be added and not have the system unstable? (b) Solve for the roots of the cubic equation resulting from adding one-half the maximum integral value found in part (a) and compare ω and ζ with and without N. (c) Check ζ of part (b) by plotting the inverse transfer locus.

7.6. Prove that, in a second-order mechanical system with constant velocity input, the transfer plot approaches as an asymptote the negative real value $-1/4\zeta^2$ as $\omega \to 0$. Also prove that this is inversely proportional to the steady-state error.

7.7. Determine if the following systems are stable and approximate their degree of damping:

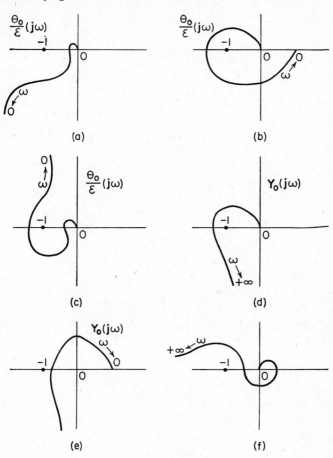

(a)

(b)

(c)

(d)

(e)

(f)

Prob. 7.7

CHAPTER 8

REGULATION

Regulation implies the automatic monitoring and adjustment of some physical quantity such as voltage, position, velocity, frequency, temperature or a variety of other quantities, according to some predetermined plan. Most frequently it is desired to hold the regulated quantity constant, as in the case of the speed of an alternator or the tension in a strip of material in a mill. Except in the most elementary cases, regulators are essentially servomechanisms, the basic theory of which has been discussed in Chapter 7. The present chapter will show the application of this theory to several types of regulator. Emphasis is placed on voltage regulation for several reasons. First, it is a quantity which electrical engineers are familiar with, and hence it is appropriate for the explanation of basic ideas. Second, a great many other quantities which must be regulated, such as velocity, temperature, current or position are, in practice, most easily converted into proportional voltages by suitable transducers, and this equivalent voltage then becomes a sort of secondary quantity which is to be regulated. It is convenient to convert or transduce various quantities into voltages, because in many cases the operations of addition, multiplication, differentiation or integration which may be required to produce certain system characteristics may be most conveniently carried out or approximated by electric circuits.

8.1 Voltage Regulation by Proportional Control

Figure 8-1 shows a simple regulator circuit for a d-c generator supplying a resistance load. The circuit elements are arranged in the figure to correspond to the elements of the servomechanism block diagram of Fig. 7-1. The general symbol θ now represents voltage, so the symbol e will replace θ. The power amplifier designated by K in Fig. 7-1 corresponds to the triode part of the circuit. The voltage input to the grid is the error voltage E obtained from the junctions enclosed by dotted lines. This "junction box" corresponds to the differential device x of Fig. 7-1.

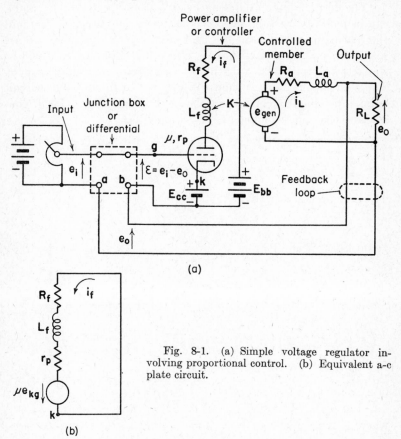

Fig. 8-1. (a) Simple voltage regulator involving proportional control. (b) Equivalent a-c plate circuit.

The controlled member is the generator. The input voltage is the potentiometer voltage e_i which in this case is adjustable to some constant desired value in practice. In theory it will be desirable to allow e_i to change, either as a step function of time or as a sinusoidal function of time, in order to determine the characteristics of the regulator. In practice, the load resistance would be the quantity most likely to change.   However, it will be shown that the stability and response speed for such a change are the same as for a change of e_i, and since the servomechanism theory of Chapter 7 is developed on this basis and because the relations are simpler, the study of regulators will be based largely on changes of e_i.

The desired differential equation, in terms of e_i and e_o or e_o and ϵ, can be found by writing the loop equations around the plate circuit, the armature circuit, and the grid circuit.   At this point we are interested only in *changes* of e_i, e_o and other variables, so it will be simplest to replace the tube by its equivalent a-c voltage source. The equivalent circuit is shown in Fig. 8-1(b) for the plate circuit only.   All circuit elements will be considered linear.   Then, considering changing components of voltages only,

$$\mu e_{kg} = \mu(e_i - e_o) = \mu\epsilon = (R_f + r_p)i_f + L_f p i_f. \tag{8.1}$$

$$e_{gen} = k i_f = (R_a + L_a p)i_L + e_o. \tag{8.2}$$

To eliminate i_L, note that

$$i_L = \frac{e_o}{R_L}. \tag{8.3}$$

From Eqs. 8.2 and 8.3,

$$i_f = \frac{(R_a + R_L + L_a p)e_o}{R_L k}. \tag{8.4}$$

Substitution of this result into Eq. 8.1 and rearrangement gives

$$\left(1 + \frac{L_f}{R_f + r_p}p\right)\left(1 + \frac{L_a}{R_a + R_L}p\right)e_o = \frac{\mu R_L k}{(R_a + R_L)(R_f + r_p)}\epsilon \tag{8.5}$$

or

$$(1 + T_1 p)(1 + T_2 p)e_o = K'\epsilon. \tag{8.5a}$$

where

$$T_1 = \frac{L_f}{R_f + r_p} \quad \text{and} \quad T_2 = \frac{L_a}{R_a + R_L}.$$

Equation 8.5a is identical with Eq. 7.64 for the similar system of Fig. 7-6.   Equation 8.5a may also be written in the form of Eq. 7.28:

$$\left(p^2 + \frac{T_1 + T_2}{T_1 T_2}p + \frac{1}{T_1 T_2}\right)e_o = \frac{K'}{T_1 T_2}\epsilon = \frac{\mu R_L k}{L_a L_f}\epsilon. \tag{8.6}$$

To write this equation in terms of the damping constant ζ and the natural frequency ω_n rewrite Eq. 8.6 in terms of e_o and e_i.

$$\left(p^2 + \frac{T_1 + T_2}{T_1 T_2}p + \frac{1 + K'}{T_1 T_2}\right)e_o = \frac{K'}{T_1 T_2}e_i. \tag{8.7}$$

This is the same as Eq. 7.68, which, incidentally, was obtained for a mechanical system, and hence we may write immediately that

$$(p^2 + 2\zeta\omega_n p + \omega_n{}^2)e_o = \frac{K'}{T_1 T_2}e_i, \tag{8.8}$$

where

$$\omega_n{}^2 = \frac{1 + K'}{T_1 T_2} \qquad (7.72) \quad \text{or} \quad (8.9)$$

$$\zeta^2 = \frac{(T_1/T_2) + (T_2/T_1) + 2}{4(1 + K')}. \qquad (7.73) \quad \text{or} \quad (8.10)$$

It should be recalled from Sec. 7.5 that K' is the open loop d-c or zero frequency gain of the system. This fact is most easily shown by starting with Eq. 8.6. If the loop of Fig. 8-1 be opened by eliminating the feedback connections and shorting across terminals a and b of the "junction box," then Eq. 8.6 is still valid if ϵ is replaced by e_i. This is the reason why Eq. 8.6 is sometimes called the open loop form (see Eq. 7.24). Making this change gives

$$\left(p^2 + \frac{T_1 + T_2}{T_1 T_2}p + \frac{1}{T_1 T_2}\right)e_o = \frac{K'}{T_1 T_2}e_i. \tag{8.11}$$

To find the steady state or zero frequency open loop gain it is only necessary to let $p \to 0$ and solve Eq. 8.11 for e_o/e_i. The result is:

$$\left.\frac{e_o}{e_i}\right|_{p=j\omega=0} = K'.$$

The same result can be found by physical reasoning from Fig. 8-1 by determining the change Δe_o due to a change Δe_i for the open loop condition.

It will be noticed from Eq. 8.10 that ζ, the damping constant, may be expressed as a function of the *ratio* T_1/T_2 and the open loop gain K'. We are interested in whether ζ is less than, equal to, or greater than unity, for if it is less than unity the system is underdamped, etc. Suppose we imagine a fictitious open loop gain of zero, and calculate a few values of ζ. The calculations are tabulated in Table 8.1. For this fictitious situation, ζ never is less than unity,

Table 8.1   Tabulation ζ versus T_1/T_2 for $K' = 0$

T_1/T_2	$\zeta^2 = \dfrac{(T_1/T_2) + (T_2/T_1) + 2}{4}$	ζ
0.0	∞	∞
0.1	3.03	1.74
0.5	1.125	1.06
1.0	1.0	1.0
2.0	1.125	1.06
10.0	3.03	1.74
10^2	25.5	5.04
10^3	2.5×10^2	15.8
10^6	2.5×10^5	500.0
∞	∞	∞

although at $T_1/T_2 = 1$, $\zeta = 1$.   In any real system the gain K' will be greater than zero, so that for $T_1/T_2 = 1$, any real system would be under-damped.   The greater K' is made, the greater will be the range of values of T_1/T_2 above and below 1 for which $\zeta < 1$. However, for any chosen value of K' it is always possible to find the value of T_1/T_2 either so high or so low that $\zeta > 1$, and the system will be over-damped.   This may or may not be desirable, depending on the application, but in any case, the above reasoning leads to a generalization.   *In any closed loop system with proportional control containing two time constants, the greater the ratio of the time constants the higher the gain can be made before the system becomes under-damped.* Thus if it is possible to choose time constants in designing a system, make them widely different.   This choice will permit larger values of K' and ω_n (see Eq. 8.9), and better transient response will result.

The characteristics of any second order closed loop system have been discussed in general in Sec. 7.5.   The response of such a system to a step input was detailed and will not be repeated here.

It might be pointed out that the open loop gain K' varies directly with μ, the triode amplification factor, and almost inversely with the plate resistance.   If $r_p \gg R_f$, then, approximately, from Eq. 8.5,

$$K' \cong \frac{\mu R_L k}{(R_a + R_L)r_p} = \frac{g_m R_L k}{R_a + R_L} = \frac{g_m k}{1 + R_a/R_L}. \qquad (8.12)$$

Therefore g_m should be large for high gain.   Also the ratio k, of generated voltage to field current should be larger, and the ratio

R_a/R_L should be small. The actual frequency of oscillation is found from Eq. 7.51,

$$\omega = \omega_n \sqrt{1 - \zeta^2}.$$

The damping ratio is given by Eq. 7.57,

$$\frac{\alpha}{\omega} = \frac{\zeta}{\sqrt{1 - \zeta^2}} = \frac{1}{\sqrt{(1/\zeta^2) - 1}}.$$

From these relations it is evident that all the essential facts about the system's response can be found from the ratio of time constants and the open loop zero frequency gain.

8.2 Inverse Transfer Function in Second-order Systems

It is interesting to plot the inverse transfer function, $Y_0(j\omega) = \frac{\epsilon}{\theta_o}(j\omega)$, for the second-order system discussed in section 8.1. Equation 8.5a is the general differential equation in terms of time constants for the second-order system. From Eq. 8.5a,

$$K' \frac{\epsilon}{e_o}(p) = (1 + T_1 p)(1 + T_2 p). \tag{8.13}$$

For sinusoidal input, where $p = j\omega$,

$$K' \frac{\epsilon}{e_o}(j\omega) = (1 - T_1 T_2 \omega^2) + j(T_1 + T_2)\omega. \tag{8.14}$$

This equation is plotted for four values of the ratio T_1/T_2 in Fig. 8-2. Actually the curves are symmetrical about the real axis, but only the upper halves are plotted. The curves are parabolas which depend *only* on the ratio of time constants, or, in view of Eqs. 8.9 and 8.10, on ζ and K'. These statements are easily verified by representing the imaginary part of Eq. 8.14 by y and the real part by x and eliminating ω between the two relations. Thus,

$$x = 1 - T_1 T_2 \omega^2$$

$$y = (T_1 + T_2)\omega.$$

Eliminating ω and rearranging gives

$$y^2 + \left(\frac{T_1}{T_2} + \frac{T_2}{T_1} + 2\right) x - \left(\frac{T_1}{T_2} + \frac{T_2}{T_1} + 2\right) = 0. \tag{8.15}$$

It is thus evident that the loci of the inverse transfer function are parabolas depending only on T_1/T_2. Also, since T_1/T_2 and T_2/T_1 always appear as the sum $T_1/T_2 + T_2/T_1$, a curve for a given value of T_1/T_2 is also the curve for the same value of T_2/T_1.

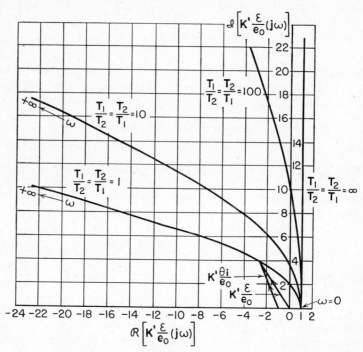

Fig. 8-2. Inverse transfer functions for second-order regulator, branches for positive ω only.

$$K' \frac{\epsilon}{\epsilon_0} (j\omega) = (1 - T_1 T_2)\omega^2 + j(T_1 + T_2)\omega$$

From Eq. 8.10, relating ζ and the time constants, Eq. 8.15 can be written in the form

$$y^2 + 4(1 + K')\zeta^2 x - 4(1 + K')\zeta^2 = 0. \tag{8.16}$$

The curves of Fig. 8-2 may be regarded as dimensionless plots of the inverse transfer functions for any regulator whose differential equation is of second order. They may be used directly for a zero frequency gain K' of unity, or all dimensions may be *divided* by K' for a general gain of K'. Thus, the larger the gain, the closer the parabolas will lie to the negative real axis and the closer they will come to the point -1. In Sec. 7.7 it was shown that the minimum distance from the point -1 to the locus is

$$\frac{1}{M_{max}} = \left|\frac{\theta_i}{\theta_o}(j\omega)\right|_{min}. \tag{8.17}$$

From Eq. 7.79, Eq. 8.17 becomes

$$\left|\frac{\theta_i}{\theta_o}(j\omega)\right|_{min} = 2\zeta\sqrt{1 - 2\zeta^2}. \tag{8.18}$$

Equation 8.18 may be expressed in terms of time constants and K' by use of Eq. 8.10.

$$\left|\frac{\theta_i}{\theta_o}(j\omega)\right|_{min}$$
$$= \left[\left(\frac{(T_1/T_2) + (T_2/T_1) + 2}{1 + K'}\right)\left(1 - \frac{(T_1/T_2) + (T_2/T_1) + 2}{2(1 + K')}\right)\right]^{\frac{1}{2}}. \tag{8.19}$$

This result shows why it is that increasing K' brings the inverse transfer function loci closer to the point -1. It also confirms the statement made in Chapter 7 that the closer the locus of $Y_o(j\omega)$ comes to the point -1, the smaller is the damping. This is apparent from Eq. 8.10, which states that

$$\zeta^2 = \frac{(T_1/T_2) + (T_2/T_1) + 2}{4(1 + K')}. \tag{8.10}$$

The discussion in Sec. 8.1 of the effect of the ratio of time constants on damping, or stability, may now be restated in terms of the inverse transfer function plot of Fig. 8-2. Here we see that the minimum distance $\left|\frac{\theta_i}{\theta_o}(j\omega)\right|_{min}$ occurs for $T_1/T_2 = 1$, which means that minimum damping occurs for this ratio. For all other ratios, the damping is greater. This is the same conclusion that was reached in Sec. 8.1 by a different argument.

8.3 Conditions in Proportional Control System at Quiescence

The problem of determining the quiescent values of i_b, e_o, and e_i in Fig. 8-1 is important. Consider first a graphical method which is quite general in that it does not require linearity of either the tube or generator characteristics. However, for simplicity of drawing and later analysis it has been assumed in Fig. 8-3 that both the tube and generator characteristics are linear. On the left side of Fig. 8-3 is plotted tube plate current against e_o, the total grid voltage, for a fixed value of supply voltage E_{bb}. On the right is a family of curves of output voltage, e_o, plotted against plate current for various values of $r = R_a/R_L$. With these curves, which can be obtained from machine and tube characteristics, a number of cases may be analyzed. In Sec. 8.1, e_o was used to refer only to *changes* in output

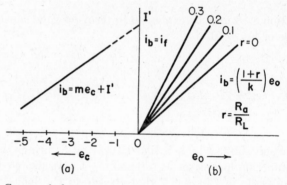

Fig. 8-3. Curves of plate current versus output voltage and grid voltage for determining quiescent conditions.

voltage. It is used here to refer to the *total* output voltage, that is, the sum of the quiescent and changing components.

Case 1. Given r and e_o: Find the value of e_i required to produce the given value of e_o.

From Fig. 8-3(b) the given values of r and e_o determine uniquely a value of i_b. Figure 8-3(a) gives directly the value of e_c required to produce the necessary plate current. Then from Fig. 8-1, $e_i = e_c + e_o + E_{cc}$. Notice here that e_c is a negative number for most triodes.

Case 2. Given e_i and r: Find e_o and i_b.

First assume a value of e_o, for example, equal to e_i. Then locate i_b for this assumed value of e_o on the appropriate curve of Fig. 8-3(b). Now calculate a value $e_c = e_i - e_o - E_{cc}$. From this value of e_c obtain a value of i_b from Fig. 8-3(a). If this value of i_b is the same as that obtained from Fig. 8-3(b), the first guess for e_o was correct. If not, then a second guess for e_o must be made and the process repeated. Three or four guesses should yield good values of e_o and i_b.

Case 3. Given e_i, i_b, r and e_o: Find e_o for a new value of r corresponding to a different load resistance.

Here one proceeds exactly as in Case 2, assuming a new value of e_o, etc.

It will be noticed that the graphical method does not require linearity, although the curves were so drawn in Fig. 8.3. If, however, linearity is assumed, simple relations exist for solving the problem analytically. Even if the system is not strictly linear, such relations are useful to indicate roughly the interdependence of the various parameters, voltages, and currents.

The straight line in Fig. 8-3(a) can be written

$$i_b = me_c + I' \qquad (8.20)$$

where m is the slope of the line, as yet unknown, and I' is the i_b intercept.

The family of lines in Fig. 8-3(b) can be written

$$i_b = \left(\frac{1+r}{k}\right) e_o.$$

At quiescence these two equations for i_b must be equal to each other.

$$me_c + I' = \frac{1+r}{k} e_o. \qquad (8.21)$$

But from Fig. 8-1,

$$e_c = -e_o + e_i - E_{cc}.$$

Substituting this into Eq. 8.21 and solving for e_o gives

$$e_o = \frac{I' + m(e_i - E_{cc})}{(1+r)/k + m}. \qquad (8.22)$$

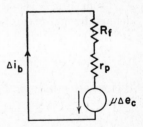

Fig. 8-4. Equivalent a-c plate circuit of a triode.

The value of I' is the value of plate current at the intersection of the load line with the e_b, i_b characteristic of the tube *at zero bias* and must therefore be found from the plate characteristics of the tube. The value of m, which is really the slope of the mutual characteristic, can be found by the use of the equivalent a-c plate circuit.

$$m = \frac{\Delta i_b}{\Delta e_c}$$

From the equivalent a-c plate circuit,

$$\Delta i_b = \frac{\mu \, \Delta e_o}{R_f + r_p}.$$

Therefore

$$m = \frac{\mu}{R_f + r_p} = g_m \frac{r_p}{R_f + r_p} \tag{8.23}$$

Substituting Eq. 8.23 into Eq. 8.22 gives

$$e_o = \frac{I' + \mu(e_i - E_{cc})/(R_f + r_p)}{(1 + r)/k + g_m r_p/(R_f + r_p)},$$

$$e_o = \frac{I'k/(1 + r) + K'(e_i - E_{cc})}{1 + K'}, \tag{8.24}$$

where the zero frequency gain is

$$K' = \frac{k\mu}{(R_f + r_p)} \frac{R_L}{(R_L + R_a)} = \frac{k\mu}{(R_f + r_p)(1 + r)}.$$

Equation 8.24 gives the steady-state value of e_o for a constant value of e_i.

8.4　Voltage Regulation in the Proportional Control Regulator

From Eq. 8.24 the voltage regulation for change in load as defined by de_o/dr can be found in terms of r. Differentiation gives

$$\frac{de_o}{dr} = \frac{-e_o}{1 + r + kg_m r_p/(R_f + r_p)}. \tag{8.25}$$

But we are interested in the variation of e_o with R_L, so we can write

$$\frac{de_o}{dR_L} = \frac{de_o}{dr} \cdot \frac{dr}{dR_L}$$

since

$$r = \frac{R_a}{R_L}, \qquad \frac{dr}{dR_L} = \frac{-R_a}{R_L^2}.$$

Hence

$$\frac{de_o}{dR_L} = \frac{e_o R_a}{R_L^2[1 + (R_a)/(R_L) + kg_m r_p/(r_p + R_f)]}$$

$$= \frac{e_o r}{R_L(1 + r)(1 + K')}. \tag{8.26}$$

It is interesting to compare this result with the voltage regulation with no feedback. In this case the generated voltage stays constant, and one may write

$$\frac{e_o}{e_{gen}} = \frac{R_L}{R_a + R_L},$$

or

$$e_o = e_{gen} \frac{R_L}{R_a + R_L},$$

$$\frac{de_o}{dR_L} = e_{gen}\left[\frac{-R_L}{(R_L + R_a)^2} + \frac{1}{R_L + R_a}\right] = \frac{e_o R_a}{R_L(R_L + R_a)}$$

$$= \frac{e_o r}{(1 + r)R_L}. \qquad (8.27)$$

Obviously the regulation with feedback is superior to that without, since the denominator of Eq. 8.26 is larger than that of Eq. 8.27. As was mentioned in Chapter 7, this type of regulator must always exhibit some steady-state error, which is evident from the fact that $de_o/dR_L \neq 0$. Inspection of Eq. 8.26 shows that the regulation will be best if the smallest value of $r = R_a/R_L$ and the largest possible value of K' are used. These are also the conditions stated in Sec. 8.1 for the best transient response.

8.5   Sudden Change of Load in Proportional Regulator

It will be recalled from Chapter 7 that the important characteristics of servomechanisms resulting in second order differential equations could be predicted from a knowledge of the differential equation alone. It is not necessary to solve the differential equation, but only to know the characteristic equation, in order to predict stability, the damping ratio, frequency of oscillation, and the damping constant. The derivation of the differential equations for any regulator does not depend at all on the cause of a disturbance in the system. Therefore, in considering the effect of a sudden change of load in the circuit of Fig. 8-1, which initially would change e_o suddenly to a new value, it is proper to start with Eq. 8.8 or one of its equivalent forms. The important characteristics of the resulting transient are therefore exactly the same as for a sudden change in e_i. The change in steady-state conditions for a change of load has been discussed in Sections 8.3 and 8.4.

8.6   Regulator with Proportional-plus-derivative Control

The circuit of a simple regulator with proportional-plus-approximate derivative control is shown in Fig. 8-5. This circuit is identical to that of Fig. 8-1 except for the insertion of the R-C network between the "junction box" and the amplifier. The R-C network is the same as the one in Fig. 7-21 for producing a voltage output with terms approximately proportional to ϵ and $d\epsilon/dt$ or $p\epsilon$. The

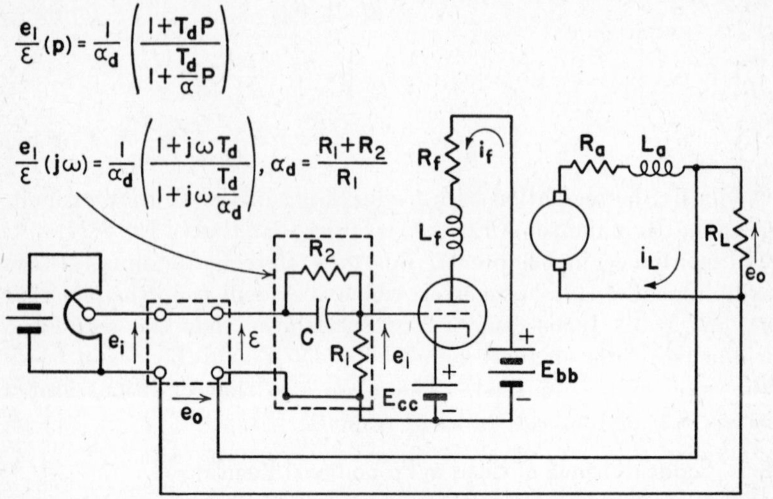

$$\frac{e_1}{\epsilon}(p) = \frac{1}{\alpha_d}\left(\frac{1+T_d P}{1+\frac{T_d}{\alpha}P}\right)$$

$$\frac{e_1}{\epsilon}(j\omega) = \frac{1}{\alpha_d}\left(\frac{1+j\omega T_d}{1+j\omega\frac{T_d}{\alpha_d}}\right), \quad \alpha_d = \frac{R_1+R_2}{R_1}$$

Fig. 8-5. Regulator with proportional-plus-approximate derivative control.

differential equation of the system may be found by starting with Eq. 8.1, which is valid here if ϵ is replaced by e_i.

$$\mu e_{kg} = \mu e_1 = (R_f + r_p)i_f + L_f p i_f. \tag{8.28}$$

The exact relationship between e_1 and ϵ is given by Eq. 7.113.

$$e_i = \frac{\epsilon}{\alpha_d}\left[\frac{1 + T_d p}{1 + (T_d p/\alpha_d)}\right]. \tag{8.29}$$

From Eq. 8.4

$$i_f = \left(\frac{R_a + R_L + L_a p}{R_L k}\right)e_o. \tag{8.30}$$

Substitution of Eqs. 8.29 and 8.30 into Eq. 8.28 gives

$$\frac{\mu\epsilon}{\alpha_d}\left[\frac{1 + T_d p}{1 + (T_d/\alpha_d)p}\right] = \frac{(R_f + r_p)(R_a + R_L + L_a p)}{R_L k}e_o$$

$$+ \frac{L_f p(R_a + R_L + L_a p)e_o}{R_L k}$$

which can be arranged in the form

$$\frac{\mu R_L k \epsilon}{\alpha_d (R_a + R_L)(R_f + r_p)}$$

$$= \left[\frac{1 + (T_d/\alpha_d)p}{1 + T_d p} \right] \left(1 + \frac{L_a}{R_a + R_L} p \right) \left(1 + \frac{L_f}{R_f + r_p} p \right) e_o = K'_d \epsilon \tag{8.31}$$

where $\qquad K'_d = \dfrac{K'}{\alpha_d} = \dfrac{\mu R_L k}{\alpha_d (R_a + R_L)(R_f + r_p)}.$

In terms of time constants,

$$K'_d \frac{\epsilon}{e_o} (p) = \frac{[1 + (T_d/\alpha_d)p]}{(1 + T_d p)} (1 + T_1 p)(1 + T_2 p), \tag{8.32}$$

where $\qquad T_1 = \dfrac{L_f}{R_f + r_p}, \qquad T_2 = \dfrac{L_a}{R_a + R_L}.$

Equation 8.32 is the general differential equation for the system of Fig. 8-5 with no approximations involved. It will be recalled from Sec. 7.8 that the R-C network used here may be adjusted so that one of the other time constants, T_1 or T_2, may be replaced by a smaller time constant. Thus, if T_d is adjusted to equal T_2 for example, T_2 is replaced in effect by T_2/α_d, and the system behaves as a second order system with T_2 reduced by the factor $1/\alpha_d$, as is evident from Eq. 8.32, which becomes

$$K'_d \frac{\epsilon}{e_o} (p) = (1 + T_1 p) \left(1 + \frac{T_2}{\alpha_d} p \right). \tag{8.33}$$

This manipulation therefore simply changes the ratio of time constants and the open loop gain by the factor $1/\alpha_d$. The open loop gain may, of course, be increased by using greater amplification. In this way the performance of the system may be very much improved, as reference to Fig. 8-2 and the related discussion will show, since by increasing the time constant ratio one shifts the inverse transfer function locus away from the point $(-1 + j0)$.

If the R-C network is adjusted to give an approximation to pure proportional-plus-derivative control by making

$$2\omega_n = \frac{T_d}{\alpha_d} \le 0.2, \tag{7.115}$$

then, approximately, Eq. 8.32 becomes

$$K'_d \frac{\epsilon}{e_o} (j\omega) = \frac{(1 + T_1 j\omega)(1 + T_2 j\omega)}{1 + T_d j\omega} = \frac{(1 - T_1 T_2 \omega^2) + j(T_1 + T_2)\omega}{1 + jT_d \omega}$$

(8.34)

To give an idea of the effect of a pure derivative term on the inverse transfer function, Eq. 8.34 has been plotted for several values of T_d in Fig. 8-6. All the curves are plotted for $T_1 = T_2 = 1$ and for various values of T_d equal to 1, 5, and 0.2 respectively. It will be noticed that for $T_d = 1$, Eq. 8.34 reduces to $1 + j\omega$, which is the equation of a straight line through $1 + j0$. When $T_d = 5$, the inverse transfer function drops below the real axis as ω increases from zero toward $+\infty$ and then swings back above the real axis. As the time constant of the feedback circuit becomes smaller, the inverse transfer function approaches the shape it would have with no derivative feedback at all. This fact is apparent from curve 3 for $T_d = 0.2$. For comparison, the curve of $T_d = 0$, curve 4, is plotted. It is identical to the curve for $T_1/T_2 = T_2/T_1 = 1$ in Fig. 8-2. The reader can easily show, by expanding and rationalizing Eq. 8.34 to obtain its real and imaginary parts, that this equation approaches $(T_1 + T_2)/T_d - (T_1 T_2/T_d^2) \pm j\omega$ as ω approaches $\pm \infty$. Thus, curve 3 for $T_1 = T_2 = 1$, $T_d = 0.2$ approaches $-15 + j\infty$. In all cases however, the curves lie above the curve for $T_d = 0$, indicating a more stable system in which higher gain can be used to obtain faster response.

Curves 1, 2 and 3 presuppose that $2\omega_n(T_d/\alpha_d) \leq 0.2$, which enables one to neglect $(T_d/\alpha_d)j\omega$ in comparison with 1 in Eq. 8.32. This assumption is equivalent to assuming pure proportional-plus-derivative control. In order to show how this assumption departs from reality, the inverse transfer function resulting from the exact relation is plotted. Equation 8.32 with $j\omega$ substituted for p gives the result:

$$K'_d \frac{\epsilon}{e_o} (p) = \frac{\left(1 + \dfrac{T_d}{\alpha_d} j\omega\right)(1 + T_1 j\omega)(1 + T_2 j\omega)}{1 + T_d j\omega}.$$

(8.35)

Equation 8.35 is plotted for $T_1 = T_2 = 1$, $T_d = 0.2$ and $\alpha_d = 5$. Curve 3 is the approximate curve for $T_d = 0.2$, and it is evident that the two curves are nearly the same for low values of ω, but that they are quite different as ω gets large. In fact as $\omega \to \infty$, curve 3 approaches $-15 + j\infty$, but curve 5 approaches $-\infty + j\infty$. The close approximation of curve 5 to curve 3 for pure proportional-plus-derivative control at low frequencies is reasonable when it is recalled

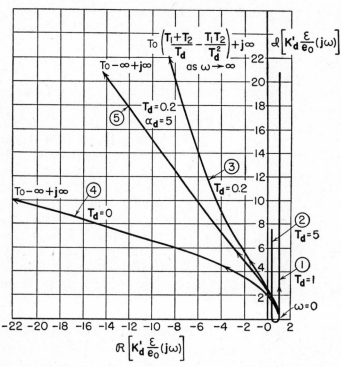

Fig. 8-6. Effects of derivative control on inverse transfer function. For curves 1, 2, and 3,

$$K'_d \frac{\epsilon}{e_0}(j\omega) = \frac{(1 + T_1 j\omega)(1 + T_2 j\omega)}{1 + T_d j\omega}, \text{ Eq. 8.34,}$$

with $T_1 = T_2 = 1$. For curve 5,

$$K'_d \frac{\epsilon}{e_0}(j\omega) = \frac{[1 + (T_d/\alpha_d)j\omega](1 + T_1 j\omega)(1 + T_2 j\omega)}{1 + T_d j\omega}, \text{ Eq. 8.35,}$$

with $T_1 = T_2 = 1$.

from Sec. 7.8 and Fig. 7-22 that the R-C network approximates this ideal condition only at low frequencies. The important conclusion is that although the true performance of the circuit with the R-C network lies between the ideal case and the case for no derivative control on the inverse transfer function plot, still the performance of the circuit can actually be vastly improved by the use of the somewhat less than ideal R-C network. This statement has even more meaning when it is recalled from Fig. 7-8 of Sec. 7.5 that the amplitude versus frequency curve drops rapidly at frequencies above $2\omega_n$, so that the system has little or no response at these higher frequencies anyway.

8.7 The Amplidyne[1,2]

The use of a triode to control directly the field current of a d-c generator is impractical except for the smallest generators. One

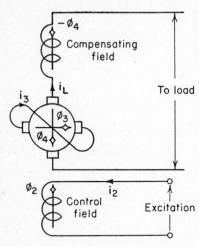

device which is extremely useful in controlling the field current of large generators is the amplidyne, a simple form of which is shown schematically in Fig. 8-7. The amplidyne consists essentially of a d-c generator with two poles (not shown) and four brushes located 90° apart. When an existing voltage is applied to the control field, current i_2 causes flux ϕ_2 to generate a voltage in the rotating armature conductors. The brushes on which this voltage would appear are short circuited, so that a relatively small flux ϕ_2 causes a large short circuit current i_3. The current i_3 sets

Fig. 8-7. Schematic diagram of simple amplidyne.

up a flux ϕ_3 at 90° to ϕ_2. Conductors cutting this flux produce voltage at the other pair of brushes, which are connected to a load. The load current i_L flowing in the armature produces flux ϕ_4 which is opposite to ϕ_2. This bucking flux would produce degenerative feedback if it were not for the addition of a compensating series field winding which carries the load current i_L. This winding produces a flux $-\phi_4$ which balances out the original degenerative flux ϕ_4, thus

[1] Crever, F. E., "Principles of Amplidyne Applications," *Trans. AIEE,* Sept. 1943, Vol. 62, p. 603.

[2] Fisher, A., "Design Characteristics of Amplidyne Generators," *Gen. Elec. Rev.,* Vol. 43, No. 3, pp. 107–113, 1940.

leaving only the controlling flux ϕ_2. The machine is so designed that only a small control magnetomotive force is required to control the full output of the machine. The amplidyne may be considered as a two stage power amplifier combined into one rotating machine. The first stage is the control field and the short circuited brushes. The second stage is the short circuit field ϕ_3 and the load brushes and circuit.

The time constants of each circuit are smaller than those found in an ordinary d-c machine, and for this reason the response speed of the amplidyne is very high. It is therefore very suitable for use as an exciter for large d-c or a-c generators in a system requiring voltage control or in various other regulating systems. Voltage regulation is one important application.

The amplidyne can also be operated as a motor, and as such it will develop large torques in very short times. Such a motor, driven by an amplidyne generator, the latter being controlled electronically, makes an ideal system for applications requiring rapidly changing torques which must be accurately controlled. There are many applications for this sort of system, and its advantages lie in the fact that an amplidyne generator of very large power capabilities can be controlled by high vacuum tubes directly, thus permitting direct application of the many and versatile methods of electronics. An important advantage of the use of electronic control is that feedback, including proportional, derivative and integral types, can be used at very low power levels, so that very little energy need be drawn from the system being controlled. The required energy for corrections is supplied from amplifiers, either electronic or rotating.

The excitation requirements for amplidynes in the range from 0.5 to 2.5 kw output vary from about $\frac{1}{4}$ to $\frac{3}{4}$ watt. Thus the *power* amplification may range from about 2000 to 1 to about 35,000 to 1.

For purposes of approximate design or analysis the amplidyne may be considered as equivalent to two machines in series. The analogous circuit is shown in Fig. 8-8. Here the control field resistance and inductance are R_2 and L_2, the short circuit path resistance and inductance are R_3 and L_3, and those of the load armature circuit are R_a and L_a. It will be noticed that each of these RL circuits has a time constant, and each of these time constants may be thought of as introducing a time delay in the progress of a signal through the system from input to output. It will be shown in Section 8.9 that when there are 3 or more such time delays in a closed system self sustained oscillations, or hunting, may occur. Before analyzing the amplidyne, the general differential equation for a system of n time delays will be set up.

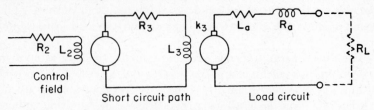

Fig. 8-8.   Equivalent circuit of amplidyne.

8.8   Differential Equation for n-Stage Regulator

Consider the system shown in Fig. 8-9, in which there are several stages of amplification, each of which contributes a time constant,

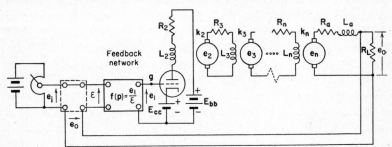

Fig. 8-9.   Voltage regulator with n time delays or time constants exclusive of the feedback network.

or time delay, to the system.   The voltage e_n, which is a generated voltage, is

$$e_n = k_n i_n,$$

$$e_{n-1} = i_n R_n + L_n p i_n = (R_n + L_n p)i_n = R_n(1 + T_n p)i_n,$$

$$e_n = \frac{k_n e_{n-1}}{R_n(1 + T_n p)},$$

$$e_{n-1} = \frac{k_{n-1} e_{n-2}}{R_{n-1}(1 + T_{n-1}p)} \cdot \cdot \cdot ,$$

$$e_3 = \frac{k_3 e_2}{R_3(1 + T_3 p)}.$$

The voltage E_o in the equivalent circuit shown in Fig. 8-10 is necessary in order to provide the quiescent plate current in the circuit which actually exists in the triode. The quiescent current, and hence E_o, will depend on quiescent circuit conditions just before the occurrence of a transient. Therefore E_o can be determined by the method of Section 8.3. At this point, however, we are not par-

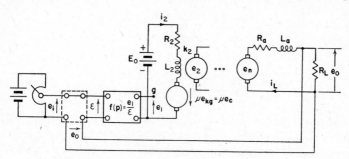

Fig. 8-10.   Equivalent circuit of n-stage regulator of Fig. 8-9.

ticularly interested in the value of E_o, as will be shown immediately. In Fig. 8.10

$$e_2 = k_2 i_2.$$

Also

$$\mu e_c = i_2 R_2 + L_2 p i_2.$$

E_o is not included because we are interested only in changes.

$$i_2 = \frac{\mu e_c}{(R_2 + L_2 p)} = \frac{\mu e_c}{R_2(1 + T_2 p)}.$$

Therefore

$$e_2 = \frac{k_2}{R_2} \frac{\mu e_c}{(1 + T_2 p)}.$$

By combining all the above results it is possible to write in operational form the differential equation for e_n in terms of e_c.

Therefore

$$e_n = \frac{(k_n \cdots k_2)\mu e_c}{(R_n \cdots R_2)(1 + T_n p) \cdots (1 + T_2 p)}. \tag{8.36}$$

Also

$$e_n = i_L R_a + L_a p i_L + e_o = \left(\frac{R_a + R_L}{R_L} + \frac{L_a}{R_L} p \right) e_o$$

$$e_n = \frac{R_a + R_L}{R_L} \left(1 + \frac{L_a}{R_a + R_L} p \right) e_o = (i + r)(1 + T_L p)e_o \tag{8.37}$$

where
$$r = \frac{R_a}{R_L}.$$

Equating Eqs. 8.36 and 8.37 and rearranging gives

$$[(1 + T_L p)(1 + T_n p) \cdots (1 + T_2 p)]e_o = \frac{(k_n \cdots k_2)\mu e_c}{(1 + r)(R_n \cdots R_2)}. \quad (8.38)$$

The d-c or steady-state gain of the system for increments of e_c with no feedback can be found from Eq. 8.38 by putting $pe_o = 0$ and solving for e_o/e_c. The result is

$$\frac{e_o}{e_c} = K' = \frac{(k_n \cdots k_2)\mu}{(1 + r)(R_n \cdots R_2)}. \quad (8.39)$$

Comparison of this result with the value of K' as used in Eq. 8.5a shows that they are of the same form and have the same meaning, except that K' in Eq. 8.39 applies for n time delays, whereas the previous value of K' is for $n = 2$ time delays. Equation 8.38 can now be written

$$[(1 + T_L p)(1 + T_n p) \cdots (1 + T_2 p)]e_o = K'e_c. \quad (8.40)$$

The voltage e_c is the voltage rise from cathode to grid of the triode, and where we are concerned only with changes, e_c becomes

$$e_c = e_1 = f(p)\epsilon. \quad (8.41)$$

Combining Eqs. 8.40 and 8.41 gives

$$[(1 + T_L p)(1 + T_n p) \cdots (1 + T_2 p)]e_o = K'f(p)\epsilon. \quad (8.42)$$

As an example of the use of this result, Eq. 8.32 will be derived from it. The circuit is that of Fig. 8-5, where $n = 2$. Equation 8.42 then becomes

$$(1 + T_L p)(1 + T_2 p)e_o = \frac{k_2\mu}{(1 + r)R_2}f(p)\epsilon.$$

From Fig. 8-5, $\qquad f(p) = \frac{1}{\alpha_d}\frac{1 + j\omega T_d}{(1 + j\omega T_d/\alpha_d)},$

and $r = R_a/R_L$.

$$(1 + T_L p)(1 + T_2 p)e_o = \frac{k_2\mu R_L}{(R_L + R_a)R_2}\frac{1}{\alpha_d}\frac{1 + j\omega T_d}{(1 + j\omega T_d/\alpha_d)}\epsilon. \quad (8.43)$$

Here R_2 corresponds to $R_f + r_p$ in Eq. 8.31, and k_2 corresponds to k. Also, in Eq. 8.43, T_2 and T_L correspond respectively to T_1 and T_2 of Eq. 8.32. With these changes, Eq. 8.43 will be the same as Eq. 8.32.

8.9 Differential Equation for Amplidyne Regulator

The results of Sec. 8.8 make it possible to write at once the differential equation of the simple amplidyne whose equivalent circuit is shown in Fig. 8-8. The equivalent circuit of the whole regulator will then be the same as Fig. 8-10 with $n = 3$. Thus Eq. 8.42 becomes

$$(1 + T_L p)(1 + T_3 p)(1 + T_2 p)e_o = \frac{k_3 k_2 \mu}{(1 + r)R_3 R_2} \frac{(1 + T_d p)}{\alpha_d \left(1 + \dfrac{T_d}{\alpha_d} p\right)} \epsilon$$

or $\quad K'_d \dfrac{\epsilon}{e_o}(p) = \dfrac{\left(1 + \dfrac{T_d}{\alpha_d} p\right)(1 + T_L p)(1 + T_3 p)(1 + T_2 p)}{(1 + T_d p)}, \quad$ (8.44)

where $\qquad\qquad K'_d = \dfrac{k_3 k_2 \mu}{(1 + r)R_3 R_2 \alpha_d}.$

Here, as before, K'_d is the zero frequency open loop gain of the system.

Several cases may now be considered. The simplest would be to assume that T_d is adjusted to be equal to one of the other time constants, say T_2. In that case the differential equation is of the third order.

$$K'_d \frac{\epsilon}{e_o}(p) = \left(1 + \frac{T_d}{\alpha_d} p\right)(1 + T_L p)(1 + T_3 p). \qquad (8.45)$$

To study the system's stability one may examine the inverse transfer function plot, which is Eq. 8.45, or one may write the differential equation for e_o/e_i and examine the roots of the characteristic equation for positive real parts. The second of these procedures will be carried out first, followed by the inverse transfer plot method.

As was shown in Chapter 7,

$$\frac{e_o}{e_i}(p) = \frac{1}{1 + \dfrac{\epsilon}{e_0}(p)}. \qquad (8.46)$$

Substituting Eq. 8.45 into this gives

$$\frac{e_o}{e_i}(p) = \frac{K'_d}{K'_d + \left(1 + \frac{T_d}{\alpha_d}p\right)(1 + T_L p)(1 + T_3 P)}.$$

If this is expanded and rearranged, the result is

$$\left[p^3 + \left(\frac{1}{T_L} + \frac{\alpha_d}{T_d} + \frac{1}{T_3}\right)p^2 + \left(\frac{\alpha_d}{T_L T_d} + \frac{\alpha_d}{T_3 T_d} + \frac{1}{T_3 T_L}\right)p \right.$$
$$\left. + \frac{(1 + K')\alpha_d}{T_3 T_d T_L}\right]e_o = \frac{\alpha_d K'_d}{T_3 T_d T_L} e_i \quad (8.47)$$

The roots of the auxiliary equation for finding the transient solution will be either (a) all real roots, or (b) one real root and a pair of conjugate complex roots. They will determine whether the system is overdamped or underdamped, and if the latter, whether the oscillations decay or increase in amplitude, etc. The roots of third and higher order algebraic equations with numerical coefficients can be found by various methods, but nearly always they are laborious and time consuming. However, certain information may be obtained about the roots without actually solving for them. Routh's rule, explained in section 7.6, will show how many roots there are with positive real parts. This information is useful because it tells whether or not the system is stable. If Routh's rule is applied to Eq. 8.47, the resulting array is as shown below.

1	$\left(\dfrac{\alpha_d}{T_d T_L} + \dfrac{\alpha_d}{T_3 T_d} + \dfrac{1}{T_3 T_L}\right)$
$\left(\dfrac{1}{T_L} + \dfrac{\alpha_d}{T_d} + \dfrac{1}{T_3}\right)$	$\dfrac{(1 + K'_d)\alpha_d}{T_3 T_L T_d}$
$\dfrac{\left(\dfrac{\alpha_d}{T_d T_L} + \dfrac{\alpha_d}{T_d T_3} + \dfrac{1}{T_3 T_L}\right)\left(\dfrac{1}{T_L} + \dfrac{\alpha_d}{T_d} + \dfrac{1}{T_3}\right) - \dfrac{\alpha_d(1 + K'_d)}{T_3 T_L T_d}}{\dfrac{1}{T_L} + \dfrac{\alpha_d}{T_d} + \dfrac{1}{T_3}}$	0
$\dfrac{\alpha_d(1 + K'_d)}{T_3 T_L T_d}$	0

Since α_d and all the time constants are inherently positive, it is possible for only the third term in the first column to be negative. If it should be negative, there would then be two changes of sign in the terms of the first column, and hence, two roots with positive real parts. This condition of course is to be avoided in a stable system, so a criterion for stability would be that the third term be positive. It will be positive if

$$\left(\frac{\alpha_d}{T_d T_L} + \frac{\alpha_d}{T_d T_3} + \frac{1}{T_3 T_L}\right)\left(\frac{1}{T_L} + \frac{\alpha_d}{T_d} + \frac{1}{T_3}\right) > \frac{\alpha_d(1 + K'_d)}{T_3 T_L T_d}. \quad (8.48)$$

Inequality 8.48 may be arranged in a number of ways. It may be expanded and rearranged into the form of Eq. 8.49:

$$\alpha_d\left(\frac{T_L}{T_d} + \frac{T_3}{T_d}\right) + \left(\frac{T_3}{T_L} + \frac{T_L}{T_3} + 3\right) + \frac{1}{\alpha_d}\left(\frac{T_d}{T_L} + \frac{T_d}{T_3}\right) > 1 + K'_d. \quad (8.49)$$

From this inequality it is apparent that stability may be determined from values of T_d/T_L, T_d/T_3, α_d and K'_d. From these dimensionless ratios the stability of a design may be quickly checked. No matter what values T_d/T_1, T_d/T_3 and α_d may have, it will always be possible to find a zero frequency gain, K'_d, large enough to cause instability. Suppose for example that

$$\frac{T_d}{T_L} = \frac{T_d}{T_3} = \alpha_d = K'_d.$$

Then inequality 8.49 will give

$$9 > 1 + K'_d,$$

and for $K'_d > 8$ the system will be unstable.

The stability of this same system may also be determined by use of the inverse transfer function plot. Expansion of Eq. 8.45 and division by K'_d gives the inverse transfer function.

$$\frac{\epsilon}{e_o}(p) = \frac{1}{K'_d}\left[p^3 + \left(\frac{1}{T_L} + \frac{\alpha_d}{T_d} + \frac{1}{T_3}\right) p^2 \right.$$

$$\left. + \left(\frac{\alpha_d}{T_L T_d} + \frac{\alpha_d}{T_3 T_d} + \frac{1}{T_3 T_L}\right) p + \frac{\alpha_d}{T_3 T_d T_L}\right] \frac{T_3 T_d T_L}{\alpha_d}.$$

Now let $p = j\omega$.

$$\frac{\epsilon}{e_o}(j\omega) = \frac{1}{K'_d}\left\{ -\left(\frac{T_d T_3}{\alpha_d} + T_L T_3 + \frac{T_L T_d}{\alpha_d}\right)\omega^2 \right.$$

$$\left. + 1 + j\left[\frac{-\omega^3 T_L T_d T_3}{\alpha_d} + \left(T_3 + T_L + \frac{T_d}{\alpha_d}\right)\omega\right]\right\} \quad (8.50)$$

The loci of this equation are plotted in Fig. 8-11 for the same values of time constant ratios α_d and K'_d as were used in discussing stability from the differential equation viewpoint. As before, it is assumed that the time constant ratios and α_2 are all equal to K'_d, and Eq. 8.50 is plotted for $K'_d = 5$ and 10. For substitution into Eq. 8.50,

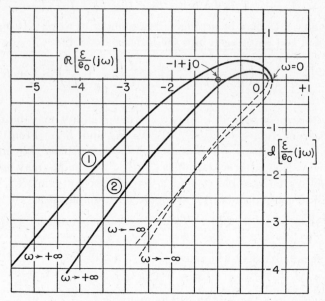

Fig. 8-11. Inverse transfer functions for simple amplidyne regulator, Eq. 8.50.

$$\text{Curve 1:} \quad \frac{T_d}{T_L} = \frac{T_d}{T_3} = \alpha_d = K'_d = 5, \text{ stable.}$$

$$\text{Curve 2:} \quad \frac{T_d}{T_L} = \frac{T_d}{T_3} = \alpha_d = K'_d = 10, \text{ unstable.}$$

the data sets assumed were
 (1) $T_d = 5$, $T_L = T_3 = 1$, $\alpha_d = K'_d = 5$
 (2) $T_d = 10$, $T_L = T_3 = 1$, $\alpha_d = K'_d = 10$.

According to the rule of Sec. 7.7, the system is stable or unstable if, as ω varies from $+\infty$ through zero to $-\infty$, the point $-1 + j0$ is to the right or left of the path as viewed by an observer moving along the path. By this rule the system for $K'_d = 5$ is stable (curve 1), and for $K'_d = 10$ it is unstable (curve 2). Thus one gets the same information about stability from both methods. The direct transfer function, which is the inverse of the curves of Fig. 8-11, will give the same result using the same rule stated above.　　Problem 8.9 is designed to show this fact.

The discussion of the amplidyne regulator has so far dealt only with the special case where $T_d = T_2$ in Eq. 8.44.　In the general case in which none of the factors of Eq. 8.44 cancel, the application of Routh's rule with literal coefficients is almost prohibitively complex, and even with numerical coefficients it may become very laborious.　The inverse (or direct) transfer functions may be relatively easily plotted, however, for numerical coefficients.　Moreover, in an existing system whose constants may be unknown or difficult to measure, a simple experimental procedure will yield the transfer function, and the effect on the system of making changes can be determined fairly quickly.　In fact, the use of the transfer function plot has been developed by Brown and Campbell[3] and others to the point where the technique can be used to design a complex system to give predetermined characteristics.

8.10　Speed Regulator

The speed regulator shown in Fig. 8-12 is designed to regulate the speed of the d-c motor, M, which is driving a load requiring a constant torque τ_L.　The field of the d-c motor is assumed to have constant separate excitation.　In addition to the load, the motor has connected to it a small tachometer generator which generates a d-c voltage e_o proportional to the motor speed.　This voltage is the signal which is fed into the feedback and comparison network. From one point of view the circuit may be considered a voltage regulator, with e_o being the regulated quantity.　Hence, since e_o is proportional to the motor speed, the circuit is also a speed regulator.

For the analysis, assume that R_3 and L_3 include the resistances and inductances of the generator and motor armatures, and consider the tachometer to be open circuited.　Let

J = moment of inertia of motor, load and tachometer,

N = motor speed, radians per sec.,

$e_o = k_3 N$ volts,

e_m = motor back emf = $k_4 N = \dfrac{k_4}{k_3} e_o$,

τ_m = torque developed by motor = $k_6 i_L$,

i_L = motor armature current.

[3] Brown, Gordon S. and Donald P. Campbell, *Principles of Servomechanisms*, John Wiley and Sons, Inc., New York.

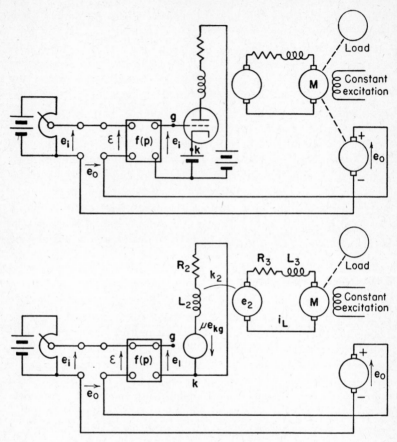

Fig. 8-12.   Speed regulator and its equivalent circuit.

Begin by using Eq. 8.36 for e_2 in Fig. 8-12.

$$e_2 = \frac{k_2 \mu e_1}{R_2(1 + T_2 p)} \tag{8.51}$$

Also

$$e_2 = i_L R_3 + L_3 p i_L + e_m. \tag{8.52}$$

Equating torques on the motor armature gives

$$\tau_m = k_6 i_L = \tau_L + J p N.$$

Therefore

$$i_L = \frac{\tau_L}{k_6} + \frac{J p e_o}{k_3 k_6}. \tag{8.53}$$

In addition,
$$e_m = \frac{k_4}{k_3} e_o. \qquad (8.54)$$

Substituting Eqs. 8.53 and 8.54 into Eq. 8.52 and equating the result to Eq. 8.51 gives

$$\frac{R_3}{k_6}\left(\tau_L + \frac{J}{k_3} p e_o\right) + \frac{L_3 J}{k_3 k_6} p^2 e_o + \frac{k_4}{k_3} e_o = \frac{k_2 \mu e_1}{R_2(1 + T_2 p)}.$$

Rearrangement gives

$$p^2 e_o + \frac{R_3}{L_3} p e_o + \frac{k_4 k_6}{L_3 J} e_o + \frac{R_3 \tau_L k_3}{JL_3} = \frac{k_2 \mu e_1}{\dfrac{L_3 J}{k_3 k_6} R_2(1 + T_2 p)}.$$

Dimensional analysis of the coefficients in this equation shows that, except for the constant term, the coefficients may be expressed in terms of time constants. Thus

$$\frac{R_3}{L_3} = \frac{1}{T_3}, \qquad \frac{k_4 k_6}{L_3 J} = \frac{R_3}{L_3} \times \frac{k_4 k_6}{JR_3} = \frac{1}{T_3 T_L}$$

$$\frac{k_3 k_6}{L_3 J} = \frac{1}{T_3 T_L}\frac{k_3}{k_4}. \qquad (8.55)$$

The differential equation then becomes

$$\left(p^2 + \frac{1}{T_3} p + \frac{1}{T_3 T_L}\right) e_o + B = \frac{k_2 \mu e_1}{(k_4/k_3) T_3 T_L R_2(1 + T_2 p)} \qquad (8.56)$$

where B is a constant which can be dropped, since we are interested in changes only. Now cross multiply and expand. The result, after dropping B, gives

$$\left[p^3 + \left(\frac{1}{T_2} + \frac{1}{T_3}\right) p^2 + \left(\frac{1}{T_3 T_L} + \frac{1}{T_2 T_3}\right) p + \frac{1}{T_2 T_3 T_L}\right] e_o$$
$$= \frac{k_2 k_3 \mu}{k_4 T_2 T_3 T_L R_2} e_1, \qquad (8.57)$$

or
$$(p^3 + \alpha_2 p^2 + \alpha_1 p) p e_o = b_1 p e_1, \qquad (8.57a)$$

where coefficients are functions of the time constants T_2, T_3 and T_L. If the modifying network is such that

$$e_1 = \frac{1 + T_d p}{\alpha_d\left(1 + \dfrac{T_d}{\alpha_d} p\right)} \epsilon,$$

then the final result in terms of e_0 and ϵ is the same as Eq. 8.44 for the amplidyne regulator. Since the case of the amplidyne has been discussed in some detail, no further discussion is necessary here except to point out that, like the amplidyne regulator, this system has three time constants. Two of them are obviously due to L_2/R_2 and L_3/R_3, and the third is introduced by the inertia J of the rotating parts of the system, as can be seen from Eqs. 8.55, from which

$$T_L = \frac{JR_3}{k_4k_6}. \tag{8.58}$$

8.11   Electronic Regulators

There are numerous all-electronic regulator circuits for regulating the voltage supply for small current loads such as vacuum tube circuits. Of these, two will be considered. The first, shown in Fig. 8-13, is a circuit designed to maintain constant the voltage

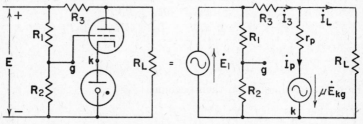

Fig. 8-13.   Mutual conductance regulator and its equivalent a-c plate circuit.

across R_L in the presence of variations in supply voltage E. Here, if E increases, the voltage rise from cathode to grid of the triode increases, causing the triode current to increase. The resulting increased drop across R_3 tends to reduce the voltage across R_L to its original value. It will be shown that with proper adjustment this regulation can be made perfect as long as the triode can be assumed linear.

The analysis can be made by assuming that E has superimposed on it a sinusoidally varying voltage of effective value $\dot{E}_1$. The resulting variation of voltage across R_L can be found from the equivalent a-c plate circuit shown in Fig. 8-13. First write voltage equations around two loops.

$$\dot{E}_1 = (\dot{I}_p + \dot{I}_L)R_3 + \dot{I}_p r_p - \mu\dot{E}_{kg}$$
$$\dot{E}_1 = (\dot{I}_p + \dot{I}_L)R_3 + \dot{I}_L R_L$$

Also, $$\dot{E}_{kg} = \dot{E}_1 \frac{R_2}{R_1 + R_2} = r\dot{E}_1$$

Simultaneous solution for $\dot{I}_L$ gives

$$\dot{I}_L = \frac{\dot{E}_1(r_p - \mu r R_3)}{R_L(R_3 + r_p) + r_p R_3}.$$

It will be noticed that $\dot{I}_L$, which is the varying part of the load current due to variation in the supply voltage, can be made zero if $r_p - \mu r R_3 = 0$, or

$$r_p = \frac{\mu R_2 R_3}{R_1 + R_2}. \tag{8.59}$$

With this adjustment the circuit will regulate perfectly for changes in supply voltage as long as the tube operates in the linear region of its characteristics. This circuit will not regulate for changes in R_L.

The circuit of Fig. 8-14 is designed to regulate the voltage across R_L for variations in either R_L or in supply voltage. The analysis will be carried out only for changes in R_L. Suppose R_L decreases. The voltages across R_L and R_1 then decrease in magnitude, so that the grid becomes more positive to the cathode, thus

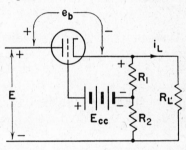

Fig. 8-14. Voltage regulator which regulates for changes in both R_L and E.

increasing the plate current and bringing the load voltage back toward normal.

In the analysis neglect the current through R_1 and R_2, and assume that the tube is linear. Assume also that E is constant. We want to know the change of voltage across R_L for a small change ΔR_L in the load resistance. From the circuit of Fig. 8-14,

$$E - e_b - i_L R_L = 0. \tag{8.60}$$

Also, for changes Δe_b and Δe_c, the change in tube current is

$$\Delta i_L = \frac{1}{r_p} \Delta e_b + g_m \Delta e_c. \tag{8.61}$$

The rise in voltage from grid to cathode is

$$e_c = -i_L R_L \times \frac{R_1}{R_1 + R_2} + E_{cc} = -i_L R_L r + E_{cc},$$

from which

$$\Delta e_c = -r(R_L \, \Delta i_L + i_L \, \Delta R_L).$$

Here

$$r = \frac{R_1}{R_1 + R_2}.$$

From Eq. 8.60,

$$\Delta e_b = -(R_L \, \Delta i_L + i_L \, \Delta R_L).$$

Substitute these values of Δe_c and Δe_b into Eq. 8.61.

$$\Delta i_L = (i_L \, \Delta R_L + R_L \, \Delta i_L)\left(-\frac{1}{r_p} - g_m r\right).$$

Let

$$\frac{1}{r_p} + g_m r = a.$$

Then, in terms of differentials,

$$i_L \, dR_L + R_L \, di_L = -\frac{1}{a} \, di_L,$$

which gives, upon integration,

$$i_L R_L = -\frac{1}{a} i_L + C.$$

If, just before the change in R_L, $i_L = I_0$ and $R_L = R_0$, then

$$C = I_0 R_0 + \frac{1}{a} I_0. \tag{8.62}$$

It is convenient, however, not to make this substitution for C at this point. Solution for i_L and multiplication by R_L will give the load voltage, e_L.

$$i_L R_L = e_L = \frac{aCR_L}{aR_L + 1} \tag{8.63}$$

We want to know the change in e_L when R_L changes. Differentiating Eq. 8.63 gives

$$\frac{de_L}{dR_L} = \frac{aC}{(aR_L + 1)^2}.$$

Substituting increments for differentials and solving for Δe_L gives

$$\Delta e_L = \frac{aC \, \Delta R_L}{(aR_L + 1)^2}.$$

If Eq. 8.62 is now substituted for C, the result is

$$\Delta e_L = I_0 \, \Delta R_L \, \frac{aR_0 + 1}{(aR_L + 1)^2}. \tag{8.64}$$

If ΔR_L is small compared to R_0, then $R_L \cong R_0$ and

$$\Delta e_L \cong \frac{I_0 R_L}{aR_0 + 1} = \frac{I_0 \, \Delta R_L}{\left(\dfrac{1}{r_p} + g_m r\right) R_0 + 1} = \frac{I_0 \, \Delta R_L}{\dfrac{R_0}{r_p}(1 + \mu r) + 1}. \tag{8.65}$$

From this result it is apparent that to minimize Δe_L one should choose a tube with as low a plate resistance and as high an amplification factor as possible. In addition the tube must be capable of carrying the load current, and this requirement usually limits the choice to a relatively few tubes with low plate resistance and, unfortunately, low μ. One would be tempted to choose $r = R_1/(R_1 + R_2) = 1$, but this is not always possible, since adjustment of r is usually necessary to obtain the correct load voltage and operating conditions for the tube. The bias supply voltage E_{cc} may be obtained from a battery, or by slight circuit changes, from a cold cathode voltage regulator tube.

Problem 8.15 is designed to show that the regulator is most effective against changes in E, the supply voltage, if the tube plate resistance is large instead of small.

8.12 Voltage Regulation with Gas Tubes

The circuit of Fig. 8-15 shows a simple voltage regulator utilizing gas tubes in the field circuit of the generator. In this circuit we will be interested only in the steady-state conditions, since the transient is not easily analyzed.

The field is excited from an a-c source, $E_m \sin \omega t$. If we suppose that the thyratron grid is controlled so that the thyratron always fires at the angle α, Fig. 8-16, then the current through the field and the voltage across the field have the forms shown. After the thyratron fires, it conducts until the voltage of point k goes negative

enough to p so that the gas diode fires.   The thyratron current then
becomes zero and the field current shifts to the diode.   The field
current then decays exponentially until the thyratron is allowed by
its grid to fire again.   The variation in field current is shown much

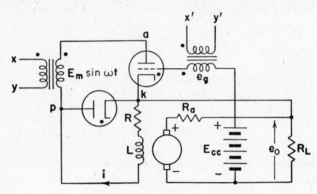

Fig. 8-15.   D-c generator voltage regulator using gas tubes in the field circuit.

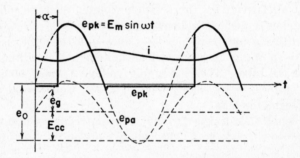

Fig. 8-16.   Current and voltage wave forms for circuit of Fig. 8-15.

exaggerated in Fig. 8-16.   Actually, since in most generators L/R is
large, there will be very little ripple.   The average field current, I, is

$$I = \frac{E_{av}}{R} \cong \frac{1}{2\pi R} \int_{\alpha}^{\pi} E_m \sin \omega t \, d(\omega t) = \frac{E_m}{2\pi R} (1 + \cos \alpha). \quad (8.66)$$

The firing angle α is determined by the thyratron cathode-to-
grid voltage rise, which is

$$e_{kg} = -e_o + E_{cc} + E_{gm} \sin \omega t.$$

If the critical firing voltage is assumed to be $-E_{crit}$ then

$$-E_{crit} = -e_o + E_{cc} + E_{gm} \sin \alpha,$$

and
$$\sin \alpha = \frac{e_o - E_{cc} - E_{crit}}{E_{gm}},$$

whence
$$\cos \alpha = \frac{\sqrt{E_{gm}{}^2 - (e_o - E_{cc} - E_{crit})^2}}{E_{gm}}. \qquad (8.67)$$

The regulating action is as follows. Suppose e_o drops; then, according to Fig. 8-16, the average level of the sinusoidal component of grid voltage is raised, causing the thyratron to fire earlier, thus raising the average field current. It should be mentioned that in this circuit the thyratron cannot be made to fire beyond $\alpha = 90°$. This fact has important significance in the operation of the system as a regulator. Suppose, for example, that E_m is made so large that the average field current required to produce the rated output voltage as determined by E_{cc} will be exceeded if the thyratron fires at $90°$. In this case e_o will become so large that the sinusoid in the grid circuit will be depressed below the level where it can intersect the critical firing voltage curve, and the thyratron will not fire at all. The output voltage will then drop until the thyratron begins to fire again, at which point the cycle of events begins over again. Thus the thyratron will fire for a few cycles at $\alpha = 90°$ and then will not fire at all for a few cycles. The ratio of the number of cycles it fires to the number it does not fire over a large number of cycles will be automatically adjusted by the regulator so that the average field current is that required to produce the necessary average output voltage demanded by E_{cc}. Under this condition voltage regulation due to changes in load should be very good. If, on the other hand, E_m is so small that, even when the thyratron fires at $\alpha = 0$, the average current is too low to give the necessary value of e_o, the regulation will be nil.

The analysis for steady state conditions is very simple in principle. We have already found the average field current, Eq. 8.66, as a function of α, and the dependence of α on e_o, Eq. 8.67. In addition e_o is related to I, the average field current, by the relation

$$k_2 I = e_o \left(1 + \frac{R_a}{R_L}\right) = e_o(1 + r). \qquad (8.68)$$

Substitute Eq. 8.67 into Eq. 8.66 and multiply the result by k_2. Thus

$$k_2 I = \frac{k_2 E_m}{2\pi R}\left(1 + \frac{\sqrt{E_{gm}^2 - (e_o - E_{cc} - E_{crit})^2}}{E_{gm}}\right).$$

Equate this result to Eq. 8.68 and solve for e_o.

$$\frac{k_2 E_m}{2\pi R(1 + r)} \cdot \frac{\sqrt{E_{gm}^2 - (e_o - E_{cc} - E_{crit})^2}}{E_{gm}} = e_o - \frac{k_2 E_m}{2\pi R(1 + r)}.$$

For simplicity, let $E_{crit} = 0$ and let

$$\frac{k_2 E_m}{2\pi R(1 + r)} = a. \tag{8.69}$$

Then $a^2(E_{gm}^2 - e_o^2 + 2e_o E_{cc} - E_{cc}^2) = E_{gm}^2(e_o^2 - 2ae_o + a^2).$

Solution for e_o gives

$$e_o = \frac{a(E_{gm}^2 + aE_{cc}) + aE_{gm}\sqrt{E_{gm}^2 + 2aE_{cc} - E_{cc}^2}}{E_{gm}^2 + a^2}. \tag{8.70}$$

The plus sign is to be used in front of the radical because if the minus sign were used e_o would come out less than E_{cc}. A glance at Fig. 8-16 will show that this is impossible. A numerical example will illustrate this point.

Example. In a system like Fig. 8-15 let $k_2 = 500$ v/amp, $E_m = 200$, $R = 238$, $r = \dfrac{R_a}{R_L} = 0.1$, $E_{gm} = 10$, $E_{cc} = 95$. From Eq. 8.69,

$$a = \frac{500 \times 200}{1.1 \times 2\pi \times 238} = 61.$$

From Eq. 8.70,

$$e_o = \frac{61(100 + 61 \times 95) \pm 61 \times 10\sqrt{100 + 122 \times 95 - 95^2}}{100 + (61)^2}$$

$$= \frac{360,000 \pm 30,200}{3820};$$

$$e_o = 94.2 \pm 7.9.$$

Obviously the positive sign must be used if e_o is to be greater than $E_{cc} = 95$.

Therefore $e_o = 102.1$ volts.

In this example it will be noticed that in several places E_{gm}^2 is negligible compared to other quantities. If, in these cases, it is dropped, Eq. 8.70 simplifies to

$$e_o \cong E_{cc} + \frac{E_{gm}}{a} \sqrt{E_{cc}(2a - E_{cc})}. \qquad (8.71)$$

8.13 Voltage Regulation of an Alternator

Figure 8-17 shows a circuit which might be used to regulate the voltage of an alternating current generator. Here the alternating voltage is rectified and filtered to produce a continuous voltage e_o which is proportional to the rms value of the generated voltage. This voltage e_o can then be treated exactly as though it were the output of a d-c generator, and in fact the circuit of Fig. 8-17 is like

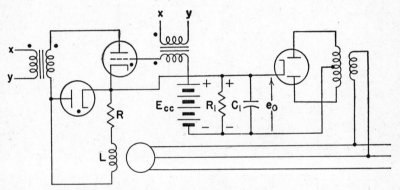

Fig. 8-17. Simple voltage regulator for a-c generator.

Fig. 8-15 except that e_o is obtained from the rectifier instead of from a d-c generator. The method of operation can easily be deduced by comparison with Figs. 8-15 and 8-16.

The transient analysis here is difficult, because the rectifier which produces the voltage e_o is a non-linear device. Thus, although e_o might follow quite faithfully rapid increases in the rms value of alternator voltage, it might not follow rapid decreases because the capacitor C_1 might not discharge through its parallel resistor fast enough. Another property of this regulator is that e_o will really be proportional to the peak value of the alternating voltage if R_1C_1 is large enough, and thus the regulator tends to hold constant the peak voltage rather than the rms value. In other words the regu-

lator is insensitive to changes in waveform.   This property may or
may not be a disadvantage depending on the application.

PROBLEMS

8.1. Show by direct definitions of ζ and ω_n (Eq. 7.45) that Eqs. 8.9 and
8.10 are true.

8.2. Show by physical reasoning that the open loop gain of Fig. 8-1 is

$$K' = \frac{\mu R_L K}{(R_a + R_L)(R_f + r_p)}.$$

8.3. Set up the differential equation for e_o for an arbitrary function $e_i(t)$.
If e_i is to be obtained from the drop across a voltage regulator tube, what is

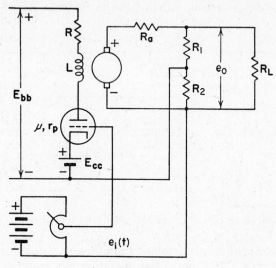

Prob. 8.3

the maximum allowable variation in e_i if e_o is to be held constant to within
± 1 per cent?

8.4. Set up the differential equation for e_o in Fig. 8-1 if the load consists of
R_L and L_L in series instead of just R_L.   Discuss the effect on e_o of adding this
load inductance.

8.5. The triode of Fig. 8-1 is assumed to be a pair of 6L6's connected as
triodes in parallel. $R_f = 1000$, $L_f = 1h$, $R_a = 1$, $L_a = 0.1h$, $R_L = 25$, $k =$
1100 v per amp.   (a) Determine the quiescent value of e_i for a steady state
value of $e_o = 120$.   Assume plate supply voltage = 400 v, and $E_{cc} = -20$ v.
(b) If e_i is held at this value and R_L is changed from 25 to 15 ohms, find the
new steady state value of e_o.   (c) If there were no feedback, calculate the value

of I_b to give $e_o = 120$ v for $R_L = 25$. With this value of I_b find e_o when $R_L = 15$.

8.6. Can this circuit be used to produce a voltage e' which is approximately $e' = m_1 e_o + m_2 p e_o$? If so, under what conditions? Evaluate m_1 and m_2 in terms of R_1, R_2 and L.

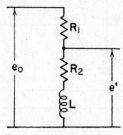

Prob. 8.6

8.7. Show analytically that the inverse transfer function

$$K'_d \frac{\epsilon}{e_o} (j\omega) = \frac{(1 + T_1 j\omega)(1 + T_2 j\omega)}{1 + T_d j\omega}$$

approaches

$$\left(\frac{T_1 + T_2}{T_d} - \frac{T_1 T_2}{T_d{}^2} \right) \pm j\infty \text{ as } \omega \to \pm\infty.$$

8.8. Show analytically that the inverse transfer function

$$K'_d \frac{\epsilon}{e_o} (j\omega) = \frac{\left(1 + \dfrac{T_d}{\alpha} j\omega \right)}{(1 + T_d j\omega)} (1 + T_1 j\omega)(1 + T_2 j\omega)$$

approaches $-\infty \pm j\infty$ as $\omega \to \pm\infty$.

8.9. Show, by selecting a few radius vectors to the curves of Fig. 8-11 and plotting their inverses, that the direct transfer function gives the same answer as the inverse transfer function regarding stability.

8.10. The differential equations in operational form for two regulators are
(a) $(p^2 + a_1 p + a_o)e_o = b_o e_i$ and
(b) $(p^3 + a_2 p^2 + a_1 p + a_o)e_o = b_o e_i$, where the coefficients are all positive. Show by Routh's rule that the second-order system cannot be unstable but that the third order system may be unstable.

8.11. The control field of an amplidyne generator is controlled by a type 6L6 connected as a triode. The amplidyne supplies a load R_L whose voltage is to be regulated. The system parameters are as follows:

$$R = 1000 \qquad R_3 = 1 \qquad R_a = 1$$
$$L_2 = 10 \text{ h} \qquad L_3 = 0.001 \qquad L_a = 0.01$$
$$k_2 = 250 \text{ v/a} \qquad k_3 = 0.5 \text{ v/a} \qquad R_L = 50$$

Is this system stable?

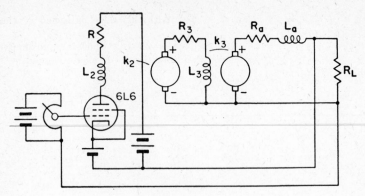

Prob. 8.11

8.12. In the circuit of Fig. 8-13 the voltage regulator tube is a VR-75 and the triode is a 6C5. The triode is to be operated normally at 6 volts bias. The load R_L is 20,000 ohms, and it is to have a normal voltage of 275 volts maintained across it. (a) Determine E, R_1/R_2, and R_3 for good regulation. (b) What is the approximate minimum value E may assume without throwing the 6C5 into a non-linear region? (c) What is the maximum value E may assume without causing greater than rated 6C5 plate dissipation?

8.13. In the circuit of Fig. 8-14, $R_L = 1000$, $E_{cc} = 45$ v, the load current I_o is to be 75 ma, and the triode is a 2A3 which is to operate normally with a 30 volt bias. (a) Find R_1/R_2. (b) Find E for the normal condition stated above. (c) Find the load voltage if R_L changes to 900 ohms.

8.14. (a) Draw a regulator circuit like that of Fig. 8-15 but add between xy and $x'y'$ the circuit elements necessary to shift the phase of the a-c grid voltage so that the thyratron may be fired over approximately 180° range instead of only 90°. (b) If $k = 500$ v per amp, $E_m = 400$ v, $R = 238$ ohms, $r = 0.1$, $E_{gm} = 10$, $E_{cc} = 95$ and $E_{crit} = 0$, find e_o and the firing angle of the thyratron. (c) Find the regulation, de_o/dR_L.

8.15. In the regulator circuit of Fig. 8-14 show that for a change ΔE in supply voltage the change ΔE_L across R_L is given by

$$\frac{\Delta E_L}{\Delta E} = \frac{R_L}{R_L + r_p + \mu r R_L}$$

8.16. Show from Eq. 8.70 that the regulation of the circuit of Fig. 8-15 improves as E_{gm} decreases and that approximately,

$$\frac{de_o}{dR_L} = \frac{rE_{gm}}{(1 + r)R_L} \left[\frac{E_{cc}}{\sqrt{E_{cc}(2a - E_{cc})}} - \frac{1}{a}\sqrt{E_{cc}(2a - E_{cc})} \right].$$

CHAPTER 9

ELECTRONIC CONTROL OF MOTORS

Electronic control of d-c motors has become widely used because it offers a number of advantages over other methods. One of the most important of these is that it permits smooth and continuous speed control of the motor over the whole range from zero to maximum speed by the adjustment of a very small potentiometer. Automatic speed regulation is possible over the whole range of available torque, and automatic torque control or limiting is easily accomplished. Current limiting for starting purposes or to prevent overloading is also a standard practice. All these operations can be made completely automatic, so that abuse of the motor at the hands of an inexperienced operator or a hurried production worker is not likely. In addition to these advantages, electronic control lends itself naturally to regulation by means of small power, small signal devices such as phototubes, thermocouple pyrometers, or instrument type relays. Such devices may be arranged to operate amplifiers which control thyratrons in the motor circuits, or they may control electronically operated relays which may or may not have electronic time delay circuits associated with them. Finally, d-c machines, with their desirable characteristics, can be operated from a-c mains.

9.1 Vacuum Tube Control

High-vacuum tubes are used occasionally to control directly the armature or field currents of very small d-c motors, and occasionally of small a-c motors. Usually these applications are in special-purpose devices such as automatic recording instruments, and because they constitute a rather small group and are usually quite special, they will not be considered here.

9.2 Gas Tube Control

Because of their high current ratings compared with vacuum tubes, gas tubes are almost always used in motor controls. Phanotrons, thyratrons, and ignitrons are all used. When control of armature current is desired, phanotrons or thyratrons can be used on motors up to 2 or 3 hp. Above about 3 hp, ignitrons can be used if they are provided with a holding anode, and baffles or shields to prevent arc-back. Such an ignitron is called a rectifier type, and it differs from the welder type in the respects just mentioned.

If the motor is to be controlled by adjustment of field current only, thyratrons can be used up to about 40 hp. Usually both armature and field control must be used if speed control over the whole speed range of the motor is required.

9.3 Control Circuits

One of the most elementary control circuits is shown in Fig. 9-1. Here the armature is supplied by a pair of phanotrons. In starting,

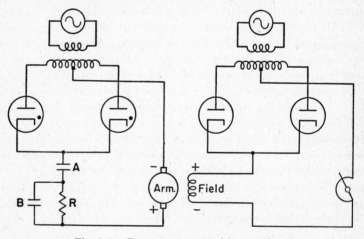

Fig. 9-1.   D-c motor operated by rectifiers.

contactor A closes first, and starting resistor R limits the inrush of current to a safe value until the motor speed rises to a point where its back electromotive force can limit the current. Contactor B then closes. The field current is shown supplied by a pair of vacuum diodes, but they could be gas-filled diodes. Manual speed control over a limited range is obtained by a field rheostat. This circuit is too elementary to lend itself readily to automatic control other than an on-off type, and its chief advantage is that it is a simple way to operate a small d-c motor from an a-c source.

Analysis of the field circuit to obtain the average d-c current for known applied voltage and circuit parameters is relatively simple by methods used on choke input filters. Analysis of the armature circuit to determine the motor speed for given applied voltage and circuit parameters is less simple. If certain assumptions are made about the motor, it can be replaced in the circuit diagram by a capacitor in parallel with a resistor. The problem then becomes that of finding the average voltage across the capacitor. This problem has been solved and the results presented graphically for the half-wave rectifier case in Chapter 6, Sec. 4. The method could be extended to cover the full-wave rectifier case.

9.4   Capacitor Analog of D-C Motor

The following analysis is intended to show that for analytical purposes a d-c motor with constant field excitation may be treated as a simple circuit containing only capacitance and resistance. In this analysis the armature inductance is considered negligible, the armature resistance is assumed constant, the field excitation is constant and great enough to saturate the iron, and all losses except armature I^2R loss are considered negligible. Two kinds of load will be considered. First a viscous friction load will be assumed, and second, a load consisting of viscous friction and constant torque will be assumed.

Case 1. *Viscous Friction Load.* Under the assumptions stated above, the armature circuit consists of a resistance R in series with a generator whose voltage equals the armature back electromotive force e_g, as shown in Fig. 9-2. By Kirchhoff's voltage law,

$$e = iR + e_g, \qquad (9.1)$$

where e is the applied voltage. Also, since the field excitation is constant,

$$e_g = K_1 N, \qquad (9.2)$$

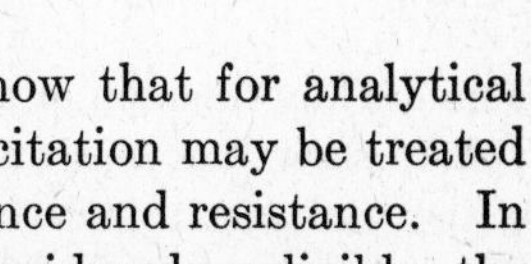

Fig. 9-2. Armature circuit of a d-c motor.

where N is the speed in radians per second, and K_1 is a constant depending on the machine. For constant field excitation the torque developed by the motor is

$$T = K_2 i,$$

and this torque must equal the load torque plus the torque required for angular acceleration. Thus

$$K_2 i = J\alpha + K_3 N = J\frac{dN}{dt} + K_3 N, \tag{9.3}$$

where J = moment of inertia of armature and load; α = angular acceleration dN/dt; and K_3 is a constant depending on the friction load. By use of Eqs. 9.3 and 9.2, both e_g and i in Eq. 9.1 can be expressed in terms of N. Thus Eq. 9.1 becomes

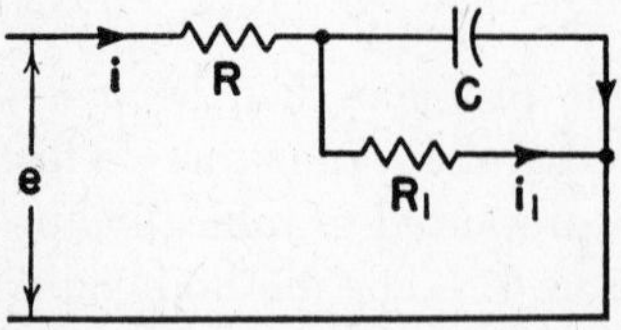

$$e = \frac{JR}{K_2}\frac{dN}{dt} + \frac{K_3 RN}{K_2} + K_1 N,$$

$$\frac{dN}{dt} + \left(\frac{K_3}{J} + \frac{K_1 K_2}{RJ}\right) N = \frac{K_2}{RJ} e,$$

$$\dot{e}_g + \left(\frac{K_3}{J} + \frac{K_1 K_2}{RJ}\right) e_g = \frac{K_1 K_2}{RJ} e. \tag{9.4}$$

Fig. 9-3. Equivalent circuit of d-c motor with viscous friction load.

Here e is any function of time. Now consider the circuit of Fig. 9-3. We wish to show that the voltage e_c across the capacitor is of the same form as the back electromotive force of the motor. To do this we write two differential equations involving i and i_1, and eliminate i between them:

$$e = iR + i_1 R_1,$$

$$e = iR + \frac{1}{C}\int (i - i_1)\, dt,$$

or

$$e = i\left(R + \frac{1}{Cp}\right) - \frac{1}{C}\cdot\frac{i_1}{p}.$$

Solution for i_1 and multiplication by R_1 gives

$$i_1 R_1 = \frac{eR_1}{RR_1 Cp + R + R_1} = e_c,$$

$$e_c\left(p + \frac{R + R_1}{RR_1 C}\right) = e\frac{R_1}{RR_1 C},$$

$$\frac{de_c}{dt} + \left(\frac{1}{R_1 C} + \frac{1}{RC}\right) e_c = \frac{1}{RC} e. \tag{9.5}$$

Comparison of Eq. 9.5 with Eq. 9.4 shows that they are of the same form, and they will be identical if

$$\frac{1}{R_1 C} = \frac{K_3}{J},$$

and

$$\frac{1}{RC} = \frac{K_1 K_2}{RJ}.$$

From the above two equations,

$$C = \frac{J}{K_1 K_2},$$

$$R_1 = \frac{K_1 K_2}{K_3}, \tag{9.6}$$

$$R = R.$$

Equations 9.6 allow us to replace the shunt motor with viscous friction load by the circuit of Fig. 9-3, in which the voltage e_c across C is equal to the motor back electromotive force, and therefore proportional to the speed N.

In this analogy the series resistance of the motor is replaced by the equal series resistor R. The inertia of the rotating parts is proportional to the capacitance C. The kinetic energy of rotation is analogous to the energy stored in the capacitor. The loss caused by the viscous friction load is proportional to $K_3 N^2$, and in Fig. 9-3 the analogous loss is $e_c{}^2/R_1$.

Case 2. *Viscous Friction and Constant Torque Load.* As in Case 1, the motor voltage equation is

$$e = iR + e_g = iR + K_1 N.$$

The torque equation is

$$T = K_2 i = J \frac{dN}{dt} + K_3 N + \tau,$$

where τ is the constant torque, and all other symbols are the same as in Case 1. Elimination of i between these equations gives

$$\frac{dN}{dt} + \left(\frac{K_3}{J} + \frac{K_1 K_2}{RJ}\right) N + \frac{\tau}{J} = \frac{K_2}{RJ} e.$$

Then, as before, since $e_g = K_1 N$,

$$\dot{e}_g + \left(\frac{K_3}{J} + \frac{K_1 K_2}{RJ}\right) e_g + \frac{K_1 \tau}{J} = \frac{K_1 K_2}{RJ} e. \tag{9.7}$$

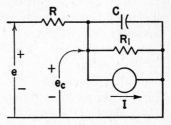

Fig. 9-4. Equivalent circuit of d-c motor with viscous friction and constant torque loads.

This differential equation for e_g contains the constant term $K_1 \tau/J$, which did not appear in Eq. 9.4. This constant term may be introduced into the equivalent circuit by the addition of a constant current generator in parallel with R_1, as shown in Fig. 9-4. This circuit may be solved for e_c by writing the node voltage equation for the node between C and R.

$$\frac{e_c - e}{R} + \frac{e_c}{R_1} + C\frac{de_c}{dt} + I = 0$$

$$\dot{e}_c + \left(\frac{1}{RC} + \frac{1}{R_1 C}\right) e_c + \frac{I}{C} = \frac{e}{RC} \qquad (9.8)$$

Comparison of Eqs. 9.7 and 9.8 shows that they are identical if

$$R = R, \qquad (9.9a)$$

$$\frac{K_1 K_2}{RJ} = \frac{1}{RC}, \qquad \text{or} \qquad C = \frac{J}{K_1 K_2} \qquad (9.9b)$$

$$\frac{K_3}{J} = \frac{1}{R_1 C}, \qquad \text{or} \qquad R_1 = \frac{K_1 K_2}{K_3} \qquad (9.9c)$$

$$\frac{K_1 \tau}{J} = \frac{I}{C}, \qquad \text{or} \qquad I = \frac{\tau}{K_2} \qquad (9.9d)$$

Equations 9.9a through 9.9d give the conditions for which e_c is identical to the back electromotive force of the motor, and hence e_c is proportional to motor speed. The constants C, R, and R_1 are the same as in Case 1, and I is proportional to the constant torque τ.

A few words about the constant torque τ are in order here. This torque may be produced by an active element, such as another motor, in which case, if the driving motor armature is open-circuited, the driving motor is driven backwards by the torque τ. Its speed in reverse is limited by the viscous friction losses. In the equivalent circuit, the analog of this situation occurs if the source e is disconnected. Then the current I flows through R_1, producing a negative voltage across C proportional to the negative motor speed. In this case the power to supply the viscous friction losses is drawn from the active element producing the torque τ, or from the current source I, in the analog.

The constant torque τ may also be produced by a passive element, that is, one which can absorb power but cannot deliver power. Here the torque must always oppose the motion, and it must be zero at standstill. Therefore in the equivalent circuit the current source must deliver current as shown in Fig. 9-4 when rotation is positive and in the opposite direction when rotation is reversed. Furthermore I must become zero whenever the capacitor voltage goes to zero.

In Eqs. 9.6 and 9.9 the dimensions of the various constants are: K_1, volts per radian per second; K_2, pound-feet per ampere; K_3, pound-feet per radian per second; J, pound-feet-second^2 per radian; C, farads; R and R_1, ohms; τ, pound-feet; I, amperes.

The magnitude of $C = J/K_1K_2$ is quite large. For a 110-volt $\frac{1}{4}$-hp d-c motor the constants are approximately as follows: $J \cong$ 0.00015 for a rotor, 3 in. diameter and 3 in. long; $K_1 \cong 0.6$; $K_2 \cong$ 0.44.

$$\therefore \quad C = \frac{1.5 \times 10^{-4}}{0.6 \times 0.4} = 569 \times 10^{-6} \text{ farad.}$$

One difficulty with the above analog is that the armature inductance is not accounted for, although there is no reason why it should not be inserted. However, in some applications the inductance is of no consequence, and in such cases the capacitor analog may prove to be a useful concept.

9.5 Thyratron Control of D-C Motors[1]

An elementary circuit for control of d-c motors up to about 3 hp is shown in Fig. 9-5. In order to make the analysis of the perform-

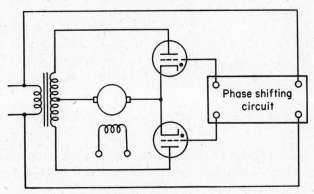

Fig. 9-5.   Basic circuit for thyratron control of a d-c motor.

ance of this circuit reasonably simple certain assumptions must be made. It will be assumed that

(1) The machine is shunt wound.
(2) The field is saturated by constant d-c excitation.
(3) The armature and circuit inductance L is constant.

---

[1] The method of analysis of thyratron controlled motors is based largely upon the paper by Vedder and Puchlowski, "Theory of Rectifier D-C Motor Drive," *Trans. AIEE*, **62**, 863–869.

(4) The total armature circuit resistance R is constant.

(5) The counter electromotive force E_g is proportional to motor speed.

(6) The transformer terminal voltage is constant.

(7) The tube drop E_t is constant.

(8) Conduction may begin as soon as the transformer voltage is equal to or greater than $E_g + E_t$.

(9) Armature reaction effect is negligible.

(10) The armature current consists of separate and discrete pulses.

Under these assumptions it is necessary to consider only half a cycle of current, and the circuit of Fig. 9-5 can be simplified to that

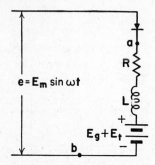

Fig. 9-6. Simplified equivalent circuit of Fig. 9-5.

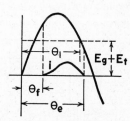

Fig. 9-7. Designation of firing and extinction angles.

of Fig. 9-6. It must be remembered, however, that the rectifier in this figure is not a simple diode rectifier but a grid controlled rectifier whose firing angle can be controlled.

Denote the firing angle of the thyratron by θ_f, Fig. 9-7, and the extinction angle by θ_e.

If time is considered zero at the firing point, the voltage applied to $a - b$, Fig. 9-6, may be written

$$E_{ab} = E_m \sin (\omega t + \theta_f); \qquad 0 \le \omega t \le \theta_e - \theta_f. \qquad (9.10)$$

If i is instantaneous armature current, its differential equation is

$$L \frac{di}{dt} + Ri = E_m \sin (\omega t + \theta_f) - (E_g + E_t). \qquad (9.11)$$

The solution of Eq. 9.11 may be written as a sum of two parts, a steady-state part i_s and a transient part i_t.

$$i_s = I_m \sin (\omega t + \theta_f - \theta) - \frac{E_g + E_t}{R}$$

$$i_s = \frac{E_m}{\sqrt{R^2 + (\omega L)^2}} \sin (\omega t + \theta_f - \theta) - \frac{E_g + E_t}{R}$$

where $\theta = \tan^{-1} \frac{\omega L}{R}$. $i_t = Ce^{-Rt/L}$.

Thus the total current i is

$$i = i_s + i_t = \frac{E_m}{Z} \sin (\omega t + \theta_f - \theta) - \frac{E_g + E_t}{R} + Ce^{-Rt/L}. \quad (9.12)$$

The constant C may be evaluated by noting that at $t = 0$, $i = 0$.

$$C = \frac{E_g + E_t}{R} - \frac{E_m}{Z} \sin (\theta_f - \theta).$$

Now let
$$\frac{E_g + E_t}{E_m} = a. \qquad (9.13)$$

Then $\quad i = \frac{E_m}{Z} \sin (\omega t + \theta_f - \theta) - \frac{aE_m}{r}$
$$+ \left[\frac{aE_m}{R} - \frac{E_m}{Z} \sin (\theta_f - \theta) \right] e^{-Rt/L}. \qquad (9.14)$$

Also let
$$\omega t + \theta_f = X.$$

$$i = \frac{E_m}{R} [\cos \theta \sin (X - \theta) - a$$
$$+ \{a - \cos \theta \sin (\theta_f - \theta)\} e^{-(X-\theta_f)/\tan \theta}]. \quad (9.15)$$

Equation 9.15 holds only for $i \geqq 0$, or for $0 < t < t_e$, or for $\theta_f \leq X \leq \theta_e$. In this circuit, the point of firing θ_f is controlled by a phase shifting circuit. The angle θ_e, the extinction angle, may be found in terms of θ_f by equating i to zero and X to θ_e in Eq. 9.15. Thus

$$\cos \theta \sin (\theta_e - \theta) - a + [a - \cos \theta \sin (\theta_f - \theta)]e^{-(\theta_e-\theta_f)/\tan \theta} = 0. \qquad (9.16)$$

The easiest way to find θ_e for various values of a, θ, and θ_f is to plot Eq. 9.16. The method is to select values of a, θ, and θ_f. Then Eq. 9.16 is plotted to find θ_e for these values. The process is repeated for a number of values of θ_f. A curve may be plotted of θ_f versus θ_e for the selected values of a and θ. For a particular machine only one value of θ is necessary, but a range of values for a between 0 and 1 must be used since $a = (E_g + E_t)/E_m$. Actually a

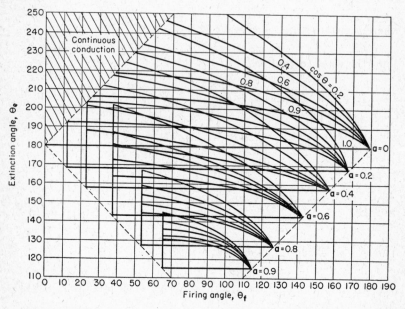

Fig. 9-8. Plots of extinction angle versus firing angle. [From a paper entitled, "Theory of Rectifier D-C Motor Drive" by E. H. Vedder and K. P. Puchlowski. Republished from *Trans. AIEE*, **62**, 863–890 (1943).]

can never quite reach 0 since E_t is assumed constant. The smaller values of a correspond to large values of torque.

Plots of θ_e versus θ_f are shown in Fig. 9-8. There are several points of interest which should be mentioned about these curves. One is that the firing angle θ_f cannot exceed the angle θ_1, Fig. 9-7, at which e, the applied voltage, becomes equal to $E_g + E_t$. This means that in Fig. 9-7, θ_f cannot exceed the angle marked θ_1. Therefore the maximum firing angle is a function of a. If $a = 0$, then θ_f could be 180°. Actually, of course, a could never be 0 because of the tube drop E_t. As $a \to 1$, which would mean that the speed would be great enough so that $E_g + E_t \to E_m$, then $\theta_{f\ max}$ would approach 90°. At speeds in between these limits $\theta_{f\ max}$ varies between 90° and 180°. The maximum possible value of θ_f is equal to the extinction angle, because if the tube fires at its maximum possible firing angle there is no voltage across the tube, so the tube extinguishes as soon as it fires. Hence the locus of maximum possible values of θ_f is a straight line of slope 1. All the curves begin on this line.

The minimum possible value of θ_f for a given value of a, and hence of E_g, would be 180° minus the maximum value of θ_f for that value of a. This fact is apparent from an inspection of Fig. 9-7, since the thyratron cannot fire until e becomes equal to or greater than $E_g + E_t$.

If $(\theta_e - \theta_f) > 180°$ the current pulses would no longer be separate and distinct pulses, and the foregoing analysis would no longer be valid. On the plot of θ_f versus θ_e, the region where $(\theta_e - \theta_f) > 180$ is the region above the dashed line starting at $\theta_f = 0$, $\theta_e = 180$, and with slope $+1$. Hence all the curves terminate on this line, since the equations are invalid for the region above the line.

9.6 Speed-torque Characteristic of Thyratron Controlled Motor

It is of interest to determine the speed-torque characteristic of a thyratron controlled d-c motor for constant firing angle θ_f and constant phase angle θ. The instantaneous torque is proportional to the instantaneous armature current i given by Eq. 9.15. The average torque is proportional to I_{av}.

$$I_{av} = \frac{1}{\pi} \frac{E_m}{R} \int_{X=\theta_f}^{X=\theta_e} \{\cos \theta \sin (X - \theta) - a$$
$$+ [a - \cos \theta \sin (\theta_f - \theta)]e^{\theta_f/\tan\theta} \cdot e^{-X/\tan\theta}\} \, dx$$

The above integration need not be carried out when it is observed that

$$I_{av}R = \frac{1}{\pi} \int_{\theta_f}^{\theta_e} e_a \, dx$$

where e_a is the instantaneous voltage across the armature resistance and inductance. This integral is simpler, since

$$e_a = E_m \sin X - (E_g + E_t)$$

$$= E_m \sin X - E_m a,$$

$$\therefore \quad I_{av} R = \frac{1}{\pi} \int_{\theta_f}^{\theta_e} (E_m \sin X - E_m a) \, dx$$

$$\frac{I_{av} R}{E_m} = \frac{1}{\pi} [\cos \theta_f - \cos \theta_e - a(\theta_e - \theta_f)]. \qquad (9.17)$$

The term $I_{av}R/E_m$ is proportional to the torque. Equation 9.17 may be written

$$\frac{I_{av}}{E_m/\pi R} = \frac{T_{av}}{T_0} = \cos \theta_f - \cos \theta_e - a(\theta_e - \theta_f). \qquad (9.18)$$

Here the term $E_m/\pi R$ is the current which would flow if a d-c voltage of value E_m/π were applied to the armature with the rotor blocked, and the torque resulting is T_0. T_{av} is the average torque under operating conditions. The maximum possible value of Eq. 9.18 would occur under the ideal conditions of $\cos \theta = 1$ and $\theta_f = 0$, so that $\theta_f = 0$; $E_t = 0$; $\theta_e = 180$; $E_g = 0$ (blocked rotor). Then Eq. 9.18 gives

$$\frac{I_{av}}{E_m/\pi R} = \frac{T_{av}}{T_0} = 2. \qquad (9.19)$$

The torque ratio is 2 because $E_m/\pi R$ is the average current for a half-wave rectified applied voltage assuming $\cos \theta = 1$, whereas the applied voltage for the foregoing calculations is an ideal full-wave rectified voltage.

Equation 9.18 for T_{av}/T_0 is plotted in solid lines in Fig. 9-9 for several firing angles and a power factor of 0.6. The abscissa, which is $a = (E_g + E_T)/E_m$, is not quite proportional to the speed because of the additive constant E_T/E_m. However, it is nevertheless obvious that the speed-torque curve for a constant firing angle has a very undesirable droop and is very similar to that of a series motor. It should be mentioned that for firing angles less than 90°, $a = (E_g + E_t)/E_m \le \sin \theta_f$, since for larger values of a the generated voltage would be so large that the tubes could not fire. Thus all

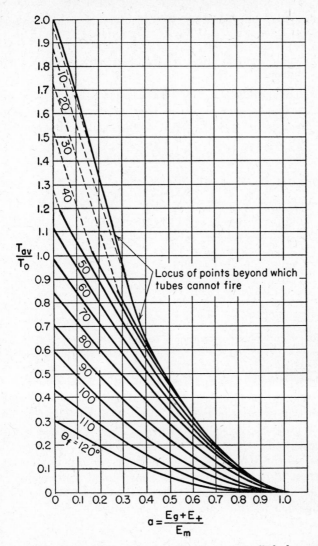

Fig. 9-9. Speed-torque curves for thyratron controlled d-c motor for various firing angles θ_f, and $\cos \theta = 0.6$. Solid lines show intermittent conduction: $T_{av}/T_0 = \cos \theta_f - \cos \theta_e - a(\theta_e - \theta_f)$. Dashed lines show continuous conduction: $T_{av}/T_0 = 2 \cos \theta_f - a\pi$.

curves of Fig. 9-9 for $\theta_f \leq 90°$ terminate at the points where $\sin \theta_f = a$.

9.7 Thyratron Controlled D-C Motor Characteristics Under Continuous Conduction

The shaded portion of Fig. 9-8 represents a region of continuous conduction, and Fig. 9-10 shows the voltage across the armature under this condition. We want to determine the speed-torque

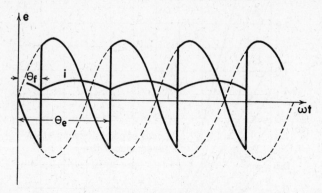

Fig. 9-10. Figure showing firing and extinction angles for continuous conduction in the circuit of Fig. 9-5.

characteristic under this condition of continuous conduction, and it is desirable to establish the conditions under which current flow changes from discrete pulses to continuous flow.

For these purposes we may start with Eq. 9-11, which is valid for this case as well as for the case of discrete pulses. The evaluation of the constant C will be different. It can be evaluated by noting that the current at the firing angle θ_f must equal the current at the extinction angle $\theta_f + \pi$, since the extinction angle for one tube is also the firing angle for the other tube. Therefore

$$i\big|_{\omega t=0} = i\big|_{\omega t=\pi}.$$

Substituting $\omega t = 0$ and $\omega t = \pi$ in Eq. 9.12 and equating the results gives

$$\frac{E_m}{Z} \sin (\theta_f - \theta) - \frac{aE_m}{R} + C = \frac{E_m}{Z} \sin (\theta_f - \theta + \pi) - \frac{aE_m}{R} + C\epsilon^{-R\pi/\omega L}.$$

From this
$$C = \frac{(2E_m/Z)\sin(\theta_f - \theta)}{\epsilon^{-R\pi/\omega L} - 1};$$

and
$$i = \frac{E_m}{Z}\sin(\omega t + \theta_f - \theta) - \frac{aE_m}{R}$$
$$+ \frac{(2E_m/Z)\sin(\theta_f - \theta)}{\epsilon^{-R\pi/\omega L} - 1}\epsilon^{-Rt/L}. \quad (9.20)$$

Here
$$a = \frac{E_g + E_t}{E_m}.$$

Now let $\omega t + \theta_f = X$ and $\omega L/R = \tan\theta$. Equation 9.20 then becomes

$$i = \frac{E_m}{R}\left[\cos\theta\sin(X - \theta) - a + \frac{2\cos\theta\sin(\theta_f - \theta)}{\epsilon^{-\pi/\tan\theta} - 1}\epsilon^{-(X-\theta_f)/\tan\theta}\right],$$
$$(9.21)$$

and
$$\theta_f \leq X \leq \theta_f + \pi.$$

Equation 9.21 gives the instantaneous current for continuous conduction between $X = \theta_f$ and $X = \theta_f + \pi$.

Under conditions where continuous flow is about to become intermittent flow, the current given by Eq. 9.21 should just go to 0 at $X = \theta_f$. Making this substitution in Eq. 9.21 and letting θ'_f represent this special firing angle gives

$$0 = \frac{E_m}{Z}\sin(\theta'_f - \theta) - \frac{aE_m}{R} + \frac{(2E_m/Z)\sin(\theta'_f - \theta)}{\epsilon^{-\pi/\tan\theta} - 1}.$$

$$\sin(\theta'_f - \theta) = \frac{aZ/R}{1 - 2/(1 - \epsilon^{-\pi/\tan\theta})} = \frac{a/\cos\theta}{1 - 2/(1 - \epsilon^{-\pi/\tan\theta})}.$$
$$(9.22)$$

Equation 9.22 gives the transition condition between intermittent and continuous current flow. For given values of a and θ, the value of θ'_f is found by Eq. 9.22. If θ_f is made less than θ'_f, continuous conduction results, corresponding to operation in the shaded region of Fig. 9-8. If θ_f is greater than θ'_f, current flows in discrete pulses.

The torque under continuous current flow is proportional to the average value of the current. This average value could be found by integrating the instantaneous current from θ_f to $\theta_f + \pi$, but it is much easier to find I_{av} by the method already used in Sec. 9.6 for discrete pulses.

$$I_{av}R = \frac{1}{\pi} \int_{\theta_f}^{\theta_f+\pi} e_a \, dx = \frac{1}{\pi} \int_{\theta_f}^{\theta_f+\pi} [E_m \sin X - (E_g + E_t)] \, dx$$

$$= \frac{1}{\pi} \int_{\theta_f}^{\theta_f+\pi} (E_m \sin X - aE_m) \, dx.$$

$$I_{av}R = \frac{E_m}{\pi} (2 \cos \theta_f - a\pi).$$

$$\frac{I_{av}}{E_m/\pi R} = \frac{T_{av}}{T_0} = 2 \cos \theta_f - a\pi. \tag{9.23}$$

This equation is plotted on Fig. 9-9 for various firing angles. Consider, for example, the curve for $\theta_f = 30°$. For low speeds, where a is small, conduction is continuous and Eq. 9.23 applies. At standstill, or at $a \cong 0$, $T_{av}/T_0 = 1.732$, and as a increases T_{av}/T_0 decreases linearly, as shown by the dashed line. At the critical value of a given by Eq. 9.22 for this particular firing angle, conduction changes from the continuous to the intermittent condition. From here on, Eq. 9.18 applies, and the curve is plotted as a solid line. As the firing angle is made larger, the speed range over which continuous conduction can occur becomes smaller. When $\theta_f = \theta$, Eq. 9.22 gives $a = 0$, which means that at zero value of a there is continuous conduction, but for all values of a greater than zero, conduction is intermittent. For $\theta_f \geq \theta$, the sign of a must be *negative* if conduction is to be continuous that is, the motor must be driven backwards.

9.8   Determination of Maximum Current

In the design of a motor control circuit the determination of the maximum instantaneous value of tube current is important, since this consideration may determine the selection of tubes.

Two conditions must be distinguished, one for discontinuous conduction and one for continuous conduction. The case of discontinuous conduction will be considered first in detail.

Start with Eq. 9.15, which is the equation for the current.

Differentiate it, set it equal to 0, and let $X = \theta_p$, the angle at which peak current occurs.

$$\frac{di}{dX} = \frac{E_m}{R}\left[+ \cos\theta\cos(\theta_p - \theta) \right.$$
$$\left. - \frac{1}{\tan\theta}\{a - \cos\theta\sin(\theta_f - \theta)\}\epsilon^{-(\theta_p - \theta_f)/\tan\theta} \right] = 0.$$

$$\cos\theta\cos(\theta_p - \theta) = \frac{1}{\tan\theta}[a - \cos\theta\sin(\theta_f - \theta)]\epsilon^{-(\theta_p - \theta_f)/\tan\theta}.$$

Divide by $\cos\theta$ and rearrange.

$$\cos(\theta_p - \theta)\epsilon^{\theta_p/\tan\theta} = \left[\frac{a}{\sin\theta} - \frac{\sin(\theta_f - \theta)}{\tan\theta}\right]\epsilon^{\theta_f/\tan\theta}. \quad (9.24)$$

This equation can be solved for θ_p for various values of θ_f and the parameters by plotting. Equation 9.24 is of the form

$$f(\theta_p) = \phi(\theta_f). \quad (9.25)$$

The method is to plot $f(\theta_p)$ versus θ_p for a given set of parameters and to plot $\phi(\theta_f)$ versus θ_f for the same parameters. To find θ_p for a given θ_f, first find ϕ and then find the value of θ_p for which f equals ϕ. In this way plots of θ_p versus θ_f can be obtained. Such plots are shown in Fig. 9.11. These are the curves to the right of the sloping straight line in the region marked "Intermittent conduction." Now to obtain I_p, the values of θ_p obtained above must be substituted in Eq. 9.15. It is convenient to write the equation in the form

$$\frac{I_p}{E_m/R} = \frac{I_p}{I'_0}$$
$$= \cos\theta\sin(\theta_p - \theta) - a + [a - \cos\theta\sin(\theta_f - \theta)]\epsilon^{-(\theta_p - \theta_f)/\tan\theta}. \quad (9.26)$$

If the equation is written in this form, the current I'_0 is the current which would flow if a d-c voltage E_m were applied to the blocked rotor. I'_0 is thus easy to calculate for any motor, and Eq. 9.26 can be used to find I_p for any motor. Equation 9.26 has been plotted for various values of θ in Fig. 9-12 for $a = 0$. Again these are the curves to the right of the curved line separating the inter- mittent and continuous conduction regions. It will be observed that the greatest values of I_p occur for $a = 0$ and $\cos \theta = 1$, that is, for blocked rotor, zero tube drop, and unity power factor.

The curve of θ_p versus θ_f for $a = 0$ and $\cos \theta = 1$ can be obtained from purely physical reasoning. If $a = 0$, then $E_g + E_t = 0$, and if $\cos \theta = 1$, then $L = 0$. Hence the circuit becomes a pure resistance

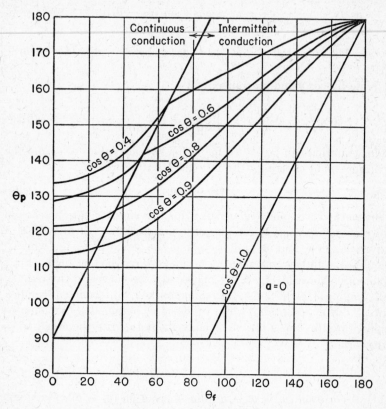

Fig. 9-11. Peak current angle θ_p versus firing angle θ_f.

in series with a switch. Obviously then if the firing angle is less than 90°, the peak current angle must be 90°. If θ_f is greater than 90°, then θ_p must be equal to θ_f. This is the way the curve is drawn. Similar reasoning will show that the ratio I_p/I'_0 must be unity from $\theta_f = 0$ to $\theta_f = 90°$.

Now similar curves for continuous conduction must be determined. The procedure is the same except that Eq. 9.21, which gives the current for continuous conduction, must be used instead of Eq. 9.15.   Otherwise, the procedure is the same and will not be carried out here.   The results are the portions of the curves in Figs. 9-11 and 9-12 to the left of the dividing lines between the regions of continuous and intermittent conduction.

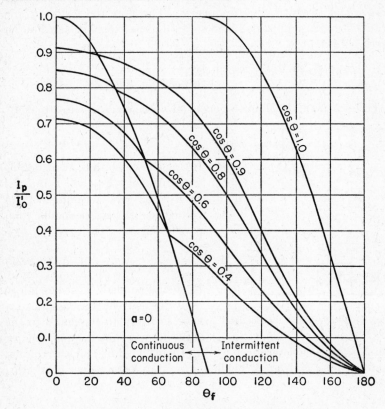

Fig. 9-12.   Peak current factor I_p/I'_0 versus firing angle θ_f.

9.9   Feedback Circuit for Speed Regulation

In order to correct for poor speed regulation, it is necessary to obtain a voltage from the system which is proportional to the speed. E_g is such a voltage, but it cannot be measured directly.   A circuit which produces a voltage nearly proportional to E_g is shown in Fig. 9-13.   It will be shown that e_c, the voltage across C, is a function of E_g under certain conditions.   The voltage divider is connected across the armature, and thus it has applied to it the voltage,

$$e_a = iR + L\frac{di}{dt} + E_g.$$

The current i is pulsating (see Eq. 9.15), with a fundamental frequency of twice the line frequency. Therefore the terms iR and $L(di/dt)$ are also pulsating, and e_a can thus be expressed as a Fourier series of the form

$$e_a = E_0 + E_1 \sin 2\omega t + E_2 \sin 4\omega t + \cdots$$
$$+ E'_1 \cos 2\omega t + E'_2 \cos 4\omega t + \cdots.$$

The term E_0 is the d-c component of voltage across the armature, and its value is

$$E_0 = E_g + I_{av}R.$$

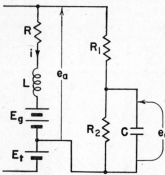

Fig. 9-13. Circuit for obtaining a voltage nearly proportional to speed.

If C is chosen so that X_c at double line frequency is small compared to R_1, all the a-c components of voltage across C are negligible compared with E_0. Then

$$e_c = \frac{R_2}{R_1 + R_2}(E_g + I_{av}R). \quad (9.27)$$

R_1 should be made large enough to limit the current through it to a very small value compared to the armature current, 0.1 per cent or less. R_2 is then determined by the proportion of E_0 which is required across C. If X_c is made small compared to R_1, say 1 per cent of R_1, then

$$0.01R_1 = \frac{1}{2\omega C}$$

and

$$C = \frac{1}{0.02R_1\omega}. \quad (9.28)$$

Equation 9.27 contains both E_g and $I_{av}R$. If the voltage e_c above is used for correcting the drooping speed-torque characteristic, the correction is not adequate, since when E_g drops, $I_{av}R$ increases. It is therefore necessary to provide an additional correction for armature resistance voltage drop. In the Mototrol circuit of Westinghouse this correction is obtained by taking the drop across a small resistor in series with the armature and applying it to the grid of an amplifier stage. The output of this stage controls the bias on a pentode control grid. The plate resistor of the pentode is shunted by a capacitor large enough to eliminate the ripple caused by the voltage across the series resistor in the armature circuit.

9.10 Regulation of Motor Speed

Figure 9-14 is a schematic diagram showing the method of using the back electromotive force of the motor to regulate the motor

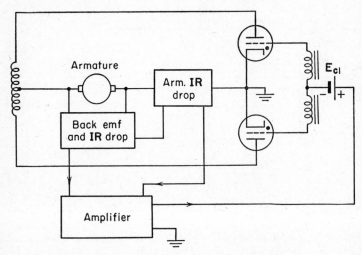

Fig. 9-14.   Schematic arrangement of feedback for speed control of a d-c motor.

speed.   The thyratron grid voltages are supplied by the secondary windings of a transformer whose primary is excited by a voltage shifted 90° behind the thyratron plate supply voltage.   Also there is a constant bias voltage component E_{c1} which makes the grids more negative to the cathode, and a variable d-c component produced by the amplifier.   The variable component shifts the a-c component up or down, thus advancing or retarding the firing angle θ_f.   The input to the amplifier is a voltage proportional to E_g, the generated voltage.   If E_g drops due to an increase in load, the amplifier output voltage rises, thus advancing the firing angle and bringing the speed back toward the original value.

The principal features of the feedback circuit are shown in Fig. 9-15. The resistors R_1, R_2, and capacitor C_2 constitute the circuit for producing a voltage proportional to $E_g + I_{av}R$. The voltage from cathode to grid of tube 1 is the important one in determining the d-c component of bias on the thyratron grids. The circuit from cathode to grid can be traced as follows. Starting at the cathode there is a drop in voltage to the tap on P_2, then a rise across R_2,

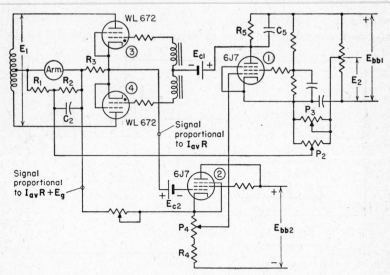

Fig. 9-15. Simplified diagram of automatic motor speed control by armature current. (From *Electronics Laboratory Manual for Educational Institutions*, Westinghouse Electric Corporation, East Pittsburgh, Pennsylvania, 1945.)

and finally a drop across part of P_4. The setting of P_2 is a manual speed control adjustment, and its setting determines the speed. The rise across R_2 is proportional to the sum $E_g + I_{av}R$. The drop across P_4 is proportional to $I_{av}R$. Thus the total *change* of voltage from cathode to grid on tube 1 due to a speed change is proportional only to the change in E_g.

The regulating process may now be traced. If the motor speed drops below normal, E_g decreases, thus decreasing the potential of the grid of tube 1. The tube 1 plate voltage then rises, the firing angle is advanced, and the motor tends to return to its original speed. Obviously the motor cannot return to exactly the original speed if the decrease is due to increased load, because there must be a change in the drop across R_2 in order to maintain the lower grid bias on tube 1 and the higher voltage on the plate. The change in voltage required at the grid of tube 1 is smaller the greater the gain of tube 1. Hence, as in the case of voltage regulators, the greater the gain of the feedback circuit, the better is the regulation.

One point has not been mentioned. The circuit for obtaining a voltage proportional to $E_g + I_{av}R$ was designed with some care to produce a voltage free of ripple, and that is the purpose of C_2. No provision is made to remove the ripple from the drop across R_3, and as a matter of fact this voltage is proportional to the armature current at any instant. This ripple appears at P_4, Fig. 9-15, and at the grid of tube 1. It is removed from the output of tube 1 by shunting R_5 by a suitable capacitor. The reason R_3 is not shunted is that R_3 must be very small in order to keep from adding an objectionable I^2R loss in the armature circuit. A capacitor across R_3 big enough to reduce the ripple appreciably would be enormous. Hence it is put across R_5 where it can be made of reasonable magnitude.

9.11 Steady-state Performance of System with Feedback

The determination of the steady-state performance of the system of Figs. 9-14 or 9-15 is not as simple as the voltage regulators previously considered, because this system is not a linear system. Not only is the curve of torque versus thyratron grid voltage nonlinear, but the thyratrons themselves are unidirectional devices. Both of these facts affect the transient behavior and make analysis difficult. Only the first affects the steady-state conditions.

If enough data are available in the form of curves, the performance of the system can be estimated. Figure 9-16 shows a set of curves like those of Fig. 9-9 which has already been discussed. If a vertical line is drawn at a chosen value of a (or speed), say at $a = 0.6$, the intersection of the curves of Fig. 9-16 with this line will give another curve of T_{av}/T_0 versus θ_f for constant speed. A set of such curves is shown in Fig. 9-17. These curves can be used to find the required change in θ_f to maintain constant speed or constant value of a. It is also necessary to know the relation between the firing angle and the voltage E'_c between the thyratron cathodes and the center tap of their grid transformer. For a fixed value of the sinusoidal component of grid voltage, the curve of θ_f versus E'_c can

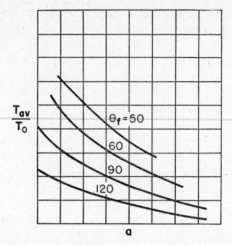

Fig. 9-16.   Speed-torque curves without feedback.

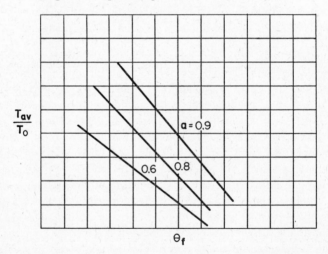

Fig. 9-17.   Torque-firing angle curves for constant speeds.

be obtained from Fig. 9-18.   Figure 9-19 shows the variation of E'_c/E_{gm} with θ_f.   If the thyratron critical grid voltage were always 0 instead of a small negative voltage, the curve of Fig. 9-19 would be a sinusoid in form.   It is very nearly so if the critical voltage is small compared with E_{gm}.   This is the condition which should exist, because a large value of E_{gm} is desirable.   If E_{gm} is small (of the order of a few volts), the slopes of the grid voltage and critical voltage curves are not much different from each other, and the firing angle θ_f shifts about erratically from cycle to cycle. If E_{gm} is of the order of 50 to 150 volts, this shifting is not serious. On the other

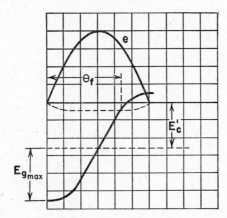

Fig. 9-18.   Figure for determining θ_f versus E'_c.

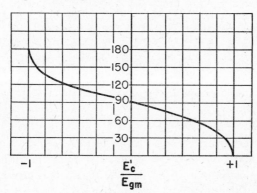

Fig. 9-19.   Firing angle versus cathode to grid voltage of tubes 3 or 4, Fig. 9-15.

hand, use of a large value of E_{gm} requires a correspondingly large gain in the feedback circuit to shift the phase appreciably.

The curve of Fig. 9-19 can be made universal by plotting E'_c/E_{gm} against θ_f and assuming that the critical firing voltage is always 0. This is a good approximation for any value of E_{gm} greater than about 50 volts. Such a curve is plotted carefully in Fig. 9-20.

It is necessary to know the ratio of the voltage across R_2, Fig.

9-15, to the speed of the machine. This ratio can be found from Eq. 9-27, by setting $I_{av}R$ equal to zero. If the gain of the amplifier is known, all the information necessary for estimating the system performance is available.

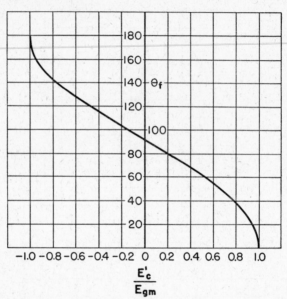

Fig. 9-20. Variation of firing angle with d-c grid bias, E'_c. Critical grid voltage assumed equals zero, or $E_{gm} > 50$.

9.12   Constant Torque System

In manufacturing processes involving the winding of strips or wires of material on spools or drums it is sometimes necessary to maintain a constant torque on the winding spool or drum regardless of the speed of the motor driving the drum. Such a circuit is shown in Fig. 9-21.

It is assumed that the motor field excitation is constant, and that the armature resistance and the inductance are constant. The excitation of the grid transformer is phase shifted so that the grid voltages lag their respective anode voltages by 90°.

The operation of the circuit is based on the fact that the average torque is proportional to the average armature current, which must flow through the low resistance R_3. The voltage drop across R_3 is fed back to the control grid of the pentode. If the torque should drop, due to an increase in motor speed for example, the drop across R_3 would decrease, and the pentode plate voltage would rise. The net d-c bias on the thyratrons would therefore decrease, thus advancing the firing angles and increasing the average current and torque.

There is a considerable amount of ripple voltage across R_3, and it is the purpose of C_1 to eliminate the ripple from the pentode plate voltage, for otherwise the amplified ripple might cause spurious

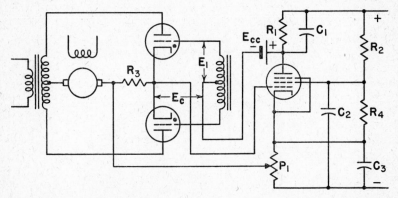

Fig. 9-21. Simple circuit for maintaining constant torque on a motor.

firing of the thyratrons. A similar precaution was observed in the circuit of Fig. 9-15.

The pentode is self-biased by means of potentiometer P_1 and capacitor C_3. The tap on P_1 is for adjusting the motor torque to the desired value at zero motor speed. The resistance of P_1 should be low enough so that changes in pentode current do not change the bias appreciably.

The design of the essential parts of the circuit can be based on a set of speed-torque curves similar to those of Fig. 9-9. It is first necessary to decide upon the allowable variation of torque over the expected variation of speed. Suppose, for example, that a stand-still torque of $T_{av}/T_0 = 0.25$ is required and that the speed is expected to vary from zero to a value such that $a = (E_g + E_t)/E_m = 0.5$. Let the value of a at zero speed be $a_0 = E_t/E_m$. Suppose for this example that the power factor of the armature, including R_3, is 0.6, so that the curves of Fig. 9-9, part of which is reproduced

in Fig. 9-22, can be used.   For any other power factor a different
set of curves should be constructed.   If E_t, the tube drop, and E_m
the maximum value of supply voltage, are such that $a_0 = 0.08$, the
thyratrons should be fired at $\theta_f = 120°$ to give the required torque
at standstill.   Let this firing angle be θ_{f1}.   As the speed increases,
the firing angle must be advanced to maintain constant torque.
Thus, at $a = 0.5$, the firing angle must be about 86° for $T_{av}/T_0 = 0.25$.   However, the regulator is not perfect, because there must be

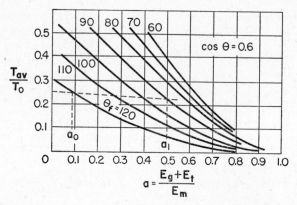

Fig. 9-22.   Speed-torque curves for thyratron controlled d-c motor for various
firing angles.

some drop in torque in order to provide the pentode grid voltage
change necessary to shift the thyratron firing angle.   The amount of
decrease in torque depends on the gain of the pentode and on the
amplitude of E_c, the grid transformer voltage.   Suppose that at
$a = 0.5$ the torque is allowed to drop to 0.225.   The resulting
speed-torque curve would then resemble the dashed line on Fig. 9-22.
The change in the torque *ratio* is 0.025, and this allowable change is
called $\Delta\tau$.   The firing angle at standstill is θ_{f0} and at the highest
expected speed, designated by a_1 on Fig. 9-22, the firing angle is
θ_{f1}.   In this example $\theta_{f0} = 120°$ and $\theta_{f1} = 90°$.

Figure 9-23 shows the anode and grid voltages of one of the
thyratrons for the case where the tube is firing at θ_{f0}.   The a-c component of grid voltage E_1 is biased below the cathode by the amount
E_c, and it is this bias which is changed by the pentode.

The amplifier gain necessary to maintain the torque ratio con⌄

stant within the allowable limit of $\Delta\tau$ can easily be found.   From Eq. 9.18 it is evident that

$$\Delta\tau = \frac{\pi R}{E_m}\Delta I_{av}.$$

Here R includes both R_3 and the armature resistance.   The change of voltage across R_3 is

$$\Delta e = R_3\Delta I_{av} = \frac{E_m R_3}{\pi R}\Delta\tau = K_1\Delta\tau.$$

This change of voltage, when amplified, must change E_c enough to shift the firing angle from θ_{f0} to θ_{f1}.   If it is assumed that the thyra-

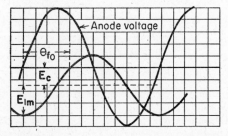

Fig. 9-23.   Thyratron grid and anode voltages for the circuit of Fig. 9-21.

tron fires when the grid voltage e_{kg} is $-E_{crit}$, then

$$e_{kg} = -E_c - E_{1m}\cos\theta_f = -E_{crit},$$

$$E_c = -E_{1m}\cos\theta_f + E_{crit},$$

$$\Delta E_c = -E_{1m}(\cos\theta_{f0} - \cos\theta_{f1}).$$

This voltage must equal the gain times $\Delta e + \Delta e$.   Therefore

$$A = \frac{-E_{1m}(\cos\theta_{f0} - \cos\theta_{f1})}{(E_m R_3/\pi R)\Delta\tau} - 1. \qquad (9.29)$$

Equation 9.29 gives the gain necessary for the pentode amplifier in order to maintain the torque ratio T_{av}/T_0 within $\Delta\tau$ of its value at zero speed.   The gain becomes larger as $\Delta\tau$ decreases.   Also the required gain varies directly with E_{1m}, so one would be tempted to make E_{1m} very small.   However, the smaller E_{1m}, the a-c grid voltage, is made, the more sensitive the firing angle becomes to small variations in the tube temperature, line voltage, etc. For best sensitivity, E_{1m} should be made as small as possible within the above limitations.

PROBLEMS

9.1. In the accompanying figure R and L are, respectively, the resistance and inductance of a d-c motor field, which is to be excited from the a-c source as shown. Assume that the diode is a perfect rectifier. (a) Does the field current flow intermittently or continuously? (b) Show that if R is zero the average current is $E_m/\omega L$, and sketch the current wave form. (c) Write the

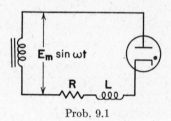

Prob. 9.1

differential equation for i for any values of R, L, and ω, and solve it for i as a function of time after the circuit has operated for a large number of cycles. (d) Plot i for 1 cycle if $e = 100 \sin \omega t$, $\omega = 377$, $R = 100$ ohms, $L = 0.01$ h.

9.2. This is the same circuit as problem 9.1, except for the added diode. Assume both diodes to be perfect rectifiers. (a) Sketch the voltage across the field terminals. (b) Show that the average current is $E_m/\pi R$. (c) If E_m,

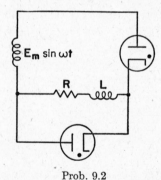

Prob. 9.2

R, and L are the same as in problem 9.1, estimate the maximum amplitude of the ripple current through L. *Hint:* Express the voltage as a Fourier series.

9.3. The phase-shifting circuit is arranged to fire the thyratron at any desired phase angle. Assume zero tube drops. Calculate the average field current as a function of θ_f, the firing angle, and other circuit parameters.

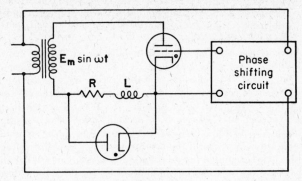

Prob. 9.3

9.4. In the circuit of Fig. 9-1 the armature circuit contains a pair of FG-17 thyratrons whose grids are connected to the cathodes. Assume that the anode must be 50 v positive to the cathode before the tube will fire. The armature resistance is 1 ohm and the inductance is zero. At 100 v d-c, the motor runs at 1500 rpm under no load. The plate-to-plate supply voltage is 220 v rms. The maximum allowable instantaneous tube current is 2 a. (a) What is the necessary starting resistance? (b) What ultimate speed will the motor attain assuming no losses or load?

9.5. A $\frac{3}{4}$-hp d-c shunt motor is to be operated using two thyratrons to control the armature current as shown in the sketch. The field is to be excited from a separate source of constant current. The armature inductance is 0.0169 h, its resistance 2.78 ohms. When the machine is operated from direct current with $\frac{3}{4}$ hp shaft output at rated speed of 1800 rpm and at 110 v armature voltage, the armature current is 6.0 a. Assume a tube drop $E_t = 15$ v. (a)

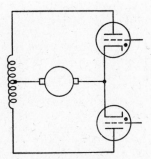

Prob. 9.5

Calculate and plot a curve of T_{av}/T_0 versus $(E_g + E_t)/E_m$ for a firing angle of 90°. (b) If the rms voltage from plate-to-plate of the thyratrons is 220 v find the motor speed in rpm for a shaft torque of 0.73 lb-ft. (c) For the conditions of part (b) what is the extinction angle? (d) If the motor is at standstill and the thyratron grids are suddenly excited so as to fire the tubes at 90°, what will be the peak current during the first half cycle of operation? Assume zero tube drop for this calculation.

9.6. A d-c motor is rated as follows: 2 hp output at 1750 rpm, 220 v, 8 amp armature current. Armature resistance is 1.5 ohms. Field constant. (a) In the circuit of Fig. 9-15 compute suitable values for R_1, R_2, R_3, and C_2. Design R_3 so that the power dissipated by it is 5 per cent of the I^2R loss in the armature. Assume a gain of 15 for tube 2. (b) It is found that to maintain motor speed constant at 1750 rpm from no load to full load, the firing angle must shift from 150° to 40°. If the grids are excited by a 60-c sinusoidal component of rms value 50 v, and if the thyratrons fire at zero grid voltage, what change in d-c bias is required to maintain motor speed? (c) What change in voltage at the grid of tube 1 of the amplifier results if the speed changes from 1750 to 1700 rpm?

9.7. In problem 9.6 assume an armature inductance such that $\cos \theta = 0.5$. Also assume that tube 1 has a gain of 90 and tube 2 has a gain of 15. At no load the speed is such that $a = 0.5$ and the friction and windage produce a ratio of $T_{av}/T_0 = 0.05$. (a) Redesign R_1 and R_2 based on a value of $R_3 = 0.075$ ohm and the above gains. (b) If the plate-to-plate supply voltage is 80 v peak, and the rms voltage across one grid transformer is 50 v, find the change in speed if the torque is increased to 7 times the value caused by friction and windage. Assume a tube drop of 12 v.

CHAPTER 10

RADIO FREQUENCY HEATING[1]

Radio frequency heating has become widespread in industry because of certain characteristics that permit rapid completion of operations which are either slow and difficult, or impossible, with other methods of heating. In many applications it puts the heat "where you want it when you want it." These advantages are possible because of two effects which radio frequency fields exhibit. One is *skin effect*. Here the currents induced in a good (but not perfect) conductor immersed in a radio frequency field are constrained to flow in a shallow layer of surface material, so that any heat thus generated by I^2R loss is near the surface. The other effect is that of *uniform heating* throughout the body of a good (but not perfect) insulator in a radio frequency field because of losses in the dielectric.

An example of the use of skin effect is the case-hardening of steel parts where only a thin shell of hardened steel is wanted. The surface is quickly heated in a radio frequency field; then it is automatically quenched, when the field is removed, by the rapid cooling of the surface as the heat flows into the cold interior. A typical use of the uniform heating effect in a dielectric is the curing of glued plywood by application of a radio frequency field.

There are numerous applications for this method of heating, where an important consideration is that no physical connection other than the electromagnetic field is required between the source of energy and the object to be heated. For example, in the manufacture of vacuum tubes it is frequently desirable to heat the metal parts after they are sealed into a glass envelope. This can be done

---

[1] A large part of the material in this chapter is based on the methods of Brown, Hoyler, and Bierwirth used in their book *Theory and Application of Radio-Frequency Heating*, D. Van Nostrand Company, Inc., New York, 1947.

by passing radio frequency current through a coil surrounding the glass envelope. The same technique may be used to heat metal parts in a hydrogen atmosphere, where a flame may cause an explosion. The method is useful in operations such as brazing of certain metals, where the contaminating influence of a flame is not tolerable, or where the operation must be done in hydrogen. In a recently developed method of concentrating penicillin, the liquid in which the penicillin is suspended is evaporated rapidly in a vacuum by uniform heating with a radio frequency field. Certain cooking and pasteurizing processes requiring great cleanliness are made simpler by the use of radio frequency energy.

These are but a few of the many applications for this method of heating, each of which has been more or less a development problem in itself. An intelligent approach to any new application is greatly facilitated by a knowledge of the fundamental processes involved in the phenomena. These processes involve not only the heating effects of electromagnetic fields but also heat transfer phenomena. The electrical engineer may be able to compute the rate of energy loss in a material, but he must also know something about heat transfer if he is to compute the temperature rise of the material. One of two problems frequently arises. Either the desired temperature rise is specified, and the necessary power input must be computed, or the temperature rise for a given power input must be found. In either case heat transfer relations must be considered. For this reason a brief discussion of pertinent power and heat transfer relations will precede the discussion of the electromagnetic field phenomena.

10.1   Power and Heat Transfer Relations

Almost any radio frequency heating process involves a thermal transient, and in many cases the engineer may need to know how the transient may be expected to behave. In other cases he may be interested only in the final or steady state condition, but he may also need to know the time required to attain the steady state. Before proceeding with the analysis of certain particular problems some of the factors affecting thermal transients and the steady state in radio frequency heating will be pointed out.

Heat input to a mass may be used or dissipated in several ways. Some of it must be used to raise the temperature of the mass, and here the specific heat of the material and its mass determine the temperature rise. In some cases liquid must be evaporated, in which case the latent heat of vaporization must be supplied. In other cases a solid must be melted, so that the heat of fusion must be supplied. In the heating of alloys, such as carbon steel, a change from one solid state to another solid state may take place; such a change may require the addition of heat or it may produce heat. Two or more of these sinks for heat absorption may be present simultaneously. In general, the heat absorbed by these sinks does useful work. In addition to being absorbed by the sinks mentioned, heat is dissipated by one or more losses. These losses are caused by radiation, conduction, and convection, and they represent no useful work. Usually all three losses are present at the same time, but frequently one or more effects may be negligible compared to another. It is usually the losses which determine the steady-state condition in a given heating problem. Thus, even a brief study of such losses is important.

10.2 Thermal Transient for Heating in a Vacuum

A problem which occurs often is that of determining the thermal transient when heat is supplied at a known rate to a body in a vacuum. Frequently it can be assumed in such a problem that conduction and convection losses are negligible compared to radiation losses. This assumption will be made here. Let us compute the time required to raise the temperature of a mass of M kilograms from an ambient temperature $\theta_0°$ to a temperature $\theta°$K for a constant power input P watts. The heat input is used to raise the temperature of the mass and to supply losses, which in this case will be due to radiation only.

The amount of heat Δh required to raise the temperature $\Delta\theta$ degrees is

$$\Delta h = M\rho\,\Delta\theta,$$

where ρ = specific heat, joules per °K per kg. If this increase in temperature is accomplished in Δt seconds, the rate of heat input is

$$\frac{\Delta h}{\Delta t} = M\rho\,\frac{\Delta\theta}{\Delta t} \text{ joules per sec,}$$

$$= M\rho\,\frac{\Delta\theta}{\Delta t} \text{ watts.}$$

W = JQ

If t is made vanishingly small,

$Q = mc\Delta t$

$$\frac{dh}{dt} = M\rho \frac{d\theta}{dt} \text{ watts.} \qquad (10.1)$$

Energy is also dissipated by radiation. For a black body (a perfect radiator or absorber) the power radiated, P_r, is given by

$= \dfrac{JQ}{At} = \dfrac{\dot{E}\rho}{A*t} = P_r = C(\theta^4 - \theta_0^4) \text{ watts per sq m}$

where $C = 5.73 \times 10^{-8}$ watts per sq m (°K)^4. The constant C is derived from the Stefan radiation constant, 5.73×10^{-5} erg per sec per m^2 per (°K)^4, and upon the assumption of black-body emissivity of unity. Actually, no material in nature has an emissivity of unity, so that if calculation of the temperature is based on the assumption of unit emissivity, the result will be lower than the true temperature. Or, if the power required to bring a body to a given temperature is computed assuming black-body properties, the answer will be greater than the true power required. In many problems it is sufficient to determine only the order of magnitude of the power requirement, so that the simplifying assumption of unit emissivity is permissible.

If A is the area in sq m of the body, the total power input is

$$P = M\rho \frac{d\theta}{dt} + CA(\theta^4 - \theta_0^4), \qquad (10.2)$$

$$\frac{d\theta}{dt} = \frac{CA}{M\rho}\left[\frac{P}{CA} + \theta_0^4 - \theta^4\right]. \qquad (10.3)$$

Let $\tau^4 = (P/CA) + \theta_0^4$. Then

$$\frac{d\theta}{dt} = \frac{CA}{M\rho}(\tau^4 - \theta^4),$$

$$dt = \frac{M\rho}{CA}\frac{d\theta}{\tau^4 - \theta^4},$$

$$\frac{1}{\tau^4 - \theta^4} = \frac{1}{(\tau^2 - \theta^2)(\tau^2 + \theta^2)} = \frac{N}{\tau^2 - \theta^2} + \frac{Q}{\tau^2 + \theta^2}.$$

$$1 = \frac{\tau^4 - \theta^4}{\tau^2 - \theta^2}N + \frac{\tau^4 - \theta^4}{\tau^2 + \theta^2}Q,$$

$$1 = (\tau^2 + \theta^2)N + (\tau^2 - \theta^2)Q.$$

This equation must be true for any θ. Hence, N and Q may be found by letting $\theta^2 = \pm\tau^2$, so that

$$N = Q = \frac{1}{2\tau^2}.$$

Therefore
$$dt = \frac{M\rho}{CA}\frac{1}{2\tau^2}\left(\frac{d\theta}{\tau^2 - \theta^2} + \frac{d\theta}{\tau^2 + \theta^2}\right),$$

$$t = \frac{M\rho}{2CA\tau^3}\left[\left(\tan^{-1}\frac{\theta}{\tau} + \frac{1}{2}\ln\frac{m + \theta}{\tau - \theta}\right)\right]_{\theta_0}^{\theta} \tag{10.4}$$

$$t = \frac{M\rho}{2CA\tau^3}\left[\tan^{-1}\frac{\theta}{\tau} - \tan^{-1}\frac{\theta_0}{\tau} + \frac{1}{2}\ln\frac{(\tau + \theta)(\tau - \theta_0)}{(\tau - \theta)(\tau + \theta_0)}\right]. \tag{10.5}$$

Equation 10.5 gives the time in seconds required to attain a temperature θ for a constant power input P. The ultimate temperature attained will be the temperature for $t = \infty$. This temperature θ_∞ can be found easily by setting Eq. 10.3 equal to zero and solving for θ. The result gives

$$\theta_\infty = \sqrt[4]{\frac{P}{CA} + \theta_0^4} = \tau. \tag{10.6}$$

Thus the quantity τ may be thought of as the limiting or ultimate temperature attained by a black body with constant power input P, and losses sustained by radiation only. Equation 10.6 may be used to find the power required to bring a black body to a given temperature θ_∞ in infinite time. In practice, a power somewhat greater than this value would be used in order to make the heating time practical.

Example. As an example of the use of the preceding relations, suppose that a cylinder of Monel metal, 5 cm long and 2 cm in diameter, is to be heated in a vacuum by induction heating. Let the power input be 100 watts, the room temperature, 27°C. Monel has a specific heat, ρ, of 0.128 cal per g per °C, and a density of 8.8 g per cc.

As a first approximation, assume an emissivity of unity. Calculate the ultimate temperature which will be attained after a long period of time.

$$\theta_\infty = \tau = \sqrt[4]{\frac{P}{CA} + \theta_0^4},$$

$$A = \text{area} = 5 \times 2\pi + 2\,\frac{\pi \times 4}{4}$$

$$= 12\pi \text{ cm}^2 \text{ or } 12\pi \times 10^{-4}\text{m}^2,$$

$$\theta_0 = 27 + 273 = 300°\text{K}.$$

$$\theta_\infty = \tau = \sqrt[4]{\frac{100}{5.73 \times 10^{-12} \times 12\pi} + (3)^4 \times 10^8} = 830°\text{K} = 557°\text{C}.$$

Now calculate the time required to bring the cylinder up to 500°C or 773°K. Using Eq. 10.5,

$$t = \frac{M\rho}{2CA\tau^3}\left[\tan^{-1}\frac{\theta}{\tau} - \tan^{-1}\frac{\theta_0}{\tau} + \frac{1}{2}\ln\frac{(\tau + \theta)(\tau - \theta_0)}{(\tau - \theta)(\tau + \theta_0)}\right].$$

$$\tau^3 = (830)^3 = 5.72 \times 10^8,$$

$$M = \text{density} \times \text{volume} = \frac{8.8\pi \times 5}{1000} = 0.138 \text{ kg}.$$

$$\tan^{-1}\frac{\theta}{\tau} - \tan^{-1}\frac{\theta_0}{\tau} = \tan^{-1}\frac{773}{830} - \tan^{-1}\frac{300}{830} = 0.403 \text{ radian},$$

$$\frac{1}{2}\ln\frac{(\tau + \theta)(\tau - \theta_0)}{(\tau - \theta)(\tau + \theta_0)} = \frac{1}{2}\ln\frac{(830 + 773)(830 - 300)}{(830 - 773)(830 + 300)} = 1.289.$$

$$t = \frac{0.138 \times 0.128 \times 4186}{2 \times 5.73 \times 10^{-8} \times 12\pi \times 10^{-4} \times 5.72 \times 10^8}[0.403 + 1.289].$$

$$t = 505 \text{ seconds}.$$

The actual time required to reach 500°C will probably be a little less than this because the true emissivity is less than unity. Also, the ultimate temperature attainable will be larger than 557°C for the same reason.

10.3   Losses by Conduction

Because of the large variety of configurations which may be encountered in the calculation of heat losses by conduction, it seems best to present here only the differential equations of heat flow which apply to any heat flow problem. Their solutions will of course depend upon particular circumstances. Consider first the case of heat flow in one direction only in a homogeneous medium. Let the flow be along the x axis of a system of rectangular coordinates. Suppose that heat is generated within the medium at a rate $H(x,t)$ joules per sec per m^3. For brevity the symbol H will be used, but it is, in general, a function of both x and t, the time. Consider now the small rectangular box in Fig. 10-1, whose dimensions are 1 meter in the y and z directions and dx meters in the x direction. Let Q_0 equal the heat generated in the box in time dt. The heat Q_0 generated within the box must, by the principle of conservation of energy, equal the sum of Q_1, the increase in heat stored in time dt, plus Q_2, the heat flowing out through face A, plus Q_3, the heat flowing out through face B.

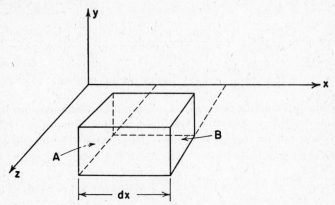

Fig. 10-1.   Elementary box for deriving heat flow equation.

Let θ be the temperature at the center O of the box. The increase in heat stored in time dt is then

$$Q_1 = c\rho \frac{d\theta}{dt} \, dt \, dx \text{ joules,}$$

where c is density, and ρ is specific heat, in joules per °K per kg. Let the temperature gradient at the center O be $\dfrac{d\theta}{dx}\Big|_0$. The gradient at B is

$$\frac{d\theta}{dx}\Big|_B = \frac{d\theta}{dx}\Big|_0 + \frac{d}{dx}\frac{d\theta}{dx}\Big|_0 \frac{dx}{2},$$

and at A,
$$\frac{d\theta}{dx}\Big|_A = \frac{d\theta}{dx}\Big|_0 - \frac{d}{dx}\frac{d\theta}{dx}\Big|_0 \frac{dx}{2}.$$

The heat flowing out through A in dt seconds is

$$Q_2 = k \frac{d\theta}{dx}\Big|_A \, dt \text{ joules,}$$

where k is the thermal conductivity in joules per m^2 per sec per °K per m. The heat flowing out through B in dt seconds is

$$Q_3 = -k \frac{d\theta}{dx}\bigg|_B \, dt.$$

But $Q_0 = Q_1 + Q_2 + Q_3$, or

$$H \, dx \, dt = c\rho \frac{d\theta}{dt} \, dt \, dx + k \left[\frac{d\theta}{dx}\bigg|_0 - \frac{d}{dx}\frac{d\theta}{dx}\bigg|_0 \frac{dx}{2} - \frac{d\theta}{dx}\bigg|_0 - \frac{d}{dx}\frac{d\theta}{dx}\bigg|_0 \frac{dx}{2} \right] dt.$$

$$H \, dx \, dt = c\rho \frac{d\theta}{dt} \, dt \, dx - k \frac{d^2\theta}{dx^2} \, dt \, dx \text{ joules.}$$

$$H = c\rho \frac{d\theta}{dt} - k \frac{d^2\theta}{dx^2} \text{ joules per m}^3 \text{ per sec.} \tag{10.7}$$

Equation 10.7 may be generalized to include three dimensions by an obvious extension of the method used for one dimension. These details will not be carried out, since the process will not add to an understanding of basic ideas. The result is given in Eq. 10.8.

$$H = c\rho \frac{\partial\theta}{\partial t} - k \left[\frac{\partial^2\theta}{\partial x^2} + \frac{\partial^2\theta}{\partial y^2} + \frac{\partial^2\theta}{\partial z^2} \right] \text{ joules per m}^3 \text{ per sec.} \tag{10.8}$$

In the notation of vector analysis this equation may be written

$$H = c\rho \frac{\partial\theta}{\partial t} - k \, \nabla^2\theta. \tag{10.8a}$$

Equations 10.7 and 10.8 are given in rectangular coordinates, but they may be converted to other coordinate systems, such as spherical or cylindrical systems, as the geometry may suggest. The solutions of these equations depend upon the particular geometry and conditions for each problem. They will not be solved here for any particular case, but they are given for future reference and as an aid in understanding the whole subject of radio frequency heating.

10.4   Admittance of a Medium

Consider a one meter cube of material. The admittance between opposite faces of the cube consists of a conductive term and a susceptive term. The equivalent circuit is shown in Fig. 10-2. The admittance is

$$\dot{Y} = \frac{1}{R} + j\omega C. \tag{10.9}$$

Here R is the resistance of a one meter cube, so that $1/R$ is the conductivity σ in mho per meter. In measuring the capacitance it is assumed that the cube has been selected from the interior of a very large volume of material, so that there are no fringing effects to consider. The capacitance of one meter cube of free space is 8.85×10^{-12} farad per meter, which is the permittivity p_0 of free space. If the material has a relative dielectric constant ϵ, then

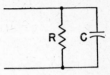

F i g . 1 0 - 2 . Equivalent circuit of cube of material.

$$C = p_0\epsilon = p \text{ farad}, \qquad (10.10)$$

where p is the permittivity of the material. Then Eq. 10.9 becomes

$$\dot{Y} = \sigma + j\omega p. \qquad (10.11)$$

If $\dot{V}$ is a sinusoidal voltage across $\dot{Y}$, the current $\dot{I}$ is

$$\dot{I} = \dot{V}\dot{Y} = \dot{V}(\sigma + j\omega p).$$

The power factor is

$$pf = \cos\theta = \frac{\sigma}{\sqrt{\sigma^2 + (\omega p)^2}} = \frac{\sigma/\omega p}{\sqrt{(\sigma/\omega p)^2 + 1}}.$$

If the material is a good dielectric, σ will be small, and, approximately,

$$pf = \frac{\sigma}{\omega p}. \qquad (10.12)$$

Here $\sigma/\omega p = \cot\theta = \tan\phi$. The angle ϕ is called the *loss angle* of the material, which, for a perfect insulator, would be 0. If σ, the conductivity, is very large, as in most metals, then $(\sigma/\omega p)^2 \gg 1$ and $\cos\theta \rightarrow 1$.

10.5 General Relations for a Right Cylinder

Consider the right cylinder of height h meters and radius a meters shown in Fig. 10-3. The ends are to be imagined as covered with perfectly conducting plates connected to a source of sinusoidal voltage. In the analysis to follow it is assumed that there is no fringing and that current flows only in the axial direction. Under these assumptions the current density and the electric and magnetic field intensities will have axial symmetry and will vary only with the radius r.

Consider now a slice 1 meter thick cut from the cylinder normal to the axis. A plan view of the slice is shown in Fig. 10-4. Let $\dot{E}$ be the electric intensity in volts per meter in the axial direction where the section is located. The current $\Delta \dot{I}$ flowing through the ring of

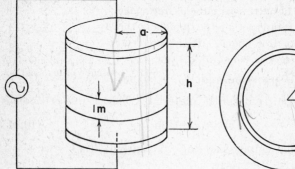

Fig. 10-3. Right cylinder.   Fig. 10-4. Plan view of one meter slice.

radial dimension dr is

$$\Delta \dot{I} = \dot{E} \dot{Y} \, dA,$$

where dA is the area of the ring. From Eq. 10.11

$$\Delta \dot{I} = \dot{E}(\sigma + j\omega p) 2\pi r \, dr \text{ amp.}$$

The current enclosed within the circle of radius r is

$$\oint_0^{2\pi} H \cdot dl,$$

and the current enclosed within the circle of radius $r + dr$ is

$$\oint_0^{2\pi} \left(H + \frac{\partial H}{\partial r} \, dr \right) \cdot dl.$$

Therefore,

$$\Delta \dot{I} = \left(\dot{H} + \frac{\partial \dot{H}}{\partial r} \, dr \right)(r + dr)2\pi - 2\pi \dot{H} r = 2\pi r \dot{E}(\sigma + j\omega p) \, dr.$$

Dropping second order differentials gives

$$\dot{H} \, dr + r \, d\dot{H} = \dot{E}(\sigma + j\omega p) r \, dr,$$

$$\frac{d\dot{H}}{dr} + \frac{\dot{H}}{r} = \dot{E}(\sigma + j\omega p). \tag{10.13}$$

Now pass a vertical plane through the axis of the cylinder and examine a small part of this plane of height dz and width dr, as shown in Fig. 10-5. Here the magnetic flux is normal to the paper. The line integral of electric intensity E around the rectangle must equal the rate of change of magnetic flux within the rectangle, by Faraday's law.

$$\oint_\square \boldsymbol{E} \cdot dl = \left(\dot{E} + \frac{\partial \dot{E}}{\partial r} \, dr \right) dz - \dot{E} \, dz = \frac{d}{dt} \left(\mu \dot{H} \, dr \, dz \right). \quad (10.14)$$

The use of the symbols $\boldsymbol{E}$, $\dot{E}$, $\boldsymbol{H}$ and $\dot{H}$ should be explained. A boldface symbol represents a true *vector* quantity having magnitude and direction in space. It may or may not vary with time. The dot over a symbol signifies that it represents a *phasor*, or a quantity which varies sinusoidally with time. Thus the diagrams used to display phase and magnitude relations between voltages and currents in circuit theory would be called *phasor* diagrams under this notation instead of vector diagrams. In a-c circuit work, where field relations are not considered,

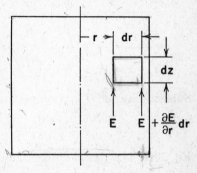

Fig. 10-5. Section through axis of cylinder.

the use of the term vector to designate a time varying quantity such as voltage leads to no confusion. But in electromagnetic field theory, where the term vector is usually used to designate a quantity possessing both magnitude and direction, and where time variation is also present, the indiscriminate use of the term vector may become confusing. Therefore, the term *phasor* will be used to designate a quantity having time variation of its magnitude. Vectors and phasors may appear in the same equation. For example, it may be necessary to express the fact that a vector representing electric field intensity lies along the z axis of a coordinate system and that its magnitude is varying sinusoidally. The fact that the quantity is a *vector* having direction and magnitude may be indicated by the symbol $\boldsymbol{E}$. The fact that its magnitude varies sinusoidally may be designated by the symbol $\dot{E}$, and the direction of this time varying quantity is specified by multiplication with the unit vector $\boldsymbol{k}$ which, by convention, lies along the z axis. Thus we may write

$$E = k\dot{E}.$$

Return now to Eq. 10.14, where, according to the above discussion, $\dot{H}$ is a sinusoidally varying quantity.

$$\dot{H} = H_m(\cos \omega t + j \sin \omega t),$$
$$\dot{H} = H_m \epsilon^{j\omega t},$$
$$\frac{d\dot{H}}{dt} = j\omega H_m \epsilon^{j\omega t} = j\omega \dot{H}.$$

Therefore,

$$\frac{d\dot{E}}{dr} = j\omega\mu\dot{H}, \tag{10.15}$$

$$\dot{H} = \frac{1}{j\omega\mu}\frac{d\dot{E}}{dr},$$

$$\frac{d\dot{H}}{dr} = \frac{1}{j\omega\mu}\frac{d^2\dot{E}}{dr^2}. \tag{10.16}$$

Substituting for $\dot{H}$ and $d\dot{H}/dr$ in Eq. 10.13 gives

$$\frac{d^2\dot{E}}{dr^2} + \frac{1}{r}\frac{d\dot{E}}{dr} - \dot{E}[j\omega\mu(\sigma + j\omega p)] = 0. \tag{10.17}$$

Eq. 10.17 is a Bessel differential equation. Let

$$\dot{m}^2 = -j\omega\mu(\sigma + j\omega p). \tag{10.18}$$

Then Eq. 10.17 becomes

$$\frac{d^2\dot{E}}{dr^2} + \frac{1}{r}\frac{d\dot{E}}{dr} + \dot{E}\dot{m}^2 = 0. \tag{10.19}$$

Now make the substitution $x = \dot{m}r$ or $r = x/\dot{m}$.

$$\frac{d\dot{E}}{dr} = \frac{d\dot{E}}{dx} \cdot \frac{dx}{dr} = \dot{m}\frac{d\dot{E}}{dx},$$

$$\frac{d^2\dot{E}}{dr^2} = \frac{d}{dr}\left(\frac{dE}{dr}\right) = \frac{d}{dx}\left(\frac{dE}{dr}\right)\frac{dx}{dr} = \dot{m}^2\frac{d^2\dot{E}}{dx^2}.$$

Then Eq. 10.19 becomes

$$\frac{d^2\dot{E}}{dx^2} + \frac{1}{x}\frac{d\dot{E}}{dx} + \dot{E} = 0. \tag{10.20}$$

The solution to this equation may be written

$$\dot{E} = Af_1(x) + Bf_2(x).$$

The method of finding $f_1(x)$ will be to write Taylor's series for $f_1(x)$ and by substitution into Eq. 10.20, to evaluate the coefficients of the series. The series is then the desired solution. By Taylor's series,

$$f_1(x) = f(0) + f'(0)x + \frac{f''(0)x^2}{2!} + \frac{f'''(0)x^3}{3!} + \cdots .$$

$$f_1(x) = a_0 + a_1x + a_2x^2 + a_3x^3 + \cdots . \tag{10.21}$$

In Eq. 10.21, $x = \dot{m}r$. It is known from the physics of the problem that at $\dot{m}r = x = 0$ the value of $\dot{E} = f_1(x)$ must be finite and different from zero. Therefore at $x = 0$, $f_1(x) = a_0$. Now

$$\frac{f'_1(x)}{x} = \frac{a_1}{x} + 2a_2 + 3a_3x + 4a_4x^2 + \cdots .$$

$$f''(x) = 2a_2 + 6a_3x + 12a_4x^2 + \cdots .$$

Substitution of these into Eq. 10.20 gives

$$\frac{a_1}{x} + (4a_2 + a_0) + (9a_3 + a_1)x + (16a_4 + a_2)x^2 + \cdots = 0.$$

This equation must be true for all values of x, which means that a_1 must be 0 and all the other coefficients of powers of x must be 0. Therefore

$$a_1 = 0,$$

$$4a_2 = -a_0 \quad \text{and} \quad a_2 = -\frac{a_0}{2^2},$$

$$a_3 = 0,$$

$$a_4 = -\frac{a_2}{16} = +\frac{a_0}{2^2 \cdot 4^2}, \text{ etc.}$$

The series expansion then becomes

$$f_1(x) = \dot{E} = a_0 - \frac{a_0}{2^2}x^2 + \frac{a_0}{2^2 \cdot 4^2}x^4 - \frac{a_0}{2^2 \cdot 4^2 \cdot 6^2}x^6 + \cdots .$$

$$\dot{E} = a_0 \left[1 - \frac{x^2}{2^2} + \frac{x^4}{2^2 \cdot 4^2} - \frac{x^6}{2^2 \cdot 4^2 \cdot 6^2} + \cdots \right].$$

The constant a_0 must be the value of $\dot{E}$ at $r = 0$, or $\dot{E}_0$. Also, since $x = \dot{m}r$, we may write

$$\dot{E} = \dot{E}_0 \left[1 - \frac{(\dot{m}r)^2}{2^2} + \frac{(\dot{m}r)^4}{2^2 \cdot 4^2} - \cdots \right]. \tag{10.22}$$

The term in the brackets is Bessel's function of the first kind and zeroth order and is written $J_0(\dot{m}r)$. Thus

$$\frac{\dot{E}}{\dot{E}_0} = J_0(\dot{m}r). \tag{10.23}$$

In addition to this solution of Eq. 10.20 or Eq. 10.19 there is the second solution $Bf_2(x)$. It may be shown that $Bf_2(x) = K_0(x)$, where $K_0(x)$ is the Bessel function of the second kind and zeroth order. An approximate formula for $K_0(x)$ is

$$K_0(x) \cong -\frac{2}{\pi} \ln \frac{2}{\gamma x},$$

from which it is apparent that $K_0(x)$ is infinite at $x = 0$. Hence B must be zero, and Eq. 10.23 is the complete solution.

Now Eq. 10.23 may be used to find $\dot{H}$ in Eq. 10.15.

$$\dot{H} = \frac{1}{j\omega\mu} \frac{d\dot{E}}{dr}.$$

From Eqs. 10.22 and 10.23

$$\frac{d\dot{E}}{dr} = \dot{E}_0 \frac{d}{dr}[J_0(\dot{m}r)] = \dot{E}_0\left[-\frac{2\dot{m}^2r}{2^2} + \frac{4(\dot{m}r)^3\dot{m}}{2^2 \cdot 4^2} - \frac{6(\dot{m}r)^5\dot{m}}{2^2 \cdot 4^2 \cdot 6^2} + \cdots\right],$$

$$\frac{d\dot{E}}{dr} = -\dot{E}_0\dot{m}\left[\frac{\dot{m}r}{2} - \frac{(\dot{m}r)^3}{2^2 \cdot 4} + \frac{(\dot{m}r)^5}{2^2 \cdot 4^2 \cdot 6} - \cdots\right]. \tag{10.24}$$

The expression in brackets is Bessel's function of the first kind and first order and is written $J_1(\dot{m}r)$.

Therefore $\qquad \dfrac{d\dot{E}}{dr} = -\dot{E}_0\dot{m}J_1(\dot{m}r),$

and $\qquad\qquad \dot{H} = \dfrac{-\dot{E}_0\dot{m}}{j\omega\mu} J_1(\dot{m}r). \tag{10.25}$

The total current flowing in the cylinder of radius a, Fig. 10-3, is, by Ampere's law,

$$\dot{I}_T = 2\pi a\dot{H}_{r=a} = \frac{-2\pi \dot{m}a\dot{E}_0 J_1(\dot{m}a)}{j\omega\mu}. \tag{10.26}$$

The electric intensity at the surface, i.e., the voltage per unit length, is, from Eq. 10.23,

$$\dot{E}_{r=a} = \dot{E}_0 J_0(\dot{m}a). \tag{10.27}$$

The impedance $\dot{Z}$ per meter is

$$\dot{Z} = \frac{-j\omega\mu J_0(\dot{m}a)}{2\pi\dot{m}aJ_1(\dot{m}a)} \text{ ohms per meter.} \tag{10.28}$$

The equations for $\dot{E}$, $\dot{H}$, $\dot{I}_T$, and $\dot{Z}$ are developed for a cylinder of a perfectly general material having conductivity σ, permittivity p, and permeability μ, the only specifications being that the material be homogeneous and isotropic.

10.6 Units

In this chapter the rationalized practical (or mksc) system[2] of units is used. For convenient reference the most important quantities and their dimensions are listed in Table 10.1 below.

Table 10.1   Units in mksc System

Quantity	Symbol	Practical Units
Length	L, l, r	Meter
Mass	M	Kilogram
Time	t	Second
Energy	W	Joule
Force	F or f	Newton, joule/meter
Power	P	Watt
Charge	q, Q	Coulomb
Current	i, I	Ampere
Resistance	R	Ohm
Electric potential	V	Volt
Electric field intensity	E	Volt/meter
Electric displacement	D	Coulomb/sq meter
Dielectric constant	ϵ	Dimensionless
Permittivity of free space	$p_0 = 10^{-9}/36\pi$	Farads/meter
Permittivity	$p = \epsilon p_0 = D/E$	Farads/meter
Capacitance	C	Farad
Magnetomotive force	MMF	Ampere-turn
Magnetic field intensity	H	Ampere-turn/meter
Magnetic induction	B	Weber/sq meter
Permeability	$\mu = \mu_r\mu_0 = B/H$	Henry/meter
Permeability of free space	$\mu_0 = 4\pi \times 10^{-7}$	Henry/meter
Relative permeability	μ_r	Dimensionless
Inductance	L	Henry

[2] Sarbacher and Edson, *Hyper and Ultrahigh Frequency Engineering*, John Wiley and Sons, New York, 1943, pp. 23–25, 53–57.

10.7 Cylinder of Perfect Insulation

It is now possible to apply the equations developed in Section 10.5 to various specific materials. The first application will be made to a perfect insulator, that is, a material with no losses and no conductivity. Such a material does not exist, but the information obtained by supposing its existence is nevertheless useful because some materials approach this ideal.

In a perfect insulator, $\sigma = 0$ and the permeability will be very nearly that of free space, μ_0. Then

$$\dot{m}^2 = -j\omega\mu(\sigma + j\omega p) = \omega^2\mu_0 p,$$

$$m = \omega \sqrt{\mu_0 p} = 2\pi f \sqrt{\mu_0 p_0 \epsilon},$$

$$m = \frac{2\pi f}{3 \times 10^8} \sqrt{\epsilon}. \tag{10.29}$$

Here $\sqrt{\mu_0 p_0} = 1/c$, where c is the velocity of light, or 3×10^8 m per sec. If λ_0 is wavelength in free space, then $\lambda_0 = 3 \times 10^8/f$ m, and

$$m = \frac{2\pi}{\lambda_0} \sqrt{\epsilon}. \tag{10.30}$$

Equation 10.23 then becomes

$$\frac{\dot{E}}{\dot{E}_0} = J_0 \left(\frac{2\pi r \sqrt{\epsilon}}{\lambda_0}\right). \tag{10.31}$$

Here r and λ_0 have been considered to be in meters, and ϵ is the relative dielectric constant. Therefore the quantity $(2\pi r \sqrt{\epsilon}/\lambda_0)$ is dimensionless, and if it is plotted against $\dot{E}/\dot{E}_0$, the resulting curve will be applicable to any cylinder of perfect dielectric material of any dielectric constant and any radius at any frequency. It will be noticed that although Eq. 10.31 expresses the ratio of two phasors, $\dot{E}$ and $\dot{E}_0$, the ratio is not complex. The equation may be evaluated for numerical values of $(2\pi r \sqrt{\epsilon}/\lambda_0)$ by substituting into Eq. 10.22 the numerical values for $\dot{m}r$. This process is laborious, and fortunately there exist tables[3] in which $J_0(x)$ has been calculated by

[3] Jahnke and Emde, *Tables of Functions with Formulas and Curves*, Dover Publications, New York, 1943. For $J_0(x)$, see pp. 126, 156–162.

evaluation of the series in Eq. 10.22.   By the use of such tables it is easy to plot Eq. 10.31, and this has been done in Fig. 10-6.   This curve may also be used in place of a table of $J_0(x)$, since it is actually a plot of $J_0(x)$.   For future reference a plot of $J_1(x)$ is shown dotted.

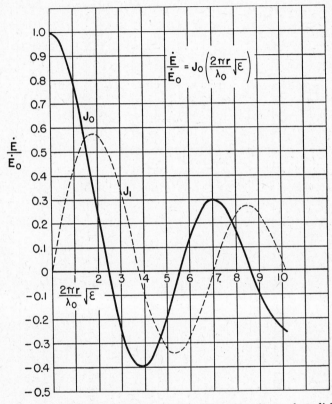

Fig. 10-6.   Variation of electric intensity with radius for perfect dielectric.

The impedance per unit length of cylinder is, from Eq. 10.28,

$$\dot{Z} = \frac{-j\omega\mu_0 J_0(\dot{m}a)}{2\pi\dot{m}a J_1(\dot{m}a)} \text{ ohms per meter.}$$

$$\dot{m} = \frac{2\pi\sqrt{\epsilon}}{\lambda_0} = \omega\sqrt{\mu_0 p_0}\sqrt{\epsilon}.$$

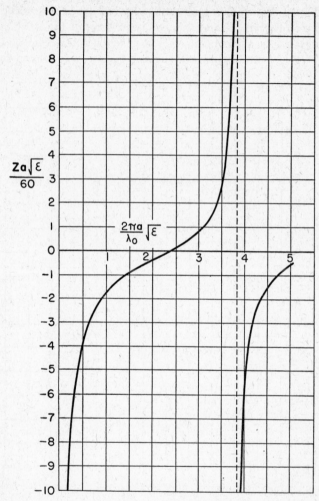

Fig. 10-7. Variation of reactance with frequency for cylinder of perfect dielectric.

Therefore,

$$\dot{Z} = \frac{-j\mu_0 J_0(\dot{m}a)}{2\pi \sqrt{\mu_0 p_0}\, \sqrt{\epsilon}\, aJ_1(\dot{m}a)} = \frac{-j\, \sqrt{\mu_0/p_0}}{2\pi \sqrt{\epsilon}\, a}\, \frac{J_0(\dot{m}a)}{J_1(\dot{m}a)},$$

$$\dot{Z} = \frac{-j60 J_0(2\pi a \sqrt{\epsilon}/\lambda_0)}{a\, \sqrt{\epsilon}\, J_1(2\pi a \sqrt{\epsilon}/\lambda_0)}. \qquad (10.32)$$

Everything in Eq. 10.32 is real except j, so $\dot{Z}$ is a pure reactance. To make the equation most useful when plotted, multiply by $a\sqrt{\epsilon}/60$.

$$\frac{\dot{Z}a\sqrt{\epsilon}}{60} = -j\frac{J_0(2\pi a\sqrt{\epsilon}/\lambda_0)}{J_1(2\pi a\sqrt{\epsilon}/\lambda_0)}. \qquad (10.32a)$$

Equation 10.32a has been plotted, with the aid of tables[3] of $J_0(x)$ and $J_1(x)$, in Fig. 10-7. It will be noticed that the impedance at low frequencies (large λ_0) is a capacitive reactance which decreases in magnitude with increasing frequency until it goes through zero and becomes an inductive reactance. Further increase in frequency results in increasing the inductive react-ance to infinity, at which point the react-ance again becomes capacitive and very large. Since both $J_0(x)$ and $J_1(x)$ are oscillatory, this variation of reactance continues indefinitely as frequency increases.

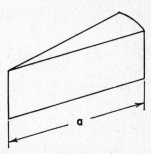

It is interesting to note that the varia-tion of impedance with frequency of the dielectric cylinder bears a striking resem-blance to the impedance of an open cir-cuited transmission line of finite length.

Fig. 10-8. Tapered trans-mission line.

Indeed, the results of this section may be derived by considering a wedge-shaped slice, Fig. 10-8, cut from the dielectric cylinder, as a tapered transmission line open at the receiving end.

10.8   Cylinder of Dielectric with Low Power Factor

If a dielectric has a very low power factor then $\sigma \ll \omega p$ in Eq. 10.18, which is rewritten here.

$$\dot{m}^2 = -j\omega\mu(\sigma + j\omega p) = \omega^2\mu p\left(1 - j\frac{\sigma}{\omega p}\right). \qquad (10.18)$$

But $\mu = \mu_0$ and $p = p_0\epsilon$.

$$\dot{m}^2 = \omega^2\mu_0 p_0\epsilon\left(1 - j\frac{\sigma}{\omega p_0\epsilon}\right).$$

Also $\mu_0 p_0 = c^{-2}$, where c = velocity of light.

Therefore $\dot{m}^2 = (2\pi f)^2 c^{-2}\epsilon(1 - j\,\delta)$

where $f = c/\lambda_0$, δ = power factor,

$$\dot{m}^2 = \left(\frac{2\pi \sqrt{\epsilon}}{\lambda_0}\right)^2 (1 - j\,\delta). \tag{10.33}$$

Here $\delta \ll 1$. From Eq. 10.23 the electric intensity is

$$\dot{E} = \dot{E}_0 J_0(\dot{m}r). \tag{10.23}$$

J_0 is given by Eq. 10.22. If Eq. 10.33 is used in Eq. 10.22 the following result is obtained.

$$\dot{E} = \dot{E}_0 \left\{ 1 - \frac{1}{2^2}\left(\frac{2\pi r \sqrt{\epsilon}}{\lambda_0}\right)^2 (1 - j\,\delta) + \frac{1}{2^2 \cdot 4^2}\left(\frac{2\pi r \sqrt{\epsilon}}{\lambda_0}\right)^4 (1 - 2j\,\delta - \delta^2) \right.$$
$$\left. - \frac{1}{2^2 \cdot 4^2 \cdot 6^2}\left(\frac{2\pi r \sqrt{\epsilon}}{\lambda_0}\right)^6 (1 - 3j\,\delta - 3\,\delta^2 + j\,\delta^3) + \cdots \right\}.$$

Now drop terms containing powers of δ greater than 1.

$$\dot{E} = \dot{E}_0 \left\{ 1 - \frac{1}{2^2}\left(\frac{2\pi r \sqrt{\epsilon}}{\lambda_0}\right)^2 + \frac{1}{2^2 \cdot 4^2}\left(\frac{2\pi r \sqrt{\epsilon}}{\lambda_0}\right)^4 - \cdots \right.$$
$$+ j\,\delta \left[\frac{1}{2^2}\left(\frac{2\pi r \sqrt{\epsilon}}{\lambda_0}\right)^2 - \frac{2}{2^2 \cdot 4^2}\left(\frac{2\pi r \sqrt{\epsilon}}{\lambda_0}\right)^4 \right.$$
$$\left.\left. + \frac{3}{2^2 \cdot 4^2 \cdot 6^2}\left(\frac{2\pi r \sqrt{\epsilon}}{\lambda_0}\right)^6 - \cdots \right] \right\}$$

$$\dot{E} = \dot{E}_0 \left[J_0\left(\frac{2\pi r \sqrt{\epsilon}}{\lambda_0}\right) + j\,\delta \left(\frac{\pi r \sqrt{\epsilon}}{\lambda_0}\right) J_1\left(\frac{2\pi r \sqrt{\epsilon}}{\lambda_0}\right) \right]. \tag{10.34}$$

If δ is small enough, Eq. 10.34 will give approximately the same distribution of electric intensity as Eq. 10.31. Reference to Fig. 10-6 will show that when J_0 approaches its first zero, J_1 still has an appreciable magnitude, so that $\dot{E}/\dot{E}_0$, which is now complex, departs considerably from Eq. 10.31 at points where the latter has zero values.

The degree of approximation involved in assuming low loss material to have the same distribution of $\dot{E}$ as a perfect dielectric can be shown by comparing the absolute values of $\dot{E}/\dot{E}_0$ in the two cases. For the perfect dielectric $|\dot{E}/\dot{E}_0|$ is given at once by Eq. 10.31 and Fig. 10-6 if the negative terms are made positive. The curve of Fig. 10-6 is redrawn in Fig. 10-9 in absolute value. For the lossy

dielectric,

$$\left|\frac{\dot{E}}{\dot{E}_0}\right| = \left[J_0{}^2(\alpha) + \frac{(\delta\alpha)^2}{4} J_1{}^2(\alpha) \right]^{\frac{1}{2}}, \qquad (10.35)$$

where $\alpha = 2\pi r \sqrt{\epsilon}/\lambda_0$. Now plot Eq. 10.35 for an assumed value of 0.1 for δ. It will be recalled that δ is the power factor of the dielectric, and a dielectric with such a power factor is a very poor one, that is, it is very lossy. In other words, 0.1 is a large value for δ

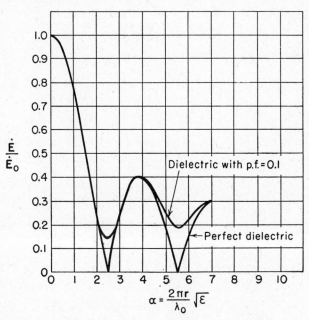

Fig. 10-9. $\left|\dfrac{\dot{E}}{\dot{E}_0}\right|$ For dielectrics with p.f. $= 0$ and p.f. $= 0.1$.

compared to the values encountered in most dielectrics. The plot of Eq. 10.35 is also given in Fig. 10-9. It will be seen that except in the neighborhood of the zeros for the perfect dielectric, the two curves nearly coincide, so that one can assume the electric field intensity distribution in a lossy dielectric to be the same as in a perfect dielectric as long as the power factor is 0.1 or less.

It is now possible to compute the power loss in a dielectric. The computation is simplified by assuming the distribution of $\dot{E}$ to be the same as in a perfect dielectric. Therefore, at any radius r,

$$P(\text{watts per m}^3) = \sigma E^2 = \sigma E_0{}^2 J_0{}^2 \left(\frac{2\pi r \sqrt{\epsilon}}{\lambda_0} \right). \qquad (10.36)$$

The total power per meter length of the cylinder of radius a meters is

$$P_T = \int_0^a 2\pi r \sigma E^2 \, dr = 2\pi \sigma E_0{}^2 \int_0^a r J_0{}^2 \left(\frac{2\pi \sqrt{\epsilon} \, r}{\lambda_0} \right) dr.$$

Let $(2\pi \sqrt{\epsilon}/\lambda_0) r = x$, $r \, dr = \dfrac{x \, dx}{(2\pi \sqrt{\epsilon}/\lambda_0)^2}$,

$$P_T = \frac{2\pi \sigma E_0{}^2}{(2\pi \sqrt{\epsilon}/\lambda_0)^2} \int_0^{\frac{2\pi a \sqrt{\epsilon}}{\lambda_0}} x J_0{}^2(x) \, dx.$$

$$P_T = \pi a^2 \sigma E_0{}^2 \left[J_0{}^2 \left(\frac{2\pi a \sqrt{\epsilon}}{\lambda_0} \right) + J_1{}^2 \left(\frac{2\pi a \sqrt{\epsilon}}{\lambda_0} \right) \right]. \qquad (10.37)$$

Equation 10.37 gives total power in watts per meter length of cylinder. The average power, P_{av}, in watts per (meter)^3 is

$$P_{av} = \frac{P_T}{\pi a^2} = \sigma E_0{}^2 \left[J_0{}^2 \left(\frac{2\pi a \sqrt{\epsilon}}{\lambda_0} \right) + J_1{}^2 \left(\frac{2\pi a \sqrt{\epsilon}}{\lambda_0} \right) \right]. \qquad (10.38)$$

Equations 10.36 and 10.38 are most useful in the dimensionless forms

$$\frac{P}{\sigma E_0{}^2} = J_0{}^2 \left(\frac{2\pi r}{\lambda_0} \sqrt{\epsilon} \right) = J_0{}^2(\alpha_1), \qquad (10.39)$$

and

$$\frac{P_{av}}{\sigma E_0{}^2} = J_0{}^2 \left(\frac{2\pi a}{\lambda_0} \sqrt{\epsilon} \right) + J_1{}^2 \left(\frac{2\pi a}{\lambda_0} \sqrt{\epsilon} \right), \qquad (10.40)$$

$$\frac{P_{av}}{\sigma E_0{}^2} = J_0{}^2(\alpha_2) + J_1{}^2(\alpha_2). \qquad (10.41)$$

Equations 10.39 and 10.40 are plotted in Fig. 10-10.

It is useful to note that σ may be expressed in terms of power factor, pf.

$$pf = \frac{\sigma}{\omega p} = \frac{\sigma}{2\pi p_0 \epsilon f} = \frac{\sigma \lambda_0}{2\pi \epsilon p_0 c},$$

$$p_0 c = \frac{10^{-9}}{36\pi} \times 3 \times 10^8 = \frac{1}{120\pi}.$$

Therefore
$$\sigma = \frac{pf \cdot \epsilon}{60\lambda_0}.$$
(10.42)

In practice it is frequently desirable to heat a large slab of dielectric material, and although the slab may not be circular in cross section as in the calculations made above, nevertheless useful conclusions may be drawn from these calculations. It is usually desirable to

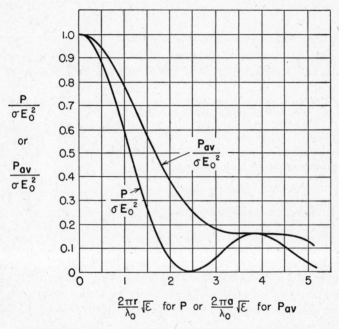

Fig. 10-10. Power dissipation in dielectric with low loss.

heat the material uniformly throughout its volume. This would be accomplished if power loss were the same at all points. A glance at Fig. 10-10 shows that in a cylinder this is not possible, and in general it is not possible for most shapes. However, a good approximation is obtained if the power per unit volume at the outer edge of the cylinder is 90 or 95 per cent of that at the center. This means that for a given radius a, the frequency must be chosen so that $2\pi a \sqrt{\epsilon}/\lambda_0$ lies in the neighborhood of 0.3 to 0.45, depending upon the amount of change between center and edge which can be tolerated. If 95 per cent is the figure chosen, then

$$\frac{2\pi a \sqrt{\epsilon}}{\lambda_0} = 0.3, \qquad \lambda_0 = \frac{c}{f}.$$

$$f = \frac{0.3c}{2\pi a \sqrt{\epsilon}} = \frac{0.3 \times 3 \times 10^8}{2\pi a \sqrt{\epsilon}},$$

$$f = \frac{14.31}{a \sqrt{\epsilon}} \text{ megacycles per sec,} \qquad (10.43)$$

where a is radius in meters and ϵ is the relative dielectric constant. Equation 10.43 gives the highest frequency for which the power density at the edge of the disk will be at least 95% of that at the center.

10.9 Cylinder of High Conductivity Material

In a good conductor, the conductance current is very much larger than the displacement current. Therefore, in Eq. 10.18 ωp is negligible compared to σ, so that

$$\dot{m}^2 = -j\omega\mu(\sigma + j\omega p) = -j\omega\mu\sigma = -j2\pi f\mu\sigma. \qquad (10.44)$$

Now introduce a new symbol s.

$$s = \frac{1}{\sqrt{\pi\mu\sigma f}} \qquad (10.45)$$

The symbol s is called the *skin thickness*, and in Section 10.12 there will be further discussion of its physical significance. In the mksc system of units used here, s is in meters. With this substitution, Eq. 10.44 becomes

$$\dot{m} = \sqrt{-j}\,\frac{\sqrt{2}}{s}. \qquad (10.46)$$

Hence Eq. 10.23 becomes

$$\dot{E} = \dot{E}_0 J_0\left(\sqrt{-j}\,\frac{\sqrt{2}\,r}{s}\right).$$

Now let $\sqrt{2}\,r/s = x$, so that, from Eq. 10.22,

$$J_0(\sqrt{-j}\,x) = 1 + j\frac{x^2}{2^2} - \frac{x^4}{2^2 \cdot 4^2} - j\frac{x^6}{2^2 \cdot 4^2 \cdot 6^2} + \frac{x^8}{2^2 \cdot 4^2 \cdot 6^2 \cdot 8^2}$$
$$+ \cdots,$$

$$J_0(\sqrt{-j}\,x) = 1 - \frac{x^4}{2^2 \cdot 4^2} + \frac{x^8}{2^2 \cdot 4^2 \cdot 6^2 \cdot 8^2} - \cdots$$
$$+ j\left(\frac{x^2}{2^2} - \frac{x^6}{2^2 \cdot 4^2 \cdot 6^2} + \frac{x^{10}}{2^2 \cdot 4^2 \cdot 6^2 \cdot 8^2 \cdot 10^2} - \cdots\right) \quad (10.47a)$$

$$J_0(\sqrt{-j}\,x) = \operatorname{ber} x + j \operatorname{bei} x. \quad (10.47b)$$

Equations 10.47 define the ber and bei functions (pronounced "bear" and "buy"). The derivatives with respect to x of ber x and bei x are written ber′ x and bei′ x and are also infinite series. These four functions are tabulated in the literature.[4,5]

$$\dot{E} = \dot{E}_0 \left[\operatorname{ber}\left(\frac{\sqrt{2}\,r}{s}\right) + j \operatorname{bei}\left(\frac{\sqrt{2}\,r}{s}\right) \right]. \quad (10.48)$$

The absolute value of $\dot{E}/\dot{E}_0$ is

$$\left|\frac{\dot{E}}{\dot{E}_0}\right| = \sqrt{\left[\operatorname{ber}\left(\frac{\sqrt{2}\,r}{s}\right)\right]^2 + \left[\operatorname{bei}\left(\frac{\sqrt{2}\,r}{s}\right)\right]^2}. \quad (10.49)$$

Equation 10.49 is plotted in Fig. 10-11. It may be regarded also as a plot of current density distribution; hence the skin effect is apparent.

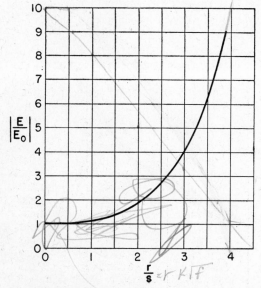

Fig. 10-11. Electric field intensity distribution in a cylinder of high conductivity, Eq. 10.49.
(Adapted from Brown, Hoyler, and Bierwirth, *Theory and Application of Radio-Frequency Heating*, D. Van Nostrand Company, Inc., New York, 1947).

[4] Reference 3, pp. 246–249 and Reference 1, p. 18.
[5] McLachlan, N. W., *Bessel Functions for Engineers*, Oxford University Press, New York, 1934, pp. 119–121.

Example.   As an example of the use of Eq. 10.48, the electric intensity at various radii inside a copper conductor 0.6 cm in diameter will be computed for a frequency of 5000 cps.   For copper, $\mu_r = 1$, $\mu_0 = 4\pi \times 10^{-7}$, and conductivity is about 5.8×10^5 mho-cm per cm^2.   This last figure must be changed to mho-meter per meter^2 for use in the equation for s.   Hence, $\sigma = 5.8 \times 10^7$ mho-m per m^2.   First calculate skin depth.

$$s = \frac{1}{\sqrt{\pi\mu\sigma f}} = \frac{1}{2\pi\sqrt{10^{-7} \times 5.8 \times 10^7 \times 5000}} = 0.937 \times 10^{-3} \text{ meter.}$$

The maximum radius a is 3×10^{-3} meter.   Thus the range of r/s in which we are interested is from 0 to $3/0.937 = 3.2$.   It is convenient to use $s/\sqrt{2}$ as the unit of measurement, in which case the radius at any point is $\sqrt{2}\,r/s$, and the outer radius is then 4.52 units, or let us say approximately 4.5 units. Write Eq. 10.48 in the form

$$\frac{\dot{E}}{\dot{E}_0} = \text{ber } \frac{\sqrt{2}\,r}{s} + j \text{ bei } \frac{\sqrt{2}\,r}{s}. \tag{10.48}$$

Now make a table for computing this equation for various values of $\sqrt{2}\,r/s$.   As an aid in this computation a very condensed table of the functions ber (x), bei (x), ber$'$ (x) and bei$'$ (x) is included in Table 10.2.   Equation 10.48 may now be tabulated.

Table 10.2   Tabulation of ber and bei Functions[4]

x	ber (x)	bei (x)	ber$'$ (x)	bei$'$ (x)
0.0	1.000	0.000	0.000	0.000
0.5	0.999	0.062	−0.008	0.250
1.0	0.984	0.250	−0.062	0.500
1.5	0.921	0.559	−0.210	0.730
2.0	0.752	0.972	−0.493	0.917
2.5	0.399	1.457	−0.944	0.998
3.0	−0.221	1.938	−1.570	0.880
3.5	−1.194	2.283	−2.336	0.435
4.0	−2.563	2.293	−3.135	−0.491
4.5	−4.299	1.686	−3.754	−2.053
5.0	−6.230	0.116	−3.844	−4.354
10.0	138.840	56.370	51.373	135.23
20.0	47583.7	11500.8	24325.1	41491.5
∞	∞	∞	∞	∞

$\sqrt{2}\,r/s$	ber $\sqrt{2}\,r/s$	bei $\sqrt{2}\,r/s$	$\dot{E}/\dot{E}_0$	r, meters
0.0	1.000	0.000	$1 + j0$	0
1.0	0.984	0.250	$0.984 + j0.250$	0.66×10^{-3}
2.0	0.752	0.972	$0.752 + j0.972$	1.33×10^{-3}
3.0	-0.221	1.938	$-0.221 + j1.938$	2.00×10^{-3}
3.5	-1.194	2.283	$-1.194 + j2.283$	2.33×10^{-3}
4.0	-2.563	2.293	$-2.563 + j2.293$	2.66×10^{-3}
4.5	-4.299	1.686	$-4.299 + j1.686$	3×10^{-3}

The various phasors representing $\dot{E}/\dot{E}_0$ are shown in the phasor diagram. It will be noticed that the electric intensity decreases as the radius decreases, and the phase angle becomes more lagging. Thus, at the center the absolute value of E/E_0 is $1/\sqrt{(4.299)^2 + (1.686)^2} = 1/4.61$ of the value at the outer radius, and the phase difference is about 158.6°.

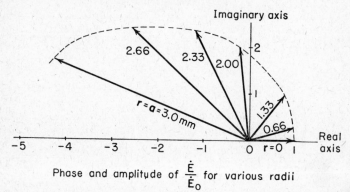

Phase and amplitude of $\dfrac{\dot{E}}{\dot{E}_0}$ for various radii

The impedance of the conductor may be found from Eq. 10.28, which is rewritten here.

$$\dot{Z} = \frac{-j\omega\mu J_0(\dot{m}a)}{2\pi\dot{m}aJ_1(\dot{m}a)} \tag{10.28}$$

$$= \frac{-j\omega\mu J_0[\sqrt{-j}\,(\sqrt{2}/s)a]}{2\pi\sqrt{-j}\,(\sqrt{2}/s)aJ_1[\sqrt{-j}\,(\sqrt{2}/s)a]}.$$

$$-\dot{m}J_1(\dot{m}a) = \frac{d}{da}J_0(\dot{m}a) = \frac{d}{da}\left(\text{ber}\,\frac{\sqrt{2}\,a}{s} + j\,\text{bei}\,\frac{\sqrt{2}\,a}{s}\right)$$

$$= \frac{\sqrt{2}}{s}\left(\text{ber}'\,\frac{\sqrt{2}\,a}{s} + j\,\text{bei}'\,\frac{\sqrt{2}\,a}{s}\right). \tag{10.50}$$

Therefore

$$\dot{Z} = \frac{j\omega\mu \, [\text{ber} \, (\sqrt{2} \, a/s) + j \, \text{bei} \, (\sqrt{2} \, a/s)]}{(2\pi a \sqrt{2}/s) \, [\text{ber}' \, (\sqrt{2} \, a/s) + j \, \text{bei}' \, (\sqrt{2} \, a/s)]}. \qquad (10.51)$$

$$\dot{Z} = R_{ac} + jX_{ac}.$$

$$R_{ac} =$$
$$\frac{\omega\mu s}{2\sqrt{2}\,\pi a} \frac{(\text{ber} \, \sqrt{2} \, a/s)(\text{bei}' \, \sqrt{2} \, a/s) - (\text{bei} \, \sqrt{2} \, a/s)(\text{ber}' \, \sqrt{2} \, a/s)}{(\text{ber}' \, \sqrt{2} \, a/s)^2 + (\text{bei}' \, \sqrt{2} \, a/s)^2}.$$

$$X_{ac} =$$
$$\frac{\omega\mu s}{2\sqrt{2}\,\pi a} \frac{(\text{ber} \, \sqrt{2} \, a/s)(\text{ber}' \, \sqrt{2} \, a/s) + (\text{bei} \, \sqrt{2} \, a/s)(\text{bei}' \, \sqrt{2} \, a/s)}{(\text{ber}' \, \sqrt{2} \, a/s)^2 + (\text{bei}' \, \sqrt{2} \, a/s)^2}$$

$R_{dc} = (\sigma\pi a^2)^{-1}$ ohms per meter. Also,

$$\frac{\omega\mu s}{2\sqrt{2}\,\pi a} \times \frac{1}{R_{dc}} = \frac{\omega\mu s}{2\sqrt{2}\,\pi a} \times \sigma\pi a^2 = \frac{1}{2}\left(\frac{\sqrt{2}\,a}{s}\right).$$

Therefore,

$$\frac{R_{ac}}{R_{dc}}$$
$$= \frac{1}{2}\left(\frac{\sqrt{2}\,a}{s}\right) \frac{(\text{ber} \, \sqrt{2}\,a/s)(\text{bei}' \, \sqrt{2}\,a/s) - (\text{bei} \, \sqrt{2}\,a/s)(\text{ber}'\sqrt{2}\,a/s)}{(\text{ber}' \, \sqrt{2} \, a/s)^2 + (\text{bei}' \, \sqrt{2} \, a/s)^2},$$
$$(10.52a)$$

and

$$\frac{X_{ac}}{R_{dc}}$$
$$= \frac{1}{2}\left(\frac{\sqrt{2}\,a}{s}\right) \frac{(\text{ber} \, \sqrt{2}\,a/s)(\text{ber}' \, \sqrt{2}\,a/s) + (\text{bei} \, \sqrt{2}\,a/s)(\text{bei}' \, \sqrt{2}\,a/s)}{(\text{ber}' \, \sqrt{2} \, a/s)^2 + (\text{bei}' \, \sqrt{2} \, a/s)^2}.$$
$$(10.52b)$$

Equations 10.52a and 10.52b are plotted in Fig. 10-12.

For values of a/s larger than about 2.5, both of these curves are straight lines, so that approximate simple equations may be written,

$$\frac{R_{ac}}{R_{dc}} = \frac{a}{2s} + 0.25, \qquad \frac{a}{s} \geq 2.5 \qquad (10.53)$$

$$\frac{X_{ac}}{R_{dc}} = \frac{a}{2s}, \qquad \frac{a}{s} \geq 2.5. \qquad (10.54)$$

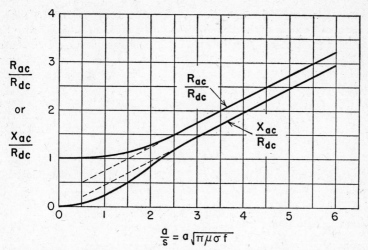

Fig. 10-12. Variation of R_{ac} and X_{ac} with s. (Adapted from Brown, Hoyler, and Bierwirth, *Theory and Application of Radio-Frequency Heating.* D. Van Nostrand Company, Inc., New York, 1947).

Example. A copper tube of the dimensions shown has a conductivity of

$$\sigma_c = 5.8 \times 10^7 \text{ mho-m/m}^2.$$

Find the ratio of R_{ac}/R_{dc} for this tube for frequencies of (a) 100,000 cps and

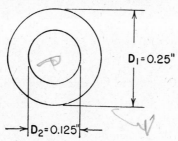

(b) 10,000,000 cps. First calculate s, the skin depth.

$$s = \frac{1}{\sqrt{\pi \mu \sigma f}} = \frac{1}{\sqrt{\pi \mu_r \times 4\pi \times 10^{-7} \sigma f}} = \frac{1}{2\pi \sqrt{10^{-7} \times 5.8 \times 10^7 \times 10^5}}$$

$$= \frac{1}{200\pi \sqrt{58}}.$$

$s = .000209$ meter at 10^5 cps,

$s = .000209 \times \sqrt{\dfrac{10^5}{10^7}} = 0.0000209$ meter at 10^7 cps.

Compare these with $(D_1 - D_2)/2 = 0.125 \times 2.54/2 \times 100 = 0.00159$ meter. At both frequencies s is small compared to the wall thickness of the tube. Therefore R_{ac} will be independent of the wall thickness, and the ratio R_{ac}/R_{dc} may be calculated assuming a solid conductor. The ratio must then be adjusted to take account of the hole, since R_{dc} will be affected by the hole.

At 10^5 cps,
$$\frac{a}{s} = \frac{0.125 \times 2.54 \times 10^{-2}}{0.000209} = \frac{0.00318}{0.000209} = 15.2.$$

At 10^7 cps,
$$\frac{a}{s} = \frac{0.00318}{0.0000209} = 152.$$

Both of these values are larger than 2.5, so the approximate equation 10.53 is valid.

At 10^5 cps,
$$\frac{R_{ac}}{R_{dc}} = \frac{a}{2s} + 0.25 = 7.6 + 0.25 = 7.85.$$

At 10^7 cps,
$$\frac{R_{ac}}{R_{dc}} = \frac{152}{2} + 0.25 = 76.25.$$

These are values assuming a solid conductor. For the tube,

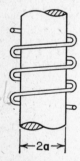

at 10^5 cps,
$$\frac{R_{ac}}{R_{dc}} = 7.85 \times \frac{(D_1{}^2 - D_2{}^2)}{D_1{}^2}$$
$$= 7.85 \times \frac{(D_1/D_2)^2 - 1}{(D_1/D_2)^2}$$

$$\frac{R_{ac}}{R_{dc}} = 7.85 \times \frac{3}{4} = 5.89 \text{ at } 10^5 \text{ cps.}$$

At 10^7 cps,
$$\frac{R_{ac}}{R_{dc}} = 76.25 \times \frac{3}{4} = 57.1.$$

$\leftarrow 2a \rightarrow$

Fig. 10-13. Long cylinder surrounded by current carrying helix.

10.10 Induced Currents in Cylindrical Conductors

Consider a long cylindrical conductor surrounded by a current carrying helix, as shown in Fig. 10-13. The helix current will induce currents in the conductor, whose temperature will then be increased by I^2R loss in the cylinder. This method of radio frequency heating, usually called induction heating, is very common, and although many shapes other than the simple cylinder are encountered, the results obtained from the analysis of this relatively simple geometry are useful.

Certain simplifying assumptions are made. The magnetic field intensity H inside the coil will be assumed everywhere axially directed, and because of cylindrical symmetry it can be assumed to vary only with radius. The cylinder and helix will be assumed long compared to their diameters, so that end effects need not be considered. As in Section 10.9, σ will be considered very much greater than ωp.

By considering elements of area in planes normal to and containing the axis of the cylinder of Fig. 10-13, the reader may easily show, by the method of Section 10.5, that the following equations are true:

$$\frac{d\dot{E}}{dr} + \frac{1}{r}\,\dot{E} = j\omega\mu\dot{H},$$

$$\frac{d\dot{H}}{dr} = \dot{E}(\sigma + j\omega p). \tag{10.55}$$

Eliminating $\dot{E}$ between these equations leads to the result

$$\frac{d^2\dot{H}}{dr^2} + \frac{1}{r}\frac{d\dot{H}}{dr} - j\omega\mu(\sigma + j\omega p)\dot{H} = 0.$$

This equation is identical to Eq. 10.17 except that $\dot{H}$ takes the place of $\dot{E}$. Therefore the solution of Eq. 10.17 which is carried out in Section 10.9 for a cylinder in which $\sigma \gg \omega p$ will apply here also if $\dot{E}$ is replaced by $\dot{H}$ in the result. Hence, from Eq. 10.48,

$$\dot{H} = \dot{A}\left(\text{ber}\,\frac{\sqrt{2}\,r}{s} + j\,\text{bei}\,\frac{\sqrt{2}\,r}{s}\right). \tag{10.56}$$

The symbol $\dot{A}$ is used rather than $\dot{H}_0$ because $\dot{H}_0$ is to be used for another purpose. From Eq. 10.55,

$$\dot{E} = \frac{1}{\sigma + j\omega p}\frac{d\dot{H}}{dr} \simeq \frac{1}{\sigma}\frac{d\dot{H}}{dr}.$$

When Eq. 10.56 is differentiated with respect to r and substituted in the above equation, the result is

$$\dot{E} = \frac{\sqrt{2}\,\dot{A}}{\sigma s}\left(\text{ber}'\,\frac{\sqrt{2}\,r}{s} + j\,\text{bei}'\,\frac{\sqrt{2}\,r}{s}\right). \tag{10.57}$$

The constant $\dot{A}$ may be evaluated from the fact that $\dot{H}$ must have the same values just outside and just inside the cylinder. If this were not true there would be a discontinuity in $\dot{H}$ at the boundary. But to produce such a discontinuity would require an abrupt change or discontinuity in ampere-turns at the boundary, and there is no way of producing such a discontinuity in the physical system under consideration.

The intensity of $\dot{H}$ just outside the cylinder is simply the mmf $\dot{H}_0$ set up by the inducing coil, in ampere-turns per meter, if the spacing between coil and cylinder is small compared to one wave length in free space, λ_0. Thus at $r = a$,

$$\dot{H} = \dot{H}_0 = \dot{A}\left(\text{ber}\,\frac{\sqrt{2}\,a}{s} + j\,\text{bei}\,\frac{\sqrt{2}\,a}{s}\right),$$

and Eq. 10.55 becomes

$$\dot{H} = \dot{H}_0\,\frac{(\text{ber}\,\sqrt{2}\,r/s) + j(\text{bei}\,\sqrt{2}\,r/s)}{(\text{ber}\,\sqrt{2}\,a/s) + j(\text{bei}\,\sqrt{2}\,a/s)}. \tag{10.58}$$

Also, Eq. 10.57 becomes

$$\dot{E} = +\frac{\sqrt{2}\,\dot{H}_0}{\sigma s}\,\frac{(\text{ber}'\,\sqrt{2}\,r/s) + j(\text{bei}'\,\sqrt{2}\,r/s)}{(\text{ber}\,\sqrt{2}\,a/s) + j(\text{bei}\,\sqrt{2}\,a/s)}. \tag{10.59}$$

Since power dissipation is the quantity desired, it is necessary to find the effective value of $\dot{E}$.

$$E = \frac{\sqrt{2}\,H_0}{\sigma s}\,\sqrt{\frac{(\text{ber}'\,\sqrt{2}\,r/s)^2 + (\text{bei}'\,\sqrt{2}\,r/s)^2}{(\text{ber}\,\sqrt{2}\,a/s)^2 + (\text{bei}\,\sqrt{2}\,a/s)^2}}. \tag{10.60}$$

The power P in watts per meter length will be

$$P = \int_{r=0}^{a} 2\pi r\sigma E^2\,dr. \tag{10.61}$$

Substituting Eq. 10.60 in Eq. 10.61 and integrating[6] gives

$$P = \frac{2\pi H_0{}^2\sqrt{2}\,a}{\sigma s}\left[\frac{(\text{ber}\,\sqrt{2}\,a/s)(\text{ber}'\,\sqrt{2}\,a/s)+(\text{bei}\,\sqrt{2}\,a/s)(\text{bei}'\,\sqrt{2}\,a/s)}{(\text{ber}\,\sqrt{2}\,a/s)^2 + (\text{bei}\,\sqrt{2}\,a/s)^2}\right]. \tag{10.62}$$

Let $F/\sqrt{2}$ = the quantity in brackets in Eq. 10.62. Then

$$P = \frac{2\pi H_0{}^2}{\sigma}\frac{a}{s}\,F \quad \text{watts per m.} \tag{10.63}$$

[6] Reference 5, p. 129, Example 21.

A plot of $(a/s)F$ against a/s is shown in Fig. 10-14. There are two regions in which the curve, as plotted on log-log paper, is very nearly a straight line. These straight lines are drawn in dashed lines and

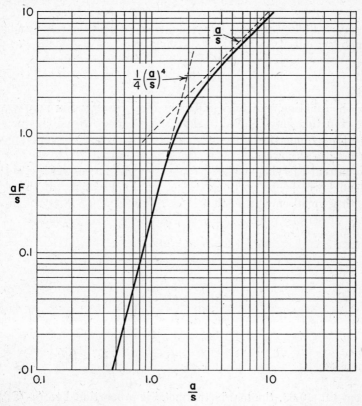

Fig. 10-14. Plot of $(a/s)F$ versus a/s. (Adapted from Brown, Hoyler, and Bierwirth, *Theory and Application of Radio-Frequency Heating*, D. Van Nostrand Company, Inc., New York, 1947).

may be represented by two simple equations. For $a/s \leq 1.5$,

$$P = \frac{\pi H_0^2}{2\sigma}\left(\frac{a}{s}\right)^4 \quad \text{watts per m.,} \qquad (10.64)$$

and for $a/s \geq 5$,

$$P = \frac{2\pi H_0^2}{\sigma}\frac{a}{s} \quad \text{watts per m.} \qquad (10.65)$$

In cases where $a/s > 5$, the power per unit area of cylinder surface is

$$P_A = \frac{P}{2\pi a} = \frac{H_0{}^2}{\sigma s} \text{ watts per m}^2. \tag{10.66}$$

Equation 10.66 will apply to any cylinder for which $a/s > 5$ and for which the initial assumptions still hold true. A flat plane surface may be considered as a cylinder of infinite radius, so that a/s is surely greater than 5. Therefore Eq. 10.66 may be applied to a flat plane.

The function F of Eqs. 10.62 and 10.63 is plotted in Fig. 10-15. This function may be used to show the efficiency of coupling power into the cylinder to be heated. The efficiency may be determined if the ratio of power loss in the metal to be heated, P_m, to the loss in the current-carrying solenoid, P_s, is known. The power loss in the solenoid will be proportional to R_{ac} of the solenoid. If the skin depth is small enough so that $a_s/s_s > 2.5$, Eq. 10.53 may be used. Here subscript s refers to the solenoid radius. Approximately,

$$\frac{R_{ac}}{R_{dc}} \cong \frac{a_s}{2s_s}.$$

But

$$R_{dc} = \frac{1}{\sigma \pi a_s{}^2},$$

$$R_{ac} \cong \frac{a_s}{2s_s \sigma \pi a_s{}^2} = \frac{1}{2\pi\sigma a_s s_s}.$$

Therefore

$$P_s \sim \frac{1}{a_s s_s}.$$

From Eq. 10.63, the loss in the metal is proportional to $(a_m/s_m)F$. Thus

$$\frac{P_m}{P_s} \sim \frac{(a_m/s_m)F}{1/a_s s_s} = \frac{a_m a_s F}{s_m/s_s}$$

$$= \frac{a_m a_s \sqrt{\pi \mu_m \sigma_m f}}{\sqrt{\pi \mu_s \sigma_s f}} F = K_2 F.$$

Therefore

$$\frac{P_m}{P_s} \sim F.$$

Figure 10-15 shows a plot of F against a/s. It is apparent that very little advantage will be gained by making a/s greater than about

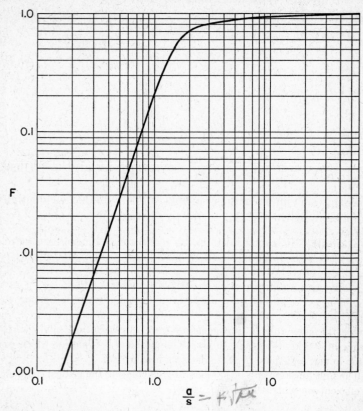

Fig. 10-15. Plot of F versus a/s. (Adapted from Brown, Hoyler, and Bierwirth, *Theory and Application of Radio-Frequency Heating*, D. Van Nostrand Company, Inc., New York, 1947).

$$F = \sqrt{2}\,\frac{\mathrm{ber}\,\dfrac{\sqrt{2}\,a}{s}\,\mathrm{ber}'\,\dfrac{\sqrt{2}\,a}{s} + \mathrm{bei}\,\dfrac{\sqrt{2}\,a}{s}\,\mathrm{bei}'\,\dfrac{\sqrt{2}\,a}{s}}{(\mathrm{ber}\,\sqrt{2}\,a/s)^2 + (\mathrm{bei}\,\sqrt{2}\,a/s)^2}$$

$$s = \frac{1}{\sqrt{\pi\mu\sigma f}}$$

2.25.   On the other hand there is a considerable disadvantage in making a_m/s_m less than 2.25, for the function F drops very rapidly for $a_m/s_m < 2.25$.   Hence the value of 2.25 for a_m/s_m may be taken to define a critical frequency, f_c, below which the efficiency of heating is likely to be low and above which very little gain will result.

$f_c = \dfrac{1.3 \times 10^6}{1 \times 10 \times 3 \times 10^3} = \dfrac{1.3 \times 10^6}{3 \times 10^4} = .4 \times 10^2 = 40$

$$\frac{a_m}{s_m} = a_m \sqrt{\pi \sigma_m \mu_m f_c} = 2.25,$$

$$f_c = \frac{(2.25)^2}{\pi a_m{}^2 \sigma_m \mu_m} \quad \text{cycles per sec.} \tag{10.67}$$

But $\mu_m = \mu_0 \mu_{rm} = 4\pi \times 10^{-7} \mu_{rm}$,

and $\qquad f_c = \dfrac{(2.25)^2}{4\pi^2 \times 10^{-7}} \dfrac{1}{a_m{}^2 \sigma_m \mu_{rm}}$,

$$f_c = \frac{1.285 \times 10^6}{a_m{}^2 \sigma_m \mu_{rm}} \quad \text{cycles per sec,} \tag{10.68}$$

where a_m = cylinder radius, meters; σ_m = cylinder conductivity mho-meters per meter^2; μ_{rm} = relative permeability.

Example. It is required to heat a nickel rod 3 mm in diameter and 10 cm long. The rod is inside an evacuated glass tube of diameter 1 inch. The nickel is polished and may be considered to have an emissivity of 0.1. Its relative permeability is unity above 350°C and its conductivity is 1.28×10^7 mho-m per m^2. The rod must be heated to an ultimate temperature of 1000°C by passing radio frequency current through a copper coil wound outside the glass tube. Two generators are available, one having a frequency of 300 kc, the other, 10 mc. One problem is to decide which generator to use, and the other is to design a heating coil.

The first question can be answered by calculating the critical frequency for efficient coupling. From Eq. 10.68,

$$f_c = \frac{1.285 \times 10^6}{a_m{}^2 \sigma_m \mu_{rm}} \quad \text{cps.}$$

$$a_m{}^2 = (1.5 \times 10^{-3})^2 = 2.25 \times 10^{-6},$$

$$\sigma_m = 1.28 \times 10^7,$$

$$\mu_{rm} = 1.$$

$$f_c = \frac{1.285 \times 10^6}{2.25 \times 10^{-6} \times 1.28 \times 10^7} = 44,600 \quad \text{cps.}$$

Therefore use the 300-kc generator, for which the coupling efficiency should be very good.

Next determine the power loss by radiation at 1000°C or 1273°K. From Section 10.2,

$$\frac{P}{A} = C(\theta^4 - \theta_0{}^4).$$

$$\mu = 4\pi \times 10^{-7} \times 5 \times 10^3 = 2\pi \times 10^{-4}$$

Assume $\theta_0 = 300°K$.   This equation is for a black body.   For an emissivity ϵ,

$$\frac{P}{A} = \epsilon C(\theta^4 - \theta_0^4) = 0.1 \times 5.73 \times 10^{-12}[(1.273)^4 - (0.3)^4]10^{12},$$

$$\frac{P}{A} = 1.5 \text{ watts per cm}^2.$$

This must be converted into watts per meter length of rod.

$$P \text{ (watts per m)} = 1.5\,\pi d \times 100 = 150\pi \times 0.3 = 141.4.$$

Now calculate $a/s = a\sqrt{\pi\mu\sigma f}$

$$\frac{a}{s} = 1.5 \times 10^{-3} \sqrt{\pi\mu_r \times 4\pi \times 10^{-7}\sigma f}$$

$$= 1.5 \times 10^{-3} \times 2\pi \sqrt{10^{-7} \times 1.28 \times 10^7 \times .3 \times 10^6}$$

$$\frac{a}{s} = 5.85.$$

Therefore to obtain the magnetomotive force H_0 required to produce the necessary power use Eq. 10.65, since $a/s > 5$.

$$P = \frac{2\pi H_0^2}{\sigma}\frac{a}{s}$$

or

$$H_0 = \sqrt{\frac{P\sigma}{2\pi\,\dfrac{a}{s}}} = \sqrt{\frac{141.4 \times 1.28 \times 10^7}{2\pi \times 5.85}}$$

$$H_0 = 7.0 \times 10^3 \text{ amp turns per m.}$$

The coil may now be designed by assuming that the mmf at the center is equal to the ampere-turns per meter of the coil if the coil is long compared to its diameter.   Assume a coil of diameter 1.5 in. and length 5 in.   If copper tubing of $\frac{3}{16}$ in. outside diameter is used and if the turns are spaced $\frac{3}{16}$ in. apart, the turns per meter will be

$$\frac{N}{l} = \frac{8}{3} \times 39.37 = 105 \text{ turns per meter.}$$

Therefore the required current at 0.3 mc is

$$I = \frac{H_0}{N/l} = \frac{7.0 \times 10^3}{105} = 66.6 \text{ amperes.}$$

For comparison the current required in this same coil at 10 mc will now be computed.

$$\frac{a}{s} = 5.85 \sqrt{\frac{10}{0.3}} = 33.8,$$

$$H_0 = 7.0 \times 10^3 \sqrt{\frac{5.85}{33.8}} = 2.92 \times 10^3,$$

$$I = \frac{2920}{105} = 27.8 \text{ amperes.}$$

10.11   Currents Induced in a Flat Sheet

Imagine a current-carrying filament of very small diameter parallel to a flat metal surface as shown in Fig. 10-16. Suppose

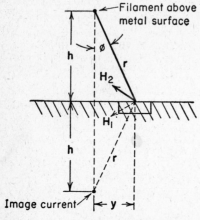

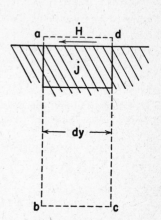

Fig. 10-16.   Current-carrying filament parallel to a flat metal surface.

Fig. 10-17.   Diagram for relating $\dot{H}$ and $\dot{J}$.

that the metal has high conductivity, so that the skin depth will be small compared to the thickness of the metal. We desire to find the current distribution in the flat sheet as a function of y. The magnetic field intensity outside the surface may be found by replacing the surface with an image current equal and opposite to the real current and located at a distance h below the surface plane. The field just outside the surface at a distance r from the filament is composed of two components, $\dot{H}_1$ and $\dot{H}_2$, due to the real and image currents respectively. The total field $\dot{H}$ is then

$$\dot{H} = \dot{H}_1 \cos \phi + \dot{H}_2 \cos \phi = 2\dot{H}_1 \frac{h}{r}. \quad (10.69)$$

If it is assumed that all the current in the metal flows in a thin layer of depth small compared to ab, Fig. 10-17, it is easy to determine a relation between the linear current density $\dot{J}$ in amperes per unit distance in the y direction and $\dot{H}$, the magnetic field at the surface. The small cross-section of area of metal indicated in Fig. 10-16 is shown enlarged in Fig. 10-17. The work required to move a unit magnetic pole around the path $abcd$ is equal, in mksc units, to the current enclosed. The current enclosed is $J\,dy$ if ab and cd are either infinite or very large compared to the depth of penetration of current. The amounts of work done along paths ab and cd are zero if $\dot{H}$ is assumed everywhere parallel to the surface. If this assumption is not valid, then these amounts of work can be made as nearly equal and opposite to each other as is desired by choosing dy small enough, so that the net work will be zero along ab and cd. The work along bc will be zero because H will be zero at a depth where there is no current. The only remaining work is that along path da, and it is $H\,dy$. Therefore,

$$H\,dy = J\,dy \quad \text{and} \quad \dot{H} = \dot{J} \tag{10.70}$$

Substituting $\dot{J}$ for $\dot{H}$ in Eq. 10.69 gives

$$\dot{J} = 2\dot{H}_1\frac{h}{r} = 2\frac{\dot{I}h}{2\pi r^2} = \frac{\dot{I}h}{\pi(h^2 + y^2)} = \frac{\dot{I}}{\pi h}\frac{1}{(1 + y^2/h^2)} \tag{10.71}$$

$$\frac{\dot{J}}{\dot{I}/\pi h} = \frac{\dot{J}}{\dot{J}_0} = \frac{1}{1 + y^2/h^2}$$

It is now of interest to determine the power dissipation in the flat sheet of metal of great thickness. First it is necessary to find the distribution of current into the metal in a direction normal to the surface. This distribution will be found in the next section.

10.12 Depth Distribution of Current Density in Flat Sheet

One way to approach the problem of determining the current density distribution in a flat sheet as a function of distance from the surface is to use the relations already obtained for a cylinder. Reference is made to Eqs. 10.58 and 10.59, which are rewritten here for convenience.

$$\dot{H} = \dot{H}_0\frac{(\text{ber }\sqrt{2}\,r/s) + j(\text{bei }\sqrt{2}\,r/s)}{(\text{ber }\sqrt{2}\,a/s) + j(\text{bei }\sqrt{2}\,a/s)}, \tag{10.58}$$

$$\dot{E} = \frac{-\sqrt{2}\,\dot{H}_0}{\sigma s}\,\frac{(\text{ber}'\,\sqrt{2}\,r/s) + j(\text{bei}'\,\sqrt{2}\,r/s)}{(\text{ber}\,\sqrt{2}\,a/s) + j(\text{bei}\,\sqrt{2}\,a/s)}. \qquad (10.59)$$

In a great many cases of practical interest the current density is negligible for distances below the surface which are greater than 1% or less of the radius of the cylinder. Thus, Eqs. 10.58 and 10.59 are of interest for values of r which are only very slightly less than a, the cylinder radius. In these cases the quantity s is very small compared to r. Values of s may be of the order of a few thousandths of a centimeter. For example, copper at 1 megacycle has the following constants:

$$\sigma = 5.8 \times 10^7 \text{ mho for a meter cube,}$$

$$\mu = \mu_0 = 4\pi \times 10^{-7},$$

$$s = \frac{1}{\sqrt{\pi\sigma\mu f}} = \frac{1}{\sqrt{\pi \times 5.8 \times 10^7 \times 4\pi \times 10^{-7} \times 10^6}}.$$

$$= 0.000066 \text{ m.}$$

For cylinders of the order of one centimeter radius, the quantity $\sqrt{2}\,r/s$ will be very large compared to unity since the values of r of interest are nearly equal to a. For such large values of $x = \sqrt{2}\,r/s$ the ber, bei, ber', and bei' functions may be approximated by the following equations.[7]

$$\text{ber } x = \frac{e^{x/\sqrt{2}}}{\sqrt{2\pi x}}\cos\left(\frac{x}{\sqrt{2}} - \frac{\pi}{8}\right), \qquad (10.72a)$$

$$\text{bei } x = \frac{e^{x/\sqrt{2}}}{\sqrt{2\pi x}}\sin\left(\frac{x}{\sqrt{2}} - \frac{\pi}{8}\right), \qquad (10.72b)$$

$$\text{ber}' x = \frac{e^{x/\sqrt{2}}}{\sqrt{2\pi x}}\cos\left(\frac{x}{\sqrt{2}} + \frac{\pi}{8}\right), \qquad (10.72c)$$

$$\text{bei}' x = \frac{e^{x/\sqrt{2}}}{\sqrt{2\pi x}}\sin\left(\frac{x}{\sqrt{2}} + \frac{\pi}{8}\right). \qquad (10.72d)$$

If Eqs. 10.72 are substituted in Eqs. 10.58 and 10.59, the results simplify to

$$\dot{H} = \dot{H}_0 \sqrt{\frac{a}{r}}\, \epsilon^{(r-a)/s} \cdot \epsilon^{j(r-a)/s}$$

$$\dot{E} = \frac{-\sqrt{2}\cdot \dot{H}_0}{\sigma s}\sqrt{\frac{a}{r}}\,\epsilon^{(r-a)/s}\cdot \epsilon^{j(r-a)/s}\cdot \epsilon^{+j\,\pi/4}.$$

Now let $a - r = x$, the distance below the surface. Also, since we are dealing with values of r nearly equal to a, $a/r \cong 1$, and $\epsilon^{j\pi/4} = (1 + j)/\sqrt{2}$. Therefore

$$\dot{H} = \dot{H}_0\epsilon^{-x/s} \cdot \epsilon^{-j\,x/s}, \qquad (10.73)$$

$$\dot{E} = -\frac{1+j}{s\sigma}\dot{H}_0\epsilon^{-x/s}\cdot \epsilon^{-jx/s}. \qquad (10.74)$$

It will be noticed that $\dot{H}$ and $\dot{E}$ are here independent of r, the only condition being that r be large enough so that $\sqrt{2}\,r/s$ be large compared to unity. It may be shown[7] that the above approximations are good for $\sqrt{2}\,r/s > 10$. Surely, therefore, Eqs. 10.73 and 10.74 will be valid for a flat surface, where $r = \infty$, and where $\dot{H}_0$ is the magnetomotive force parallel to the surface.

Now the current density $\dot{J}_x$ at depth x below the surface may be found, because $\dot{J}_x = \sigma\dot{E}$.

$$\dot{J}_x = \frac{1+j}{s}\dot{H}_0\epsilon^{-x/s}\cdot \epsilon^{-jx/s}\ \text{amp per m}^2.$$
$$(10.75)$$

The relative directions and positions of $\dot{H}$ and $\dot{J}_x$ are shown in Fig. 10-18. An element of surface area of unit dimension in the $\dot{E}$ direction and of width dy in the other

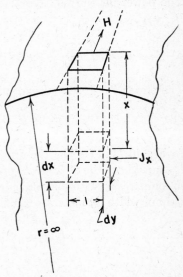

Fig. 10-18. Relative directions and locations of $\dot{H}$ and $\dot{J}_x$.

[7] Dwight, H. B., "A Precise Method of Calculation of Skin Effect in Isolated Tubes," *J. Am. Inst. Elect. Eng.*, vol. 42, no. 8, p. 829, 1923. Also Reference 5, pp. 169, 177, 178.

direction is shown. $\dot{J}_x$ is the current density entering one face of a submerged cube of material at distance x below this element of surface area. There is a time phase angle between $\dot{J}_x$ and $\dot{H}_0$ of 45° at $x = 0$, and both the magnitude and phase of $\dot{J}_x$ vary with x. The magnitude of course decreases exponentially.

The power dissipation in the submerged cube of dimensions dy, dx, 1, is

$$dP_x = [|J_x| \, dy \, dx]^2 \, \frac{1}{\sigma \, dy \, dx},$$

$$|J_x| = \frac{\sqrt{2} \, H_0}{s} \, \epsilon^{-x/s},$$

and

$$dP_x = \frac{2H_0^2}{s^2 \sigma} \, \epsilon^{-2x/s} \, dy \, dx.$$

The power for the total volume under the element of area is then $\int_0^\infty dP_x$.

$$\int_0^\infty \frac{2H_0^2}{s^2 \sigma} \, dy \, \epsilon^{-2x/s} \, dx = \frac{H_0^2}{s\sigma} \, dy \text{ watts.} \tag{10.76}$$

The power P_A dissipated per unit area of surface is

$$P_A = \frac{H_0^2}{s\sigma} \text{ watts per m}^2. \tag{10.77}$$

In Eq. 10.77, $1/s\sigma$ has the dimensions of resistance, and therefore H_0^2 must have the dimensions of (amperes per m²). It is instructive to compare H_0^2 with the total current flowing through the submerged strip of width dy meters. From Eq. 10.75 this current is

$$\dot{I} = \int_0^\infty \dot{J}_x \, dx \, dy = \frac{(1+j)H_0 \, dy}{s} \int_0^\infty \epsilon^{-x(1+j)/s} \, dx,$$

$$\dot{I} = \frac{(1+j)H_0 \, dy}{s} \times \frac{-s}{1+j} \, \epsilon^{-x(1+j)/s} \Big]_0^\infty = H_0 \, dy.$$

The current per meter of distance measured in the direction of H (or y) in Fig. 10-18 is

$$\dot{J} = \frac{\dot{I}}{dy} = H_0 \text{ amperes per m.} \tag{10.78}$$

Therefore Eq. 10.76 becomes

$$P = \frac{I^2}{s\sigma \, dy} \text{ watts,} \tag{10.79}$$

where I is the total effective current flowing under the element of area. Equation 10.79 shows the physical significance of the quantity s, the skin depth. The quantity $dy/s\sigma$ is the resistance of a block of material of length unity in the direction of current flow, of width dy and depth s. Equation 10.79 states that the total power dissipated under the element of area is the same as if the total current I were uniformly distributed for a distance s below the surface instead of being distributed according to the exponential function of x given in Eq. 10.75. This concept of the physical meaning of skin depth can be very useful, and if it is properly applied, calculations may be appreciably simplified.

We may now return to the problem, proposed at the end of Section 10.11, of finding the power dissipated in a flat sheet under a parallel current-carrying filament.

10.13 Power Loss in Flat Sheet Under Filament of Current

Figure 10-19 is a perspective view of a current-carrying filament parallel to a flat surface showing an element of surface area dA of

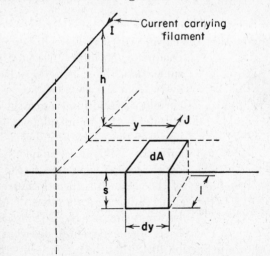

Fig. 10-19.   Current carrying filament parallel to a flat surface.

dimensions 1 and dy, located at a distance $r = \sqrt{h^2 + y^2}$ from the filament. From Eq. 10.71, the current density J in amperes per meter measured along the surface in the y direction is

$$J = \frac{I}{\pi h} \frac{1}{1 + y^2/h^2} \text{ amp per m.} \tag{10.71}$$

Therefore the total current under the element dA is $J\,dy$. From the results of Section 10.12, the power dissipated under the area dA is

$$dP_m = (J\,dy)^2 \frac{1}{\sigma_m s_m\,dy} = \frac{J^2\,dy}{\sigma_m s_m}. \tag{10.80}$$

Here the subscript m is used to distinguish power loss in the metal surface from power loss in the conductor above the surface. The total power loss in a one meter wide slice of metal cut normal to the direction of current flow is then $\int_{y=-\infty}^{+\infty} dP_m$. Combining Eqs. 10.80 and 10.71 gives

$$P_m = \int_{-\infty}^{\infty} \left(\frac{I}{\pi h}\right)^2 \frac{dy}{(1 + y^2/h^2)^2 \sigma_m s_m} = \frac{I^2 h^2}{\sigma_m s_m \pi^2} \int_{-\infty}^{\infty} \frac{dy}{(h^2 + y^2)^2},$$

$$P_m = \frac{I^2}{2\pi \sigma_m s_m h} = \frac{I^2}{h} \sqrt{\frac{\mu_{rm} f \times 10^{-7}}{\sigma_m}} \text{ watts per m,} \tag{10.81}$$

where μ_{rm} = relative permeability of metal.

Now suppose that the current carrying filament is replaced by a conductor of finite diameter. Also assume that the conductor is far enough away from the metal surface so that the current distribution around the conductor is uniform, that is, not affected by the proximity of the currents induced in the flat surface. If it is also assumed that the skin depth is small compared to the radius, a_c, of the conductor, then the current density distribution as a function of radius may be approximated by Eq. 10.75. On the basis of an exponential distribution of this type it was shown in Section 10.12 that the power loss is the same as if the current were uniformly distributed to a depth s_c. Therefore,

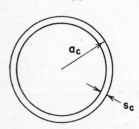

Fig. 10-20. Cross-section of current carrying conductor showing skin depth, s_c.

the power loss in the conductor per unit length will be

$$P_c = \frac{I^2}{\sigma_c \times 2\pi a_c s_c} = \frac{I^2}{a_c} \sqrt{\frac{\mu_{rc} f \times 10^{-7}}{\sigma_c}} \text{ watts per m.} \quad (10.82)$$

The ratio of power lost in the metal to that lost in the conductor is

$$\frac{P_m}{P_c} = \frac{a_c}{h} \sqrt{\frac{\mu_{rm}\sigma_c}{\mu_{rc}\sigma_m}}. \quad (10.83)$$

It can be shown from Eqs. 10.85 and 10.86 that this relation is true even for the case where the conductor is so close to the surface that the current distribution is non-uniform, as shown in Fig. 10-21.

Since in most heating applications the conductor is made of water-cooled copper, $\mu_{rc} = 1$. The coupling efficiency is then

$$\text{Eff.} = \frac{P_m}{P_m + P_c} = \frac{1}{1 + (h/a)\sqrt{\sigma_m/\mu_{rm}\sigma_c}}. \quad (10.84)$$

Examination of Eq. 10.84 reveals that for the largest possible coupling efficiency, the ratio of a, the conductor radius, to h, the height of the conductor above the surface, should be as large as possible. In other words, the conductor should be as close to the work as possible. Also, for high efficiency, σ_m should be small and σ_c and μ_{rm} should be large. The maximum practical value of a/h must be less than 1, since $h > a$. If the material being heated is copper, then Eq. 10.84 reduces to

$$\text{Eff.} = \frac{1}{1 + (h/a)},$$

and since the maximum possible value of a/h is less than one, the maximum possible coupling efficiency for heating copper with copper conductors is less than 50%. Fortunately in practice the actual situation is not quite this bad, because as soon as the work piece temperature begins to rise, its conductivity, σ_m, goes down, whereas σ_c stays constant because the conductor is water cooled. However, copper is harder to heat by this method than most other metals, not only because of the poor coupling efficiency but also because it is an extremely good heat conductor. On the other hand, iron and steel are relatively easy to heat because μ_{rm} is greater than unity, and the conductivities are relatively low.

Account may be taken of the fact that the current distribution around the conductor is non-uniform because of the proximity of the induced currents in the flat sheet.   Figure 10-21 is intended to suggest the current distribution which occurs with close spacing. If the non-uniform distribution is taken into account it may be

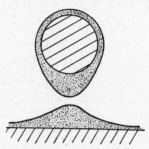

Fig. 10-21. Influence of proximity effect on current distribution. (Adapted from Brown, Hoyler, and Bierwirth, *Theory and Application of Radio-Frequency Heating*, D. Van Nostrand Company, Inc., New York, 1947).

shown that the power loss P_m in the metal surface is

$$P_m = \frac{I^2}{h} \sqrt{\frac{\mu_{rm}f \times 10^{-7}}{\sigma_m}} \frac{1}{\sqrt{1 - (a/h)^2}} \text{ watts per m.}   (10.85)$$

The power P_c lost in the conductor is

$$P_c = \frac{I^2}{a} \sqrt{\frac{\mu_{rc}f \times 10^{-7}}{\sigma_c}} \frac{1}{\sqrt{1 - (a/h)^2}} \text{ watts per m.}   (10.86)$$

It is interesting to determine the effective resistance of the conductor per unit length.   If R is the effective resistance, then

$$I^2R = P_m + P_c = \left(\frac{P_m}{P_c} + 1\right) P_c$$

$$R = \frac{P_c}{I^2} \left(1 + \frac{P_m}{P_c}\right) = R'_c \left(1 + \frac{P_m}{P_c}\right).   (10.87)$$

Here R'_c may be thought of as the resistance which causes the loss in the conductor alone, and R, the total resistance, is made up of R'_c plus an added term $R'_c P_m/P_c$ which may be thought of as the resistance of the flat surface reflected into the conductor.   If Eqs.

10.85 and 10.86 are substituted in Eq. 10.87 the result is

$$R = \left[\frac{a}{h}\sqrt{\frac{\mu_{rm}\sigma_c}{\mu_{rc}\sigma_m}} + 1\right]\frac{1}{a}\frac{\sqrt{\mu_{rc}f \times 10^{-7}/\sigma_c}}{\sqrt{1 - (a/h)^2}} \text{ ohms per m.} \quad (10.88)$$

It will be noticed that the larger a/h becomes, the greater R becomes. Also $R \sim \sqrt{f}$.

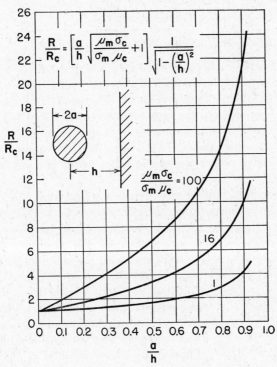

Fig. 10-22.   Ratio of conductor resistance with load to resistance without load.

Equation 10.88 may be written in slightly different form. The resistance R_c of the conductor when no load, or flat surface, is present is, from Eq. 10.86,

$$R_c = \frac{1}{a}\sqrt{\frac{\mu_{rc}f \times 10^{-7}}{\sigma_c}} \text{ ohms per m.} \quad (10.89)$$

From Eqs. 10.88 and 10.89,

$$\frac{R}{R_c} = \left[\frac{a}{h} \sqrt{\frac{\mu_{rm}\sigma_c}{\mu_{rc}\sigma_m}} + 1 \right] \frac{1}{\sqrt{1 - (a/h)^2}}. \tag{10.90}$$

Here R/R_c is the ratio of the conductor resistance when a load is present to its resistance when no load is present, and Eq. 10.89 gives the resistance per meter when no load is present. Equation 10.90 is plotted in Fig. 10-22 for three values of $\sqrt{\mu_{rm}\sigma_c/\mu_{rc}\sigma_m}$. The advantage of large values of a/h is apparent.

10.14   Single Turn Conductor Around Metal Cylinder

All the results of Section 10.13 may be applied directly to the case of a single turn conductor around a metal cylinder if the radius a_m of the metal cylinder is large compared to h, the distance from the surface of the cylinder to the center of the conductor. Thus, if $a_m > 10h$, the geometry approximates that of the straight conductor parallel to a flat plane. The equations developed in Section 10.13 then give power or resistance per meter measured along the conductor.

In designing a coil for radio frequency heating it is necessary, of course, to know the radio frequency resistance of the coil and its load.

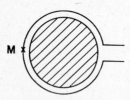

M

Fig. 10-23. Cylindrical work piece with one turn coil.

For impedance matching purposes it is desirable also to know the reactance, which may be estimated with the aid of long line theory. First assume that the work piece is grounded and that the single turn is driven by a push-pull output stage, so that the midpoint M of the coil is always at ground potential. Each half turn may then be considered as a transmission line short circuited at the receiving end. The impedance of the whole turn is then double that for each half. For a short circuited transmission line of characteristic impedance Z_0, the impedance is

$$\dot{Z}_{sc} = \dot{Z}_0 \tanh \dot{\gamma}l,$$

where $\dot{\gamma}$ is the propagation constant $\alpha + j\beta$. For the range of frequencies most often used, α will be small compared to β, so that approximately, $\dot{Z}_{sc} = \dot{Z}_0 \tanh j\beta l$. But

$$\tanh j\beta l = \frac{\sinh 0 \cos \beta l + j \cosh 0 \sin \beta l}{\cosh 0 \cos \beta l + j \sinh 0 \sin \beta l} = j\frac{\sin \beta l}{\cos \beta l} = j \tan \beta l.$$

Therefore $$\dot{Z}_{sc} = j\dot{Z}_0 \tan \beta l. \tag{10.91}$$

But $\beta = 2\pi/\lambda_0$, since the wave length of this line would not differ much from that in free space.

$$\dot{Z}_{sc} = j\dot{Z}_0 \tan \frac{2\pi}{\lambda_0} l \tag{10.92}$$

The characteristic impedance may be found by replacing the metal surface by the image conductor and using the equation for two parallel open wires. Thus

$$\dot{Z}_0 = 60 \ln \left\{ \frac{h}{a}\left[1 + \sqrt{1 - \left(\frac{a}{h}\right)^2}\right]\right\}. \tag{10.93}$$

A plot of Eq. 10.93 is shown in Fig. 10-24. Equations 10.92 and 10.93 show that the impedance is a pure reactance. The reactance for the whole coil, of circumference C meters is

$$X = 2Z_{sc} = 2Z_0 \tan \frac{2\pi C}{2\lambda_0} \text{ ohms.} \tag{10.94}$$

In all practical cases $\frac{2\pi}{\lambda_0}\frac{C}{2} \ll 1$, so that

$$\tan \frac{2\pi}{\lambda_0}\frac{C}{2} \cong \frac{2\pi}{\lambda_0}\frac{C}{2},$$

$$X = \frac{2\pi C}{\lambda_0} Z_0 = \frac{2\pi CfZ_0}{3 \times 10^8} \text{ ohms.} \tag{10.95}$$

Equation 10.95 is for a single turn, and it was derived on the assumptions that the turn was driven from a push-pull output stage and that the work piece was grounded. Actually there is nearly always a matching transformer in the circuit, one end of which may be grounded, and the work piece itself may or may not be grounded. If the turn is grounded at one end and the work is grounded, Eqs. 10.94 and 10.95 are still valid. If the work is not grounded but is allowed to float at whatever potential it assumes because of the capacitances between ground and the work and between the work and the coil, then it will float at some potential between that of

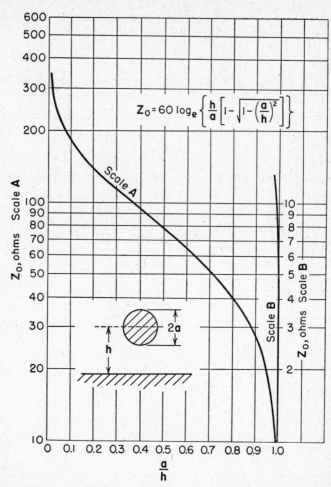

$$Z_0 = 60 \log_e \left\{ \frac{h}{a} \left[1 - \sqrt{1 - \left(\frac{a}{h}\right)^2} \right] \right\}$$

Fig. 10-24. Characteristic impedance of cylindrical conductor parallel to plane. (Adapted from Brown, Hoyler, and Bierwirth, *Theory and Application of Radio-Frequency Heating*, D. Van Nostrand Company, Inc., New York, 1947).

point A, Fig. 10-25, and ground. There will also be a point P along the coil of that potential, so that a short circuit might be introduced at P without changing the circuit. If the point P is at a distance l from A, the following equations are true. For a line of length l,

$$\dot{Z}_{sc} \cong j\dot{Z}_0 \tan \frac{2\pi l}{\lambda_0}.$$

For the coil of Fig. 10-25,

$$X = Z_0 \tan \frac{2\pi l}{\lambda_0} + Z_0 \tan \frac{2\pi(C-l)}{\lambda_0},$$

$$\cong Z_0 \left(\frac{2\pi l}{\lambda_0} + \frac{2\pi C}{\lambda_0} - \frac{2\pi l}{\lambda_0} \right),$$

therefore,

$$X = \frac{2\pi C Z_0}{\lambda_0}.$$

This result is independent of l and is also identical to Eq. 10.95, which is then valid for all the conditions considered.

If there are n turns instead of one, and if the spacing between turns is several times as large as the distance from the conductor to the work piece, Eq. 10.94 may be written

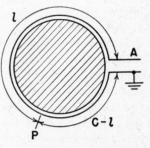

Fig. 10-25. Cylindrical work piece with heating coil grounded at one end.

$$X = 2Z_0 \tan \frac{2\pi n C}{2\lambda_0} \text{ ohms.} \quad (10.96)$$

The large spacing between turns must be specified here because otherwise the proximity of one turn to the next would affect the calculation of X. If the spacing between turns is large compared to that between the coil and the work piece, the proximity between turns will be small compared to the proximity effect between the coil and the work piece.

10.15 Summary

It has been shown in the previous sections that heat is developed in any medium which is immersed in a radio frequency electromagnetic field. The amount of heat developed depends on the material, the geometry of the system, and the magnitudes of currents, voltages and frequency. Equations have been developed for calculating the power loss in dielectrics of low power factor and in materials of high conductivity for very simple geometries. Calculations of temperature rise for very simple cases have been indicated. With these results it is possible to make approximate designs for radio frequency heating equipment for simple cases. For the more complex cases the material given here should provide the engineer with enough understanding of the basic principles to permit him to proceed with the new development in a rational way, or to enable him to read the more advanced literature intelligently.

In the case of dielectric heating the only geometry considered is that of a cylinder of material between flat conducting end plates. Equation 10.36 or 10.39 may be used to compute the power loss in such a case in watts per cubic meter. In general the power density is greater at the center of the cylinder than at the outer radius, but nearly uniform heating may be obtained by using a frequency low enough so that this variation is made small. Equation 10.43 gives the highest frequency for which the power density at the edge of the cylinder of radius a will be at least 95% of the power density at the center.

In many cases of dielectric heating, the temperatures to be attained are relatively low compared to those required in many metal heat treating operations. Accordingly, most of the heat losses sustained at these low temperatures are by conduction and convection, rather than by radiation, as would be the case in many applications involving high temperatures. Calculations involving losses by conduction and convection are likely to be complex except in the simplest cases, and so no attempt is made here to perform such calculations, although they may properly be considered part of the industrial electronics engineer's problem. The method of starting on a problem involving chiefly conduction is suggested by the development of the differential equation of heat flow, Eq. 10.8. In general this equation must be solved for the temperature as a function of time, the space coordinates, and H, the rate of heat generation. Having this solution, the value of H required to give the desired temperature at the correct time may be computed. After the desired rate of heat generation is obtained, the radio frequency heating equipment may be designed to give this power density on the basis of the results in Sections 10.7 and 10.8.

In the case of induction heating of metal parts where the temperature is high enough so that radiation is the principal cause of heat loss, the calculations may be relatively simple. First determine the properties of the material and the temperature to which it must be heated. If the work must be heated rapidly, as is the case in some industrial applications, the rate of heating may be important in determining the power requirements. If, as has been suggested above, radiation is the principal loss, Eq. 10.5 is available to compute the temperature-time transient. The power radiation in watts per square meter is given by $P/CA = \theta^4 - \theta_0{}^4$, if the emissivity is unity. If it is less than unity, as it is in all materials, the power radiated will be less.

After the power requirement is decided on, the required generator size may be fixed. If a special generator is to be selected or designed for the particular application being considered, the frequency may be selected on the basis of Eq. 10.68. On the other hand, the frequency may be fixed at one or two values which are available from existing generators, in which case the choice between generators may be based on this criterion. It is not essential that the frequency used be equal to or above the critical frequency for effective coupling, since any amount of power may be produced in a work piece if the inducing current is large enough and the generator is capable of producing the power. However, it is generally true that the higher the frequency, the smaller will be the required inducing current and the easier the problem of matching to the generator will be.

With the power requirement known and the frequency decided upon, Eq. 10.62 or Fig. 10-15, the curve of F versus a/s may be used to find the required value of H_0, the magnetomotive force needed to produce the power. Under appropriate conditions, approximate Eqs. 10.64, 10.65, or 10.66 may be used.

H_0 is in ampere-turns per meter length of solenoid, so the problem is now reduced to calculation of the required current in a coil which is proportioned properly to fit the work piece.

In many cases the work piece will not be a nice symmetrical cylinder or flat slab. Its shape may be extremely complex. In such cases, many of which have been treated in practice,[8] a good general rule to follow is to place the conductor as close to the work as possible. This rule is a direct consequence of Eq. 10.81. If it is necessary to make power and current computations, an adaptation of Eq. 10.81 for the power loss per unit length of conductor parallel to a flat surface may prove useful.

If the heating can be done by a simple solenoid the easiest

[8] Electronics Engineers of Westinghouse Electric Corp., *Industrial Electronics Reference Book*, John Wiley and Sons, New York, 1948.

procedure is to assume a coil geometry, that is, assume a coil diameter, a conductor diameter, the number of turns and the length. Since the magnetomotive force is essentially constant throughout the cross section of a long solenoid, the current required may be obtained by setting the previously determined value of H_0 equal to the ampere-turns per meter length of solenoid. Since the number of turns per meter is already assumed, the rms value of current is determined.

If the coil is close to the work, Eq. 10.95, or an adaptation of the transmission line method, will give an estimate of coil reactance. If the work piece is small compared to the coil diameter, one of the standard equations found in handbooks[9] for air coils core will be useful in estimating reactance. Coil resistance may be calculated from Eq. 10.52 or Eq. 10.53.

By the above methods the most important electrical characteristics of the coil and its load can be estimated, so that the design of the radio frequency heating equipment can be attacked rationally.

PROBLEMS

10.1. Discuss the effect on Eq. 10.5 of dropping the assumption of unit emissivity. Assume a general emissivity $\epsilon < 1$.

10.2. Make a careful plot on 3 cycle semi-log paper of P/A against θ as abscissa, from Eq. 10.6. Assume ambient temperature to be 27°C. Keep this curve for future reference.

10.3. Discuss the effect on Eq. 10.6 of assuming an emissivity $\epsilon < 1$. Derive an equation for θ_∞ with $\epsilon < 1$.

10.4. Show that in Eq. 10.29 $\sqrt{\mu_0 p_0 \epsilon}$ has the dimensions of (velocity)$^{-1}$.

10.5. Show that s in Eq. 10.45 has the dimension of length.

10.6. Derive Eq. 10.57 from Eq. 10.56.

10.7. Show from Eq. 10.71 that the total current flowing in the metal sheet is equal in magnitude to the current in the filament.

10.8. Explain why good conductors may best be heated by placing them in a current carrying coil or near a current carrying conductor, whereas good insulators are heated best by placing them between the plates of a condenser connected to a source of radio frequency power.

10.9. A round brass tube 1 in. outside diameter, $\frac{3}{4}$ in. inside diameter and 2 in. long is to be heated by induction. Assume that heat will be lost only by radiation. (a) What is the minimum power input to the tube in watts which will permit attainment of a temperature of 700°C? (b) If energy is dissipated

[9] Terman, F. E., *Radio Engineers Handbook*, McGraw-Hill Book Company, Inc., New York, 1943.

in the tube at a rate of 500 watts, make a plot of temperature θ in degrees Kelvin versus time. Assume an ambient temperature of 27°C. Take the density of brass to be 8.3 g per cm³ and its specific heat to be 0.162 cal per g per deg C.

10.10. In a certain manufacturing process it is desired to heat a plastic disc to 200°C. The disc is 15 cm in diameter and 2 cm thick. In order to make the process economical it must be done at a rate of 0.5 lb. per minute. The material has the following properties:

> power factor = 0.06,
> dielectric constant = 5.3,
> specific heat = 0.35 cal per g per °C,
> density = 2.0 g per cm³.

(a) Find the maximum frequency which can be used if the power per unit volume at the edge is to be 95 % of that at the center. (b) Find the required power input, approximately. (c) Find the required voltage gradient to produce this power at the frequency determined in part (a) and at $\frac{1}{4}$ of this frequency. In these calculations assume no losses due to conduction, convection or radiation.

10.11. Given a metal conductor in which the field intensity is H_0 at the surface and in which the current density J is

$$J = \frac{1+j}{s} \dot{H}_0 \exp\left(\frac{-x}{s}\right) \exp\left(\frac{-jx}{s}\right) \text{ amp per cm}^2.$$

Here the current flow is parallel to the surface, and x is measured perpendicular to the metal and is positive inside the metal. If σ is the conductivity, find the following equations: (a) The equation for I_t the total current flowing through a slice of conductor one m wide and of infinite depth. (b) The power dissipated in the conductor in watts per square meter of surface area in terms of H_0, and in terms of I_t. (c) Show that if this current I_t is uniformly distributed to a depth s meters from the surface, that the power dissipated would be the same as the power found in part (b) above when the current is non-uniformly distributed according to the exponential law.

10.12. A copper coil has one turn per cm made of $\frac{1}{4}$ in. outside diameter tubing. There is a cylinder of steel placed at the center as shown. The steel is to be heated to 1000°C and held there for 5 min by passing a current through

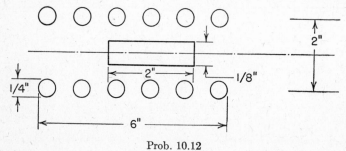

Prob. 10.12

the coil.   The coil cannot be made smaller because the steel is enclosed in a glass tube in a vacuum.   Assume that all the heat radiated passes through the glass.   Take conductivities of copper and steel to be 5.8×10^7 and 1.1×10^6 mho —m per m², respectively, and both permeabilities to be unity.   (a) Determine the power input to the cylinder for the steady state in watts.   (b) For frequencies of 0.1 mc and 10 mc determine the coil current required to heat the steel.   (c) Determine the *total* resistance of the coil including the resistance reflected by the steel for 0.1 mc and 10 mc.   (d) Describe how you would calculate the coil reactance, but do not perform the calculation.

10.13. Derive an equation for the critical frequency for good coupling of power into a flat sheet of great thickness.

10.14. Derive an equation for the power loss per meter length of cylinder for a case where a_c/h is nearly unity.   Base the derivation on Eq. 10.81, and compare the result with Eq. 10.63 or its equivalent forms.

10.15. Derive Eqs. 10.55.

CHAPTER 11

X-RAYS

Although the study of x-rays is more nearly a study of electrical physics than industrial electronics, their increasing importance in the fields of science, medicine, and industry warrant their consideration. The fact that they are produced and controlled by electronic apparatus is sufficient to justify including them in an electronics text. It is the purpose of this chapter to treat briefly the theory of their origin and the tubes and circuits used for their production.

11.1   Characteristics of X-rays and their Emission

The discovery of x-rays was made by Roentgen in 1895, while he was working with cathode rays in Germany.   It was one of the three discoveries that helped to question important areas in the classical theory of physics.

In 1890 most of the known phenomena could be explained by one or the other of the laws known and now considered as part of classical physics.   The possible exception was the photoelectric effect discovered in 1887.   These laws included Newton's laws, the conservation of energy, the kinetic theory of gases, Maxwell's equations, and Faraday's laws.   The three upsetting discoveries came in close succession: the discovery of x-rays in 1895, of radioactivity in 1896, and of the electron in 1897.   The first part of the solution of these new discoveries came with the quantum theory by Planck in 1900.

In his discovery of x-rays Roentgen found that screens of certain material glowed when brought near the cathode ray tube in the dark.   This was the beginning of what is now known as radiography. The burns suffered in the early stages of this application disclosed the x-ray's ability to destroy living tissue and brought about its ultimate use in treatment of diseases such as cancer.

Mass industrial inspection unit. (Courtesy of Westinghouse Electric Corporation.)

Reference to the radiation spectrum of Chapter 5 shows that
x-rays are electromagnetic radiations of very short wavelength.
Comparing them with light, the visible wavelengths are in the range
of 4000 to 7000 Å, while x-rays have wavelengths of the order of
0.02 to 10 Å.

$$1 \text{ Å} = 1 \text{ Angstrom unit} = 10^{-10} \text{ meter.}$$

X-rays are produced by collisions of high-speed electrons with
atoms, and are propagated with the speed of light. With large positive energies electrons are capable of going into the innermost orbits
of atoms and displacing very low-energy electrons. Since these
levels of energy remain filled in preference to those of the outer orbits,
this vacancy is filled in one or more steps by outer electrons, each
giving up a photon of energy, which if great enough is an x-ray.

Since x-rays are part of the radiation spectrum, the basic law of Eq. 11.1 holds relating wavelength, frequency, and propagation velocity:

$$c = \lambda f = 3.0 \times 10^8 \text{ meters per second,} \qquad (11.1)$$

where λ is in meters, f in cycles per second. Similar in nature to light, x-rays are affected very little by electric or magnetic fields. Their ability to penetrate solid matter and then react with photographic film or other sensitized material in proportion to their intensity has made them useful for both medical diagnosis and industrial applications.

The quantity and intensity of x-radiation may be measured in terms of its physical, chemical, or biological effects. The practical unit, the "roentgen," named after the discoverer, is expressed in terms of the ionizing effect. Thus 1 roentgen is the quantity of x-ray radiation that will ionize 1 cubic centimeter of air sufficiently at 0°C and at a pressure of 760 mm of mercury, to produce one electrostatic unit of charge at saturation current. The secondary electrons are utilized. The unit of intensity is the roentgen per second.

It was previously stated that x-rays are produced as the result of collisions of electrons possessing large kinetic energies with atoms. The x-ray photon, applying the quantum theory to x-rays since they are an electromagnetic radiation, has an energy equal to hf.[1] Here h is Planck's constant, and f is the frequency in cycles per second. It is clear then that a bombarding electron must have an energy equal to or greater than hf if the x-ray photon is to be produced. In most practical applications x-rays are produced in a vacuum tube in which electrons are accelerated from a cathode to a target by means of an electric field. The maximum kinetic energy that an electron can attain by this means is of course a direct function of the potential. Thus, $\frac{1}{2}m_0 v_{max}^2 = Ee$. It can thus be seen from the energy relation existing between the electron and the resulting x-ray photon that the maximum possible frequency of x-ray radiation depends upon the electron-accelerating potential.

$$\tfrac{1}{2}m_0 v_{max}^2 = Ee = hf_{max}.$$

Thus
$$f_{max} = \frac{Ee}{h} \text{ cps,} \qquad (11.2)$$

---

[1] The symbol f will be used in this chapter to denote frequency, although in this application it often appears in the literature as ν.

where f_{max} is the maximum frequency of x-ray radiation, E is the cathode-to-target potential in volts, e is the electron charge in coulombs, and h is Planck's constant; $h = 6.6 \times 10^{-34}$ joule-second.

Perhaps a more useful method of noting the value of this maximum energy photon would be in terms of the minimum wavelength λ_{min}.

$$\lambda_{min} = \frac{c}{f_{max}} = \frac{ch}{Ee} \text{ meter.}$$

This definite minimum cutoff wavelength, varying inversely with accelerating potential, can be seen in the experimental curves of Fig. 11-1, p. 476.

Example. What is the maximum frequency of x-radiation from a tube operating with a peak voltage of 50,000 v? By direct substitution into Eq. 11.2,

$$f_{max} = \frac{5.0 \times 10^4 \times 1.6 \times 10^{-19}}{6.6 \times 10^{-34}} = 1.212 \times 10^{19} \text{ cycles per second.}$$

The minimum wavelength is of course given by use of Eq. 11.1.

$$\lambda_{min} = \frac{2.99 \times 10^8}{f_{max}} = \frac{2.99 \times 10^8}{1.212 \times 10^{19}} = 2.465 \times 10^{-11} \text{ meter}$$

$$= 0.2465 \text{ Å.}$$

Equation 11.2 indicates that in order to produce radiation of a higher frequency or shorter wavelength, greater accelerating potentials must be used. However, as the potential difference increases, the electron velocities calculated by the relation $\frac{1}{2}m_0v^2 = Ee$ reach the speed of light at about 250,000 volts. Solutions of this relation for voltages greater than 250,000 lead to velocities greater than the speed of light, which is of course not possible. Thus it is obvious that in applications of accelerating voltages greater than about 100,000, relativity must be considered in determining the electron velocities.

The theory of relativity first proposes that the total energy of any mass can be expressed as the product of its mass and the square of the speed of light. Thus

$$W = mc^2. \tag{11.3}$$

In Eq. 11.3, c is the conventional symbol for the speed of light, and m is the rest mass, m_0, if the velocity of the mass is zero. However, any increase in velocity, and thus of kinetic energy, appears as a change in the mass m. Thus for a free electron assumed to be initially at rest and accelerated through a potential rise E to a velocity v, the energy equation becomes

$$Ee = mc^2 - m_0c^2. \tag{11.4}$$

Here m is the equivalent mass at velocity v. Differentiation of Eq. 11.4 results in

$$\frac{d(Ee)}{dt} = \frac{d(mv)}{dt} v = c^2 \frac{dm}{dt}$$

or

$$\frac{d(mv)}{dt} v = c^2 \frac{dm}{dt}. \tag{11.5}$$

Carrying out the indicated operations and evaluating, assuming $m = m_0$ at $v = 0$, the following relation is derived between the mass m at velocity v, and m_0.

$$m = m_0 \frac{1}{\sqrt{1 - v^2/c^2}}. \tag{11.6}$$

Substituting Eq. 11.6 into Eq. 11.4,

$$Ee = m_0c^2 \left(\frac{1}{\sqrt{1 - v^2/c^2}} - 1 \right). \tag{11.7}$$

This is the relation that must be satisfied at all times between the total kinetic energy of the mass above $v = 0$, and the velocity v.

Equation 11.7 may be expanded by means of the binomial theorem:

$$Ee = \frac{1}{2} m_0 v^2 + \frac{3}{8} m_0 \frac{v^4}{c^2} + \cdots. \tag{11.8}$$

This indicates that $\frac{1}{2}m_0v^2$ is only an approximation to the kinetic energy, and useful only when the velocity v is a small fraction of the speed of light. Equation 11.7 may be solved for the velocity v and results in

$$v = c \sqrt{1 - \frac{1}{(1 + Ee/m_0c^2)^2}}. \tag{11.9}$$

In both Eq. 11.7 and Eq. 11.9 the charge e of an electron should be written as a positive number.

11.2   Continuous Spectrum

Although the maximum frequency of x-ray radiation is determined by the accelerating potential, relatively few collisions result in a complete transfer of energy to produce the maximum frequency. Actually partial energy transfers, all the way from zero up to the

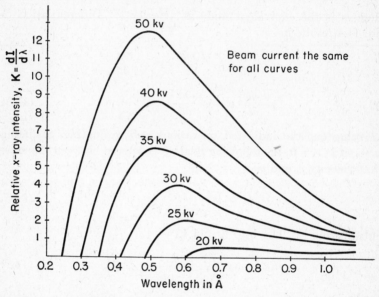

Fig. 11-1.   Relative x-ray radiation (from a tungsten target) for various voltages. (Reproduced by permission from an article by Ulrey, *Physical Review*, Vol. 11, 1918, p. 401.)

maximum, take place, and thus the x-ray emission makes up a continuous spectrum with some radiation over the entire band.   Since the energy transitions of electrons in an atom are limited to definite steps, it would seem that the radiated energy in the form of x-rays would consist of certain discrete wavelengths, rather than a continuous spectrum as indicated.   It is true that there are peaks in the amount of energy radiated, as will be discussed later, but it is also true that some energy is radiated at all wavelengths greater than the lower limit determined by the accelerating potential.   The continuous radiation is known as the continuous spectrum.   It is the result of the deceleration or sudden slowing down of the bombarding electrons as they approach the strong field near the nucleus of the atom. The amount of deceleration is random with each electron, and thus it is possible to have any frequency of radiation up to the maximum. The curves of Fig. 11-1 show the relative wavelength distribution for a series of plate voltages. It can be seen from Fig. 11-1 that below 20,000 volts the x-ray emission becomes negligible. Also, although the minimum wavelength is dependent upon the plate voltage, only a small proportion of the radiation is produced near this frequency, the greatest intensity being produced at considerably longer wavelengths.

11.3 Efficiency of Emission

It should be made clear at this point that only a few of the electrons in the accelerated beam or cathode ray convert all or even part of their energy into x-ray radiation. A great majority of the electrons have most of their energy converted into heat, which must be conducted away from the target anode. An equation for the efficiency of energy conversion into x-rays for the continuous spectrum was first postulated by Beatty[2] in 1913. Recently the relation has been substantiated by Kirkpatrick. It is

$$\text{efficiency} = \frac{\text{x-ray energy}}{\text{cathode ray energy}} = \left(\frac{\text{x-ray power}}{\text{cathode ray power}}\right)$$
$$= 1.4 \times 10^{-9} ZV.[3] \tag{11.10}$$

Here Z is the atomic number of the target material, and V is the plate potential used in the tube. This relation points out the dependency of x-radiation upon the atomic structure and indicates the decrease in efficiency at lower potentials.

Example. It is assumed that 10^{17} electrons are emitted from a thermionic cathode per second. The constant plate potential is 100 kilovolts and the target is molybdenum. (a) What is the x-ray energy radiation per minute? (b) What power must the anode be able to dissipate?

(a) Since an x-ray tube is operated under saturation conditions, all emitted electrons reach the target. The cathode ray power absorbed at the target is then

$$10^{17} \times 10^5 = 10^{22} \text{ electron volts per second.}$$

[2] Beatty, R. L., "Energy of Roentgen Rays," *Proc. Roy. Soc. (London)*, **89A**, 314 (1913).

[3] By permission from *X-rays in Practice*, by Wayne T. Sproull. Copyright 1946. McGraw-Hill Book Company, Inc., New York.

From Eq. 11.2

$$\text{x-ray power} = 1.4 \times 10^{-9}ZV \times \text{cathode ray power}$$

$$V = 10^5; \qquad Z = 42 \text{ for molybdenum.}$$

Therefore

$$\text{x-ray energy per second} = 1.4 \times 10^{-9} \times 42 \times 10^5 \times 10^{22}$$

$$= 58.8 \times 10^{18} \text{ electron volts per second,}$$

or 9.4 watts, since 1 electron volt $= 1.59 \times 10^{-19}$ joule.

(b) By Eq. 11.10, the efficiency is

$$1.4 \times 10^{-9} \times 42 \times 10^5 = 58.8 \times 10^{-4} = 0.00588.$$

Therefore the anode must dissipate the remaining part or $0.99412 \times$ cathode ray power. This is 0.99412×10^{22} electron volts per second $\cong 1.59 \times 10^3$ watts.

Refer now to the curves of Fig. 11-1. Ulrey[4] first noted that the area under the curves, which is a measure of total radiation intensity, varies in proportion to the square of the voltage. Thus the general equation for intensity I becomes

$$I_{cont} = kV^2. \tag{11.11}$$

In addition, the expression for efficiency, Eq. 11.10, states that emission is directly proportional to the atomic number Z of the target, and thus Eq. 11.11 is modified to be

$$I_{cont} = KZV^2 \tag{11.12}$$

where K is a constant. Equation 11.12 could also be derived from the expression for efficiency, Eq. 11.10. Since the tube is operated at saturation current, the cathode ray power is directly proportional to the potential V. Thus

$$\text{x-ray power, intensity} = K' \times 1.4 \times 10^{-9} \times ZV^2 = KZV^2,$$

or $$\text{x-ray power} = (\text{cathode ray power})(\text{efficiency})$$

$$= (Vi_b)(1.4 \times 10^{-9}ZV)$$

$$= 1.4 \times 10^{-9}Zi_bV^2 \text{ watts.}$$

[4] Sproull, W. T., *X-rays in Practice*, McGraw-Hill Book Company, Inc., New York, 1946.

11.4 Characteristic Radiation

In addition to the continuous x-ray spectrum whose limits are dependent upon the excitation voltage, some of the x-rays emitted are characteristic of the target material. The present theory of the atom supposes the electrons to be in a series of energy levels about the nucleus. The levels nearest the nucleus are the most stable and are in the lowest energy levels. Only a definite number of electrons can exist at a certain level, and the lowest energy levels are filled first. If an electron is removed from the innermost orbit to some higher level, an electron in an outer level falls into its place. The atom is considered to be "excited" from the time the first electron is removed from its orbit until the atom is back to its steady state. This return may be accomplished in one or several steps. It is the energy required to remove this electron from the inner orbit that must be provided by the incident electron. If previous to the collision the difference in energy levels of the displaced electron and the one taking its place is Δw, this much energy is radiated as the outer level electron falls into the vacancy created by the collision. The relation between the frequency of the radiation and Δw is of course

$$\Delta w = hf = \frac{hc}{\lambda}.$$

Expressed in electron volts and angstrom units,

$$\Delta E_{ev} = \frac{12,400}{\lambda}. \tag{11.13}$$

Transition of electrons between certain energy levels of a material is much more common than between others. Thus, if the bombarding electrons possess sufficient energy to remove electrons from the low-energy orbits, radiation of wavelengths corresponding to the more probable transitions in that material will occur. This is called characteristic radiation.

11.5 Theory of the Bohr Atom

The understanding of this phenomenon of characteristic radiation might be enhanced by a brief study of the Bohr theory of the hydrogen atom. The following four assumptions are made:

1. The atom consists of a nucleus and one electron.

2. The position of the electron is limited to orbits where its angular momentum is an integral multiple of $h/2\pi$, where h is Planck's constant.

3. No energy is radiated while the electron resides in any one of these orbits.

4. If the electron jumps from one level to another it gives up or receives an amount of energy equal to Δw, and $\Delta w = hf$.

Considering these orbits to be circular, the angular momentum of the electron in orbit n is given by

$$P_\phi = m\omega a^2 = n\frac{h}{2\pi}, \tag{11.14}$$

where m = mass of the electron; ω = angular velocity of the electron; a = radius of the orbit. The n is referred to as the quantum number. It may also be stated that the electrostatic force on the electron is just balanced by the centrifugal force of rotation. Thus

$$\frac{Ze^2}{4\pi K_0 a^2} = ma\omega^2 \text{ newtons}, \tag{11.15}$$

where Z is the atomic number; e is the charge of an electron; $K_0 = 10^{-9}/36\pi$ farad per meter. Solving Eqs. 11.14 and 11.15 for a and eliminating ω gives

$$a = \frac{n^2 h^2 K_0}{\pi m e^2 Z} \text{ meters}. \tag{11.16}$$

The total energy possessed by the electron is partly potential and partly kinetic. The potential energy w_p, if considered equal to zero at $a = \infty$, can be expressed by

$$w_p = -\frac{Ze^2}{4\pi K_0 a} \text{ joules}. \tag{11.17}$$

The kinetic energy w_k can be expressed by use of Eq. 11.15 as

$$w_k = \frac{1}{2}mv^2 = \frac{1}{2}ma^2\omega^2 = \frac{1}{2} \times \frac{Ze^2}{4\pi K_0 a} \text{ joules}. \tag{11.18}$$

The total energy then is given as

$$w_n = w_k + w_p = -\frac{1}{2} \times \frac{Ze^2}{4\pi K_0 a} = -\frac{me^4 Z^2}{8n^2 h^2 K_0^2} \text{ joules}. \tag{11.19}$$

This is the energy of the electron when in the nth quantum state.

If energy is to be radiated, the electron must jump from some energy state n_1 to a lower-energy state n_2, where $n_1 > n_2$. The radiated energy is then

$$hf = w_1 - w_2 = \frac{me^4 Z^2}{8h^2 K_0^2} \left(\frac{1}{n_2^2} - \frac{1}{n_1^2} \right) \text{ joules.} \qquad (11.20)$$

Note that in Eq. 11.20 both w_1 and w_2 are negative, but that w_1 is less negative than w_2, and thus their difference is positive.

The frequency f of the radiated energy is given from Eq. 11.20 as

$$f = \frac{me^4}{8h^3 K_0^2} Z^2 \left(\frac{1}{n_2^2} - \frac{1}{n_1^2} \right) \text{ cycles per second.}$$

The constant term $\dfrac{me^4}{8h^3 K_0^2}$ is known as Rydberg's constant and is evaluated to be

$$R = \frac{me^3}{8h^3 K_0^2} = 3.29 \times 10^{15} \qquad (11.21)$$

where $K_0 = (\frac{1}{36}\pi) \times 10^{-9}$ farad per meter; m is in kilograms, e is in coulombs, and h is in joule-seconds. Thus the frequency of radiation is

$$f = RZ^2 \left(\frac{1}{n_2^2} - \frac{1}{n_1^2} \right) \text{ cycles per second.} \qquad (11.22)$$

Since the radiated energy is hf, the ratio f/R is proportional to the radiated energy and is used as the unit of energy in Fig. 11-4, p. 484.

It is now easy to calculate from Eq. 11.22 the ionization potential of hydrogen. This potential is the energy required to take an electron from its normal state, here $n = 1$, to infinity, where $n = \infty$.

Equation 11.22, multiplied by h, gives the energy radiated by an electron in jumping from an excited state to some lower energy level. If we consider the electron initially in its normal state or $n_1 = 1$ and finally to be free of the atom or at infinity, $n_2 = \infty$, the solution is negative, since this change requires energy input rather than energy being radiated. However, the magnitude of this energy is the amount required to remove the electron of a hydrogen atom from its normal level to infinity, which is ionization. Thus

$$hf = hRZ^2 \left(\frac{1}{\infty^2} - \frac{1}{1^2} \right)$$

$$= 6.6 \times 10^{-34} \times 3.29 \times 10^{15} \times 1(-1)$$

$$= -21.65 \times 10^{-19} \text{ joules.}$$

Converting this to electron volts, the ionization potential of hydrogen is

$$E = \frac{21.65 \times 10^{-19}}{1.59 \times 10^{-19}} = 13.58 \text{ volts.}$$

This checks very closely with the accepted value of 13.53 volts. It is also possible, with this information, to calculate and plot the

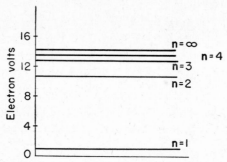

Fig. 11-2.   Energy levels above $n = 1$ for excited hydrogen atom.

energy transitions between the normal, $n = 1$, state and any other state of excitation.

If the hydrogen atom is excited by having its electron raised in energy to some one of the possible levels, it may give up this energy in one piece or in parts, depending on whether the electron jumps directly to its normal state, or arrives there by several jumps. For example, suppose the electron were in the fourth energy level, or $n = 4$. It could return to $n = 1$ in one jump, giving up 12.7 electron volts of energy as radiation. Or it could jump first from $n = 4$ to $n = 2$, giving up 2.52 electron volts of energy and then to $n = 1$, giving up a second quantum of energy equal to 10.18 electron volts. Some of these possible transitions are more likely to occur than others, and in fact, experimental evidence indicates that in more complex atoms some never take place and thus may be forbidden.

11.6 Possible Energy Levels and Transitions

From this treatment of the simple hydrogen atom it is easy to realize that in a more complicated atom a great many energy transi-

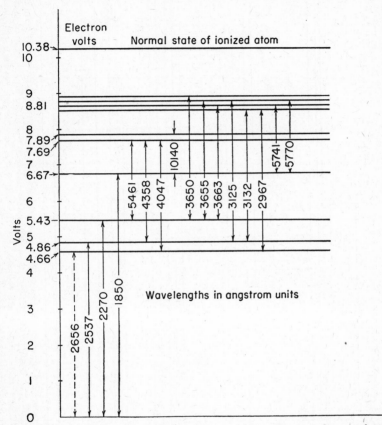

Fig. 11-3. Energy level diagram for mercury. (Energy change of two outermost electrons only.) Broken line indicates prohibited transition. (Reproduced by permission from *Gaseous Conductors*, by James Dillon Cobine, McGraw-Hill Book Company, Inc., New York, 1941.)

tions are possible. The chart of Fig. 11-4 indicates the possible transitions of an atom of uranium. This chart is plotted in a slightly different manner than the energy level diagrams for hydrogen and mercury, Fig. 11-2 and Fig. 11-3. Here the quantum numbers indicate that an electron has been displaced from this

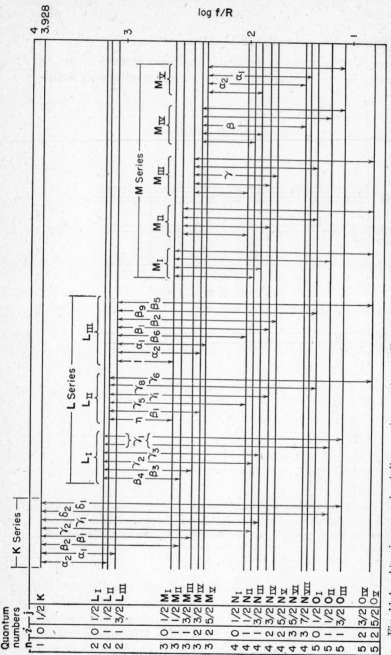

Fig. 11-4. Atomic energy level diagram for uranium. The vertical scale is a measure of the energy required to remove an electron from that level to infinity, or it might be thought of as the energy added to the atom, in the excited state. The vertical scale does not represent energies that necessarily are radiated. Only differences in energies between two levels are radiated. (Reproduced by permission from *Introduction to Modern Physics*, by F. K. Richtmeyer and E. H. Kennard, McGraw-Hill Book Company, Inc., New York, 1942.)

level and that the replacement electron may come from any one of a number of levels. Thus $n = 1$ is at the top and is indicative of the fact that there is a possibility of a photon of greatest energy being emitted, since the vacancy is at the lowest level. The K series is the summation of possible transitions to this lowest, or K, level. Similarly, the L series represent the possible energy radiations if an electron had been displaced from the $n = 2$ level, or L level. It

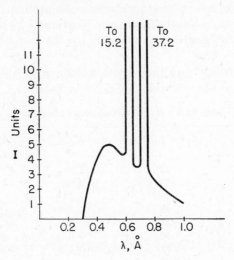

Fig. 11-5. Characteristic radiation of molybdenum at 35 kv. (Reproduced by permission from an article by Ulrey, *Physical Review*, Vol. 11, 1918, p. 401.)

should be noted that there are three possible energy levels very close together, all of which are considered to be in the $n = 2$ level.

The energy scale at the right is plotted in terms of $\log_{10} f/R$, and can be thought of as a measure of the energy of the atom above its normal value during its period of excitation.

Although it is possible to calculate the energy level diagram for any material of atomic number Z by Eq. 11.22, the probable transitions cannot be calculated. Therefore, the indicated transitions, such as those of Fig. 11-3 and Fig. 11-4, are usually arrived at by means of the spectrograph and observation of the lines of radiation.

Thus it can be seen that in addition to the continuous spectrum of x-radiation, each target material has certain predominant wavelengths of radiation which are characteristic of it alone. These constitute the characteristic spectrum of the material.

Figure 11-5 shows the relative intensity curve for molybdenum operated at 35 kv. The peaks of characteristic radiation are clearly visible. It seems strange at first that no peaks appeared on the curves of tungsten in Fig. 11-1. However, they would be present for voltages over 70 kv. Similarly, the peaks of Fig. 11-5 disappear at voltages below 20 kv. It is this property of characteristic spectra that has made the x-ray spectrometer possible and provides a fool-proof method of determining a material's composition. The possible characteristic wavelengths decrease in length with increase in atomic number, and this method served finally to place some elements in the periodic table.

A few materials with their characteristic or K wavelengths and their equivalent electron volts are given in Table 11.1.

Table 11.1 K_γ Series Radiation Characteristics

Element	Atomic number	K_γ, Å	Electron volts
Al	13	7.95	1,560
Cr	24	2.06	5,950
Fe	26	1.74	7,125
Ni	28	1.48	8,380
Cu	29	1.38	9,000
Mo	42	0.619	20,000
W	74	0.179	69,200
Pb	82	0.141	88,000

For tungsten the complete K series consists of wavelengths of 0.179, 0.184, 0.185, 0.209, and 0.213Å.

11.7   States of Atomic Excitation

In considering the possible radiation energies that may result from an accelerated electron bombarding an atom, it may be well to mention a few of the ways in which the electron's energy may be dissipated. The notation often used is similar to that utilized in chemical equations.

A; a neutral atom

A^x; an excited, neutral atom

A^+; an ionized atom

e; an electron

E; energy

E_r; energy of excitation from normal state

E_i; energy of ionization from normal state

hf; a quantum of radiant energy

1. $A + (e + E) \to (A + \text{fraction of } E) + (e + E - \text{fraction of } E)$. $\hspace{3cm}$ (11.23)

This states that the result of a neutral atom and an accelerated electron may be an atom with some additional energy as heat, and an electron with less energy. The atom is not excited to the extent of an electron leaving its normal orbit.

2. $A + (e + E) \to A^x + [e + (E - E_r)]$. $\hspace{2cm}$ (11.24)

This indicates an excited atom in which some electron has been displaced to a higher energy level at the expense of the bombarding electron. The rest of the equations will be given and assumed self-explanatory.

3. $A^x \to A + hf$. $\hspace{6cm}$ (11.25)

4. $A_3{}^x \to A_2{}^x + (hf)_{3-2}$. $\hspace{4.5cm}$ (11.26)

5. $A_2{}^x \to A_1{}^x + (hf)_{2-1}$. $\hspace{4.5cm}$ (11.27)

6. $A + (e + E) \to A^+ + (2e + E - E_i)$. $\hspace{2.5cm}$ (11.28)

7. $A^+ + (e + E) \to A^x + hf$. $\hspace{4cm}$ (11.29)

8. $A^+ + (e + E) \to A + hf$. $\hspace{4cm}$ (11.30)

Many other combinations exist, but these six represent those that are of particular importance to this text.

In concluding this section on emission four general relationships should be kept in mind.

1. A change in plate potential changes the x-ray intensity in proportion to the square of the voltage.

2. An increase in plate potential decreases the wavelength of the average radiation, making the rays more penetrating or "hard" as they are commonly known.

3. For a constant plate potential the intensity of radiation at all wavelengths is directly proportional to the tube current, this being the saturation condition of the cathode.

4. All materials emit certain characteristic wavelengths if the plate potential is sufficiently high to excite them.

11.8   Scattering and Absorption

Absorption of x-ray radiation by passage through a body results in a decrease in the beam intensity emerging from that body.

There are two mechanisms contributing to what is usually called absorption. They are scattering and photoelectric absorption. The scattering of x-ray radiation is an actual change in the direction and/or wavelength of the radiation due to an interaction of the beam with the charges on the atom nucleus and on the electrons. This new radiation may be of a longer wavelength than x-rays, or its new direction may be such as to make it useless as part of the original beam. This scattering constitutes only a small fraction of the total absorption.

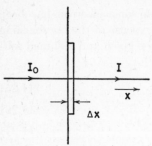

I_0 I

x

Δx

Fig. 11-6. Absorption by a thin piece of material.

Photoelectric absorption is the absorption of radiation energy by an electron to excite it from one state to another or to free the electron completely from the material as emission. This energy is then given up as longer wavelength radiation or in some other form. This absorption is most probable when the photons of x-ray radiation are of energy comparable to that required to excite an electron from one state to another in the particular material. Thus the wavelengths most likely to be absorbed are characteristic of the material.

It is generally considered that the fraction of the incident radiation absorbed in passing through a thin material is proportional to the thickness of the material and a factor called the "absorption coefficient," which is a function of the nature of the material and the wavelength of the radiation. Referring to Fig. 11-6 and considering x positive in the direction of the radiation, the change in intensity ΔI is negative in the distance Δx.

$$\frac{I - I_0}{I_0} = \frac{\Delta I}{I_0} = -\mu_l \, \Delta x. \qquad (11.31)$$

Here I_0 is the incident intensity in roentgens per second, I is the emerging intensity, μ_l is the absorption coefficient, and Δx is the thickness in meters. If Δx is allowed to approach zero in the limit, Eq. 11.31 becomes

$$\frac{dI}{I} = -\mu_l \, dx. \qquad (11.32)$$

Integrating both sides results in

$$\ln I = \mu_l x + C.$$

When $x = 0$, $C = \ln I_0$ since $I = I_0$ at $x = 0$. Therefore $\ln I - \ln I_0 = -\mu_l x$. Thus

$$I = I_0 \epsilon^{-\mu_l x}. \tag{11.33}$$

If I is the intensity per unit area normal to the direction of propagation, μ_l becomes the fraction of energy absorbed per unit volume. Practically, the absorption per unit mass is of more use because of its lack of dependence on the material's state. Thus if μ_l is divided by the material density ρ, the "mass absorption coefficient" μ is found.

$$\mu = \frac{\mu_l}{\rho} \text{ square meters per kilogram.} \tag{11.34}$$

Then Eq. 11.33 becomes

$$I = I_0 \epsilon^{-\mu x \rho}. \tag{11.35}$$

This will be recognized as Lambert's law of absorption for optics. It can be shown that μ is a function of the atomic number Z and the wavelength of the radiation.

The value of μ for any particular material and distribution of wavelengths is easily measured by use of an ionization chamber. The amount of ionization for a beam of radiation is measured with and without the absorbing material, and the value of μ is found from their ratio.

Although the total absorption is the result of both photoelectric absorption and scattering, only about 0.5 per cent is caused by the latter, and thus a study of the first is all that is usually desired.

Experimental data indicate that there is a definite variation in μ with wavelength and atomic number. The curve of Fig. 11-7 is for lead with μ plotted as a function of the wavelength of the x-ray radiation. The peaks in the curve of Fig. 11-7 result from the fact that absorption is increasingly better as the magnitude hf of a photon decreases toward the energy needed to excite an electron from a particular energy level. Absorption is best, or the transition most likely, if hf is just the required value. For wavelengths immediately above these critical values, the absorption drops off abruptly since this transition is no longer possible.

The energies involved at these different levels depend upon the atomic number of the material, and thus the discontinuities move along the horizontal axis toward longer wavelengths as the atomic number decreases.

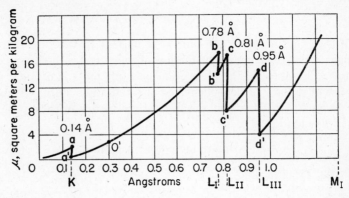

Fig. 11-7. Absorption coefficients for lead. (Reproduced by permission from *X-rays in Practice*, by Wayne T. Sproull, McGraw-Hill Book Company, Inc., New York, 1946.)

If the curve of Fig. 11-7 is plotted against λ^3 rather than λ, the curves of Fig. 11-8 result.   Thus

$$\mu = k\lambda^3 + C; \qquad 0 < \lambda^3 < a.$$

$$\mu = k'\lambda^3 + C; \qquad a < \lambda^3.$$

This indicates that μ varies linearly with λ^3.

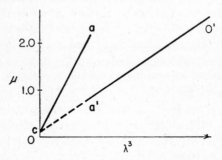

Fig. 11-8. Absorption coefficient of lead versus λ^3.

All materials are nearly opaque to radiation of long wavelength, with the cutoff value depending on the material.

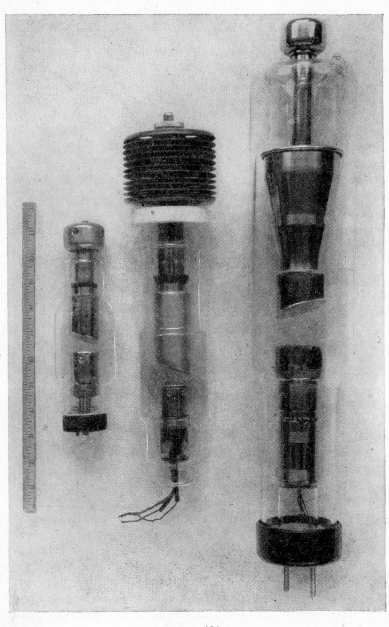

X-ray tubes. (Reproduced by permission from *Industrial Electronics Reference Book*, copyright 1948 by Westinghouse Electric Corporation, published by John Wiley & Sons, Inc.)

491

If the impinging radiation is considered to be uniform, and the specimen it is traversing is nonhomogeneous, more of the beam is transmitted through some parts than through others. Thus the originally uniform beam is modified to have intensity maxima at the points of greatest transparency. The effect of this modified radiation seen on fluoroscopic screens or on film is useful in both industrial and medical applications. In addition to this intensity change, the long wavelengths are absorbed more readily than the short ones, and thus the tendency is for the average wavelength of the beam emitted to be shorter than that of the one applied. Since the band of wavelengths covered is a function of the plate voltage, this tendency toward short wavelength emission can be overcome by using a half- or full-wave rectifier rather than a constant potential. Long wavelengths are produced over a wide range of the voltage variation, while short ones are produced only at the peaks. For ease in detection, the modified beam emerging from the test specimen should be recorded on materials sensitive to intensity differences. Fluoroscopic screens and sensitized film are both satisfactory, but a treatment of their properties will be left to a more complete text.

11.9   X-ray Tubes

Although x-ray tubes are usually divided into several classes, the basic requirements are the same. These requirements are a source of electrons, a means of accelerating these electrons, and a target for the high-energy electrons to strike.

11.10   Gas Tubes

The first x-ray tubes were gas-filled, cold-cathode tubes depending upon ionization and cathode bombardment for the source of electrons. A typical tube is shown in Fig. 11-9. The plate voltage is impressed between the cathode and the two anodes which are shown as anode and anticathode. The high plate voltage causes ionization of the gas, starting with the few stray ionized atoms. The anode with the sharp point is used in addition to the target anode to insure ionization, since the voltage gradient is very high in the vicinity of this point. The resulting positive ions are accelerated to the cathode where electrons are emitted by bombardment. These electrons are in turn accelerated to the target, or anticathode, where the x-rays are created.

Both the tube current and the hardness of the x-rays depend upon the tube voltage and the gas pressure.   Too high a pressure results in low voltage for a certain current and "soft" radiation.   Lower pressures result in increased hardness for the same current.   Since

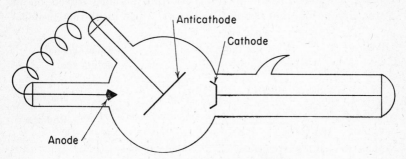

Fig. 11-9.   Gas filled x-ray tube.

the gas pressure usually decreases with age, some means of inserting gas from time to time must be provided in order to maintain any degree of constancy.

11.11   Vacuum Tubes

Although gas tubes are still used, most of the present-day tubes use a variable-current-heated filament, and a tungsten anode plate sealed in a high vacuum.   The shell is usually Pyrex to allow emission of the radiation.   A typical vacuum type is shown in Fig. 11-10.

The vacuum x-ray tube is operated at saturation, and therefore the tube current as well as the x-ray emission intensity depend upon filament current.   The wavelength spectrum of the radiation and the efficiency of energy conversion depend upon and are controlled by the plate voltage.   If the plate voltage and the filament current are both variable, the radiation may be completely controlled within the limits of the tube.

Details of construction vary with the anticipated plate voltage. The tube itself must be of sufficient length to withstand the peak plate voltage.   Since a very small percentage of the total electron energy is converted into x-radiation, most of this energy appears at the anode as heat which must be dissipated.   In terms of plate voltage, tubes may be grouped in the classes of 70–95, 100–125, 130–190, and 200–250 kv.   In the first class the tube is usually mounted in an oil-filled case with a plastic window for radiation emission. The anode is copper-backed tungsten, with the heat being conducted off by the anode and the oil. As the potential rating goes up, more elaborate means of cooling and insulating must be utilized. The cooling methods include blowers, rotating anodes, forced oil or water circulation, and external radiators. The insulation problem

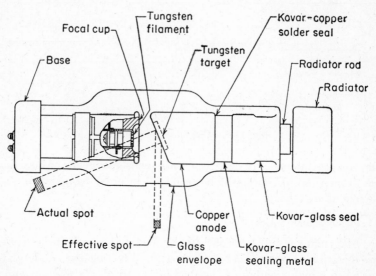

Fig. 11-10. X-ray tube. (Reproduced by permission from *Industrial Electronics Reference Book*, copyright 1948 by Westinghouse Electric Corporation, published by John Wiley & Sons, Inc.)

is handled by increasing the physical length of the tube and immersing the tube in some insulating medium as much as possible.

When the requirement is 1 or 2 million volts, it becomes necessary to build the tube in sections, limiting the voltage per section. A multisection tube has the conventional tungsten cathode at one end and a copper-backed target at the other end, usually the lower end. In between are accelerating electrodes separated by glass seals. The potential across any glass section may be determined by the potential difference between electrodes. The number of sections may reach as high as 24 for the 2-million-volt tubes. A resonance transformer, as discussed in Sec. 11.13 is used to provide the plate voltage.

11.12   The Betatron

In considering tubes for the production of x-rays, the betatron should also be mentioned.   Here the electrons are accelerated by a changing magnetic field rather than by the direct application of high potential.   Although the idea was patented in 1927 by Slepian, the first workable model was not built until 1940 by Kerst[5] at the University of Illinois.   Units have now been built producing electron energies equivalent to over 300 million volts.   In principle the

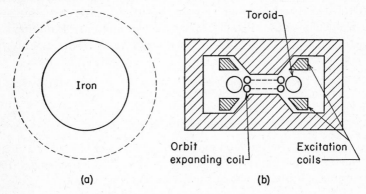

Fig. 11-11.   Basic construction of a betatron.

betatron is an induction accelerator.   It is based upon the two principles that (a) an electron moving normal to a magnetic field takes a circular path and (b) a changing magnetic field induces a voltage.   In Fig. 11-11, the iron core is surrounded by an evacuated toroid.   If the magnetic flux in this iron core is changed, a voltage is induced in the toroid, and any charges, such as electrons, which may be present, are accelerated.   Since current is the rate of flow of charge, and electrons carry a charge, this moving stream of electrons constitutes a current.   If the electrons are confined to this closed path they are accelerated each time around the path in proportion to the potential existing due to the changing flux.   Thus the electrons may attain an energy corresponding to millions of volts while actually no such voltage is present.   An evacuated ceramic tube is usually used for the path and is called a "doughnut."

[5] By permission of D. W. Kerst; Department of Physics, University of Illinois, Urbana, Ill.

Since the electrons are free and are not held in their path as part of a conductor, the chief problem is that of keeping the electron in the desired orbit while it is being accelerated. Other things being constant, the orbit of the electron would increase in a spiral as its velocity increased. This difficulty was removed by so designing the magnetic path that the flux distribution around the "doughnut" requires an orbit of constant radius.

This required flux distribution will be considered briefly. An electron of mass m and charge e, moving with velocity v in a magnetic field of density B perpendicular to its path, describes in the plane perpendicular to the magnetic field a circular motion. Equating the centrifugal force of the moving mass mv^2/r to the centripetal force on the moving charge Bev the equation of equilibrium becomes

$$\frac{mv^2}{r} = Bev \text{ newton}$$

or
$$Ber = mv \text{ kilogram-meter per second.} \tag{11.36}$$

If B is constant, the electron moves with constant velocity in a circle of constant radius. However, if the inclosed flux Φ is changed, the electron is subjected to a tangential accelerating force

$$\mathbf{E} = \frac{1}{2\pi r}\frac{d\Phi}{dt} \text{ newton per coulomb.} \tag{11.37}$$

Thus the acceleration force per electron is

$$\mathbf{E}e = \frac{e}{2\pi r}\frac{d\Phi}{dt} = \frac{d(mv)}{dt} \text{ newton.} \tag{11.38}$$

Referring to Eq. 11.36, if r is to remain constant, the flux density B must increase directly with the momentum. Integrating Eq. 11.38 gives

$$\frac{e\Phi}{2\pi r} = mv \text{ kilogram-meter per second,} \tag{11.39}$$

and equating to Eq. 11.36 gives

$$Ber = \frac{e\Phi}{2\pi r} \text{ kilogram-meter per second.} \tag{11.40}$$

Thus
$$B = \frac{\Phi}{2\pi r^2} \text{ weber per square meter.} \tag{11.41}$$

Equation 11.41 states that if the flux density B at the orbit is at all
times equal to one-half the average flux density inside the orbit, the
radius r of the orbit is constant.   By making the field highly con-
centrated at the center, tapering off very rapidly as r increases, the
electron is held in an orbit of almost constant radius.

The flux distribution also serves to limit the electron path to one
plane.   The flux bulges between pole faces as shown in Fig. 11-12.
If the electron moves away from the equilibrium plane, either up or
down, there is a horizontal component of flux as shown in Fig. 11-12.

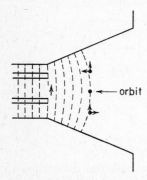

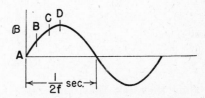

Fig. 11-12.   Cross section of   Fig. 11-13.   Magnetic field variation
betatron pole piece.   in a betatron.

If the flux is increasing, the electron is being accelerated into the page
and there is a force due to this horizontal component of flux tending
to return the electron to the original plane.

The electrons are injected into the "doughnut" with an initial
energy of 70 to 80 kv.   The magnetic field is made to vary sinusoidally, and the injection is made at point A as the flux passes
through the point of equilibrium corresponding to the initial energy.
See Fig. 11-13.

The electron is then accelerated in circling the field many times
and is pulsed out of the orbit to strike the target at some point such
as B, C, or D, depending on the energy desired.   The pulsing is
produced by a transient current through a one- or two-turn coil of
smaller diameter than the orbit of the electrons as shown in Fig.
11-11b.   The superimposed field caused by the transient current
opposes the flux at the center of the pole pieces and thus enlarges
the orbit so that the electrons strike the target (Fig. 11-14).

The betatron has thus opened the field for radiation of wavelengths below any ever previously produced. These short wavelength radiations are particularly useful because of their penetrating ability and because of their better approximation to a point source.

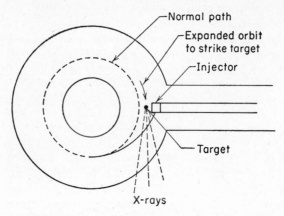

Fig. 11-14.   Cross section of betatron.

Thus they not only penetrate thicker castings but give clearer shadowgraphs. They are also finding use in medicine for the treatment of diseased tissue.

11.13   Circuits

Circuits for the application of x-ray tubes must incorporate two general controls. First, the filament voltage must be variable to give control of the emission and thus of the x-ray tube current. The beam intensity depends upon the number of electrons striking the target. Second, the plate voltage must be adjustable to determine the wavelength or "hardness" of the radiation and the efficiency of energy conversion. Most circuits include these two controls.

Basically the x-ray tube is a rectifier, and thus the plate voltage may be an alternating voltage. However, there are definite limits to the magnitude of a-c voltage that may be applied, because of the high temperature of the anode and its tendency to emit during the inverse half cycle. Half- or full-wave rectifiers are usually used. The extremely high voltages and the necessary insulation present a circuit design problem. The supply transformer is usually center-tapped to ground, and the tube is enclosed in an oil-filled,

250-kv single-column tubestand. (Courtesy of Westinghouse Electric Corporation.)

shockproof case. Often the tube and transformer are in one unit to afford better protection and safety for the operator.

Some basic plate voltage circuits are shown in Figs. 11-15, 11-17, and 11-18. In Fig. 11-15 the inverse voltage is shared by the rectifier tube and x-ray tube. The center-tapping makes it possible to have the maximum inverse voltage and the maximum voltage to ground only one-half the maximum voltage supplied to the x-ray tube. If the capacitor C is large compared to the distributed

capacitance of winding No. 2 and the interelectrode capacitance of
either tube, the inverse voltage divides equally between the two
tubes.   Since point p has the smallest rate of change of voltage with

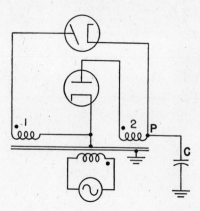

Fig. 11-15.   Half-wave, grounded center-tap x-ray voltage supply.

respect to ground (during the inverse half cycle), it is reasonable to
consider the distributed capacitance C_2 of the winding at this point,
and if it is large compared to the interelectrode capacitance of either
tube, omit C from the circuit.

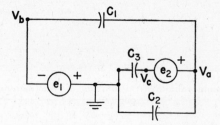

Fig. 11-16.   Equivalent circuit of Fig. 11-15 for inverse half cycle.

The proof of this voltage division can be obtained easily from an
equivalent circuit, Fig. 11-16.   The node equation about V_a is

$$0 = C_1(pV_a - pV_b) + C_2(pV_a) + C_3[p(V_a - e_2)].$$

Also

$$V_b = -e_1, \quad V_c = V_a - e_2, \quad e_1 = e_2 = e.$$

By substitution,

$$V_c = -\left(\frac{C_2 + 2C_1}{C_1 + C_2 + C_3}\right) e. \qquad (11.42)$$

This indicates that the inverse voltage V_c across the rectifier tube is equal to the voltage of one-half the transformer supply if $C_2 \gg C_1$ and C_3. Controls for timing exposures are not shown.

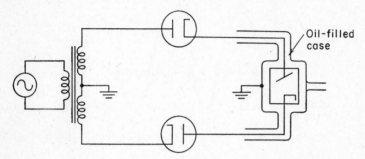

Fig. 11-17.   Two-tube half wave supply with oil-filled shockproof shield.

Figure 11-17 shows a circuit very similar to that of Fig. 11-15, but it uses two rectifiers to help divide the inverse voltage. Here the maximum voltage to ground is the peak of one-half the secondary voltage, and the inverse voltage on each tube is inversely proportional to its interelectrode capacitance. The oil-filled shockproof case is also shown.

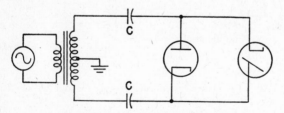

Fig. 11-18.   Villard circuit.

Figure 11-18 shows another circuit making use of the voltage doubler principle to increase the plate voltage. The circuits of Figs. 11-15 and 11-17 were half-wave rectifier circuits, and made x-ray radiation possible only half the time at best. The Villard circuit of Fig. 11-18 not only reduces the peak voltage to ground to one-half the peak plate voltage, but also allows for almost continuous radiation, since the plate never goes negative with respect to the cathode, and is zero only for an instant each cycle. Figure 11-19 shows the plate voltage as a function of time if the capacitors are assumed not to be discharged by the plate current of the x-ray tube.

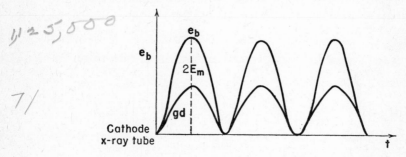

Fig. 11-19.　Plate voltage of x-ray tube in Villard circuit.

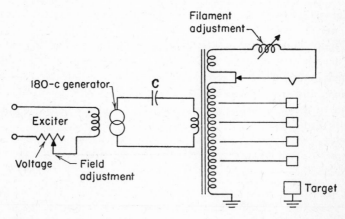

Fig. 11-20.　Resonance transformer supply for high-voltage tubes.

For the extremely high voltages that are required in the multi-section tubes it is impractical to use a conventional transformer across the line. For these applications a resonance transformer[6] as shown in Fig. 11-20 is often used. Here the large voltage is obtained without the extremely high ratio of turns that would otherwise be

[6] Kloeffler, R. G., *Industrial Electronics and Control*, John Wiley & Sons, Inc., New York, 1949.

required.   The voltage across the primary is many times that of the 180-cycle generator.

11.14   Applications

The applications of x-rays are in general threefold.   1. Radiography both in industry and medicine.   2. Medical therapy.   3. Diffraction patterns for identifying various substances.

The voltages and circuits utilized in these fields are directly dependent upon the specific application.   It is sufficient here to say that the greater the voltage the "harder" is the radiation and the greater its penetrating properties.

PROBLEMS

11.1. (a) What is the minimum wavelength of radiation that would be emitted from a tube operating at 100 kv?   (b) What velocity do the electrons have upon reaching the anode if relativity is neglected?   (c) What velocity do the electrons actually have upon reaching the anode if Einstein's equation of relativity is applied?

$$m = m_0 \frac{1}{\sqrt{1 - v^2/c^2}}$$

where m = apparent mass at velocity v; m_0 = mass at rest; c = velocity of light.   For an electron, $m_0 = 9.038 \times 10^{-31}$ kg, and the electronic charge is 1.59×10^{-19} coulomb.

11.2. A copper-backed tungsten anode is used in a tube operating at a constant plate potential of 100 kv.   The tube current is 30 ma.   Neglecting the tungsten, the copper anode weighs 4 lb.   (a) What energy is converted into x-ray radiation per second?   (b) How much energy must be dissipated from the anode as heat?   (c) Assuming all heat is dissipated by radiation and that the anode is a cylinder of 1 in. diameter and 2 in. long, radiating only from the sides, what temperature will it attain in a room at 70°F?   Assume an emissivity for copper of 0.9.   Compare with the melting point of copper.

11.3. Calculate part (a) of problem 2 if the tube voltage is a half-wave rectified supply with peak value equal to 100 kv.   Assume no emission when the voltage is under 20 kv.

11.4. What wavelength of radiation would result from an $L_{I\gamma_1}$ energy transition?   For K_{δ_1}?

11.5. What energy level transition must take place if radiation with a wavelength of 0.560 Å is to be produced?   Express in electron volts.

11.6. A lead sheet absorbing x-ray radiation is 1 in. thick.   The mass absorption coefficient for the wavelength being encountered is 6.0 m² per kg. (a) What is the ratio of the emerging beam to the incident beam?   (b) If the thickness if 0.1 in., what is I/I_0?

11.7. Assume that the magnetic flux encircled by the doughnut of a beta-tron is varying at the constant rate of 2×10^{10} lines per second. The dough-nut has a mean diameter of 1 m. Neglecting the initial energy of 70 kv, (a) What is the energy of the electron after it has circled the doughnut 10^4 times? (b) What is the actual velocity of the electron in part (a)? (c) If the average velocity was two-thirds of the final velocity, how long did the acceleration require? (d) If the flux was actually varying according to a sine law, with 2×10^{10} lines per sec being the maximum derivative and $\omega = 10^3$, how good an approximation was the constant rate of change of 2×10^{10}? Explain. What is the value of Φ_m required? (e) What is the shortest wavelength of x-radiation that could result from the electrons of this betatron striking a target?

11.8. Referring to the circuit of Fig. 10-15, plot the x-ray tube plate voltage as a function of time. If the voltage per coil is 15 kv rms, plot on the same curve the intensity of emission radiation I. Plot also as a function of time the wavelength of radiation that is most prominent. $i_b = 20$ ma, tungsten target.

11.9. Explain the operation of the circuit of Fig. 11-18. What inverse voltage must the rectifier tube withstand if the secondary has an effective voltage of 120,000 v?

11.10. Explain the operation of the resonance transformer in producing the extremely high voltages needed for the multisection tubes.

INDEX

wednesday

Date Due